NEW GCSE SCIENCE

Science
For Specification Units B1, C1 and P1
Edexcel

Series Editor: Gurinder Chadha

Authors: John Adkins, David Applin, Gurinder Chadha

Student Book

Contents

Biology   B1 Influences on life

Chemistry

C1 Chemistry in our world

Physics

P1 Universal physics

How to use this book

Welcome to Collins New GCSE Science for Edexcel!

The main content

Each two-page lesson has three sections:

> The first section outlines a basic scientific idea

> The second section builds on the basics and develops the concept

> The third section extends the concept or challenges you to apply it in a new way. It can also provide information that is only relevant to the Higher tier (indicated with 'Higher tier only').

Each section contains a set of level-appropriate questions that allow you to check and apply your knowledge.

Look for:

> 'You will find out' boxes

> internet search terms (at the bottom of every page)

> 'Did you know?' and 'Remember' boxes.

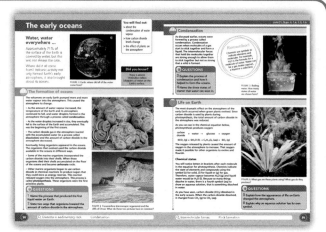

Unit introduction

Each Unit contains two Introductions – one at the start and the other midway through the Unit.

Link the science you will learn in the coming Unit with your existing scientific knowledge.

Unit checklists

Each Unit contains two graded Checklists – one midway through the Unit and the other at the end.

Summarise the key ideas that you have learnt so far and see what you need to know to progress. If there are any topics you find tricky, you can always recap them!

Exam-style questions

Every Unit contains practice exam-style questions for both Foundation and Higher tiers. There is a range of types of question and each is labelled with the Assessment Objective that it addresses.

There is a quick key to summarise the Assessment Objectives at the bottom of the page. A complete description of the Assessment Objectives – and how they apply to your written exam – can be found on pages 285–8 of this book and in Edexcel's specification.

Familiarise yourself with all the types of question that you might be asked.

Worked examples

Detailed worked examples with examiner comments show you how you can raise your grade. Here you will find tips on how to use accurate scientific vocabulary, avoid common exam errors and improve your Quality of Written Communication (QWC), and more. Any grades given in the worked example are target grades only. They are specific to the sample question and answer.

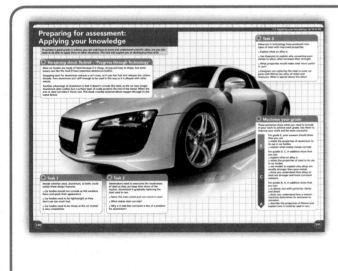

Preparing for assessment

Each Unit contains four Preparing for Assessment activities. These will help build the essential skills that you will need to succeed in your practical investigations and Controlled Assessment, and tackle the Assessment Objectives that appear throughout the Unit.

Each type of Preparing for Assessment activity builds different skills.

> Applying your knowledge: Look at a familiar scientific concept in a new context.

> Planning an investigation: Plan an investigation using handy tips to guide you along the way.

> Analysing and conclusions: Process data and draw conclusions from evidence. Use the hints to help you to achieve top marks.

Bad Science

Based on *Bad Science* by Ben Goldacre, these activities give you the chance to be a 'science detective' and evaluate the scientific claims that you hear everyday in the media.

Assessment skills

A dedicated section at the end of the book will guide you through your practical and written exams with advice on: the language used in exam papers; how best to approach a written exam; how to plan, carry out and evaluate an experiment; how to use maths to evaluate data, and much more.

B1 Influences on life (Topics 1 and 2)

What you should know

Variation and classification

Organisms can be sorted, or classified, into groups.

All organisms belong to a kingdom (e.g. the animal kingdom). Other groups that organisms belong to include: vertebrates (animals with a backbone, containing subgroups, e.g. mammals) invertebrates (animals without a backbone, containing subgroups, e.g. molluscs), fungi, protista and bacteria.

Organisms within a group have shared characteristics. As the groups get smaller the similarities increase.

Living organisms show differences even though they are the same species. This is known as variation.

Differences can be inherited through genes or caused by the environment.

⦿ Name the characteristics that all organisms belonging to the animal kingdom share.

Inheritance

Some characteristics are inherited, others are influenced by environmental conditions.

Genetic information is inherited from both parents.

⦿ Describe how genetic information is inherited from both parents.

Behaviour and health

Behaviour is influenced by internal and external factors.

The central nervous system, nerves and sense organs allow us to respond to our environment.

⦿ Name the five sense organs.

Hormones

The human reproductive cycle is controlled by hormones.

⦿ Explain what is meant by the human reproductive cycle.

You will find out about

> the characteristics used to classify organisms (including vertebrates)

> what is a species and how species are named

> how important classification is and how variation within a species complicates classification

> how to construct and use keys

> continuous and discontinuous variation

> adaptations to extreme environments

> Charles Darwin and his theory of natural selection as the mechanism of evolution

> the validation of evidence in the scientific community

> the nucleus, chromosomes, genes and alleles

> important genetic terms

> analysing and interpreting patterns of monohybrid inheritance

> the symptoms and inheritance of genetic disorders

> homeostasis regulating the body's internal environment

> receptors, the central nervous system and neurones

> the pathway from stimulus to response

> the reflex arc coordinating responses

> transmission between neurones at a synapse

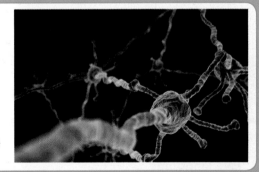

> hormones and their control of blood glucose levels

> Type 1 diabetes and Type 2 diabetes

> how hormones control plant responses

> using data

> using plant hormones commercially

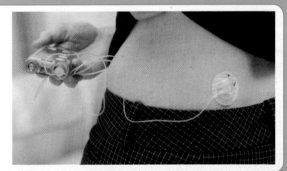

Classification

You will find out:

> about classification
> about the five kingdoms
> about the main characteristics of vertebrates

Sorting things out

Imagine that you have downloaded lots of MP3 tracks but are finding it difficult to locate the right piece of music for the right occasion. Sorting the tracks into playlists of similar types of music would make finding the right music much easier. This is an example of classification.

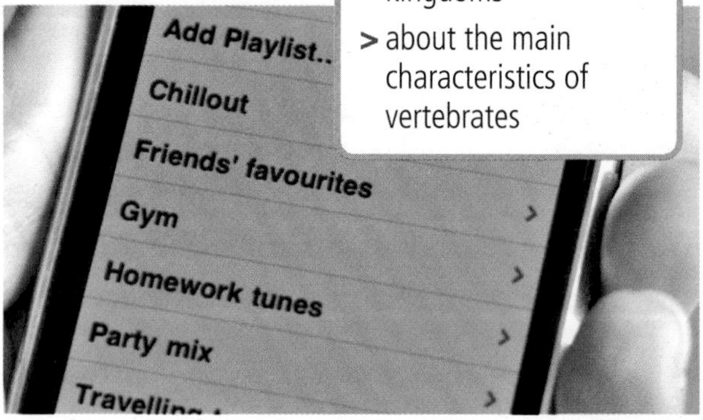

FIGURE 1: A playlist on an MP3 player.

Grouping living things

Living things are grouped together using the characteristics they have in common. Some characteristics are unique to the group, for example, feathers are a unique characteristic of birds.

The **backbone** is another characteristic of birds. However, it is also a characteristic of fish, amphibians, reptiles and mammals. Having a backbone unites these groups (including birds) into a larger group. Animals with backbones are called **vertebrates** (see Table 1).

QUESTIONS

1 Give reasons why a bird is a vertebrate animal.

2 Explain the similarities and differences between the five main vertebrate groups, providing specific examples.

TABLE 1: The five main groups of vertebrate animals.

Vertebrate	Oxygen absorption	Reproduction	Thermoregulation
Fish	Oxygen (O_2) and carbon dioxide (CO_2) are exchanged across gills	**Oviparous**; eggs are fertilised externally	**Poikilotherms**
Amphibians	O_2 and CO_2 are exchanged across moist, permeable skin	Oviparous; eggs are fertilised externally	Poikilotherms
Reptiles	O_2 and CO_2 are exchanged across lungs	Oviparous; eggs are fertilised internally	Poikilotherms
Birds	O_2 and CO_2 are exchanged across lungs	Oviparous; eggs are fertilised internally	**Homeotherms**
Mammals	O_2 and CO_2 are exchanged across lungs	Viviparous; eggs are fertilised internally	Homeotherms

Groups within groups

Five kingdoms

The **kingdom** is the largest group of all and consists of a number of phyla (singular phylum). Each kingdom represents a particular way of life that all its members share.

> **Animalia**: the animal body is **multicellular**. Its cells do not have chlorophyll and are not surrounded by a cell wall. Animals feed heterotrophically, which means that food is obtained from the environment and digested within the body.

> **Plantae**: the plant body is multicellular. Its cells have chlorophyll and are surrounded by a cell wall made of cellulose. Plants obtain food autotrophically, which means they make their food by photosynthesis.

> **Fungi**: the fungus body is usually multicellular. Its cells do not have chlorophyll and are surrounded by a cell wall, not made of cellulose. Fungi feed **saprophytically** on dead organic matter.

> **Protoctista**: the body is **unicellular** (seaweeds are an exception). The cell contains a distinct nucleus.

> **Prokaryote**: includes the bacteria. The body is unicellular. The cell does not have a distinct nucleus.

FIGURE 2: Green chlorophyll enables plants to make their own food by photosynthesis.

Vertebrates

A phylum is a group of living things with important shared characteristics such as a rod that supports the body. All chordates form the phylum **chordata** and the vertebrates are a sub-group of the larger grouping.

Mammals are a sub-group of the vertebrates, along with fish, amphibia, reptiles and birds, as we see in Table 1. Each sub-group is called a class, and a phylum usually comprises several classes.

Each sub-class of mammals comprises several orders:

> an **order** – contains several families

> a **family** – contains several genera

> a **genus** (the plural of genus is genera) – contains a number of **species** with similar characteristics

> a species – a group of organisms that have many characteristics in common. The group forms a **population**.

FIGURE 3: A chart showing the classification hierarchy.
For example, the brown rat:
kingdom – animal;
phylum – chordate;
class – mammals;
order – rodents;
family – Muroidea;
genus – *Rattus*;
species – *norvegicus*.

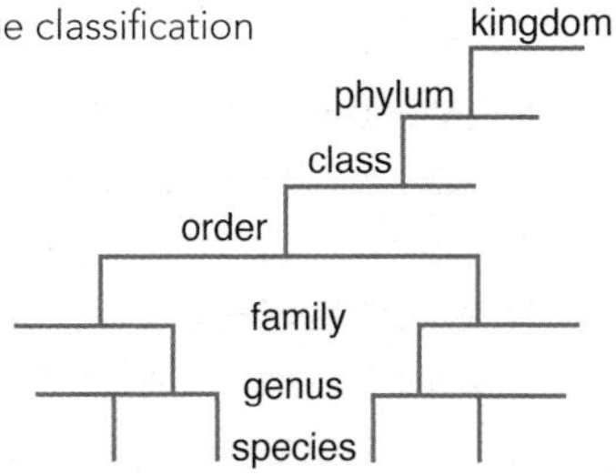

QUESTIONS

3 Choose an animal and a plant and give their group names.

4 Use the internet to investigate some of the difficulties of the five-kingdom model of classification. Summarise your conclusions from the investigation.

Classification is more than just a list

Classification helps us to understand relatedness but it also raises difficulties.

Relatedness

The more characteristics organisms have in common, the more closely they are related. By 'related' we mean that they share an evolutionary history that links them to a **common ancestor**. Most classifications highlight this. For example, the limb plan of vertebrates is a characteristic they have in common.

Compare the arrangement of bones of a human arm with the limb bones of a reptile in Figure 4. Notice that each limb consists of one upper limb bone, two lower limb bones and five (more or less) digits.

Five is the basic arrangement of digits for most vertebrates which why is the vertebrate limb is called a **pentadactyl limb** (*penta* is the Greek for five). The pentadactyl arrangement is seen in fossil fish, more than 500 million years old.

Difficulties in classifying organisms

Not all living things fit neatly into categories based on anatomy and reproductive methods. Also, new organisms with unusual characteristics are always being discovered. This makes it difficult to place them into distinct groups.

For example, the duck-billed platypus is classified as a mammal. The female produces milk for its young, like a mammal, but is oviparous, like a reptile or a bird. No wonder it's difficult to classify based purely on its anatomy.

Viruses

Are viruses living? Many scientists think not. Viruses do not seem to need food and to reproduce (replicate) they must first enter a living cell. The uncertainty means that viruses are not classified in any of the five kingdoms.

QUESTIONS

5 Explain why the pentadactyl limb is evidence that vertebrates have a shared evolutionary history.

6 Use the internet to help you explain why the slow worm is classified as a lizard and not a snake.

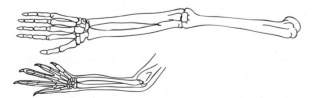

FIGURE 4: The forearms of a human (top) and reptile (bottom). Not to scale.

Naming species

You will find out:
> about defining species
> about binomial classification
> the importance of classification

What's in a name?

When Lewis Carroll wrote *Through the Looking-Glass*, he imagined Alice meeting Humpty Dumpty and talking about names. Humpty's reply to Alice suggests that his name describes his appearance. Since nobody else looks like Humpty, his name (and the appearance it describes) identifies him.

FIGURE 1: Alice and Humpty Dumpty talk about names.
Alice: "Must a name mean something?"
Humpty Dumpty: "Of course it must, my name means the shape I am."

What is a species?

Most biologists agree that if organisms are able to reproduce, and their offspring are fertile, then they belong to the same species.

However:

> Sometimes individuals of closely related species can mate and reproduce. The offspring are **hybrids**. Hybrid ducks and mules are examples. Animal hybrids are often sterile, which means that they cannot reproduce. Different species of plant can also produce hybrids between themselves. However, hybrid plants are often **fertile** and able to reproduce offspring.

> Some organisms do not always reproduce sexually. Although this is less common in animals, asexual reproduction can be seen in simpler organisms such as *Hydra*.

All this calls into question the definition of a species.

QUESTIONS

1 Explain why the definition of a species is not entirely satisfactory.

2 Explain the meaning of the word 'hybrid' and give an example.

FIGURE 4: A hybrid mallard and New Zealand blue duck (top), with the 'parent' ducks (below). Can you see the characteristics of both parents in the offspring?

Confusing names

The task of identifying and defining a **species** would be even more complicated if we did not have a universal standard system for naming species.

The species of plant shown in Figure 2 is called different everyday names depending on where you are in the UK.

On the other hand different species may be called the same everyday name. For example, the North American robin is a different species from what is called a robin in the UK.

Confusion over everyday names is avoided by scientists giving each type of living thing a Latin name in two parts:

> a *genus* name which begins with a capital letter

> a *species* name which begins with a small letter.

The two-part name is printed in *italics*. For example, the two-part name of humans is *Homo sapiens*:

> *Homo* is our genus name

> *sapiens* is our species name.

QUESTIONS

3 Explain why everyday names are not a good way to describe living things.

4 Explain the naming convention for living things.

5 Using your own research find two species that have the same everyday name but a different species and genus name. Explain how the two can be told apart.

FIGURE 2: This plant is called 'cuckoo pint', 'lords and ladies' or 'parson-in-the-pulpit', depending on where you are.

FIGURE 3: The UK robin and the North American robin. How are these birds different from and similar to one another?

Importance of binomial classification (Higher tier only)

Binomial classification

The Swedish scientist Carolus Linnaeus tackled the problem of confusing everyday names. His book *Systema Naturae* (published in 1735) set out the system of naming organisms, with each name in two parts.

Linnaeus's two-part system of names is called the **binomial system**. So, the robins in Figure 3 become *Erithacus rubecula* (the UK robin) and *Turdus migratorius* (the North American robin).

Why is binomial classification important?

Classifying living things identifies them. Binomial classification does this with particular accuracy by labelling a species with two identifiers – a genus and a species. Because it is so effective at identifying species, it has become the global scientific standard for naming species.

Accurate classification is important because it enables us to communicate information about the many

species with which we share planet Earth. It's only when we know what species exist in a given area that we can manage the area to conserve the species from the threat of extinction.

So far, we know of about ten million species, but this is only a fraction of the species awaiting discovery. **Biodiversity** refers to the number of different species living in a particular environment. This is another reason why accurate classification is important. When we can identify and study species properly we can then recognise and conserve them. This helps to target areas of greater biodiversity.

Undiscovered species can become extinct without our knowing and biodiversity suffers. Our food supplies, medicine, new drugs and how we live depend on global biodiversity. Maintaining it is a priority.

Did you know?

More than 200 species of plants and animals have been discovered recently during a two-month expedition in the remote mountain rainforests of Papua New Guinea.

QUESTIONS

6 Discuss the classification of living things and why classification is important.

7 Prepare an investigation into the species of birds in your local area. What data should be recorded? What factors need to be taken into account?

Identifying species and variation

Identification

During the Second World War (1939–45), anti-aircraft gunners were trained to spot aircraft. Charts showing the outlines (silhouettes) of different aircraft helped them with their work. The charts were keys which enabled the gunners to describe what they saw and arrive at an identification. What happened next depended on whether the aircraft were identified as friend or foe.

You will find out:
> how to use keys
> about variation within a species
> how variation complicates identification

FIGURE 1: Silhouettes of Second World War fighter aircraft.

Using keys

How many living things can you see in the photograph? Describing the animals collected from the dead leaves littering the woodland floor, and matching your description of them with the descriptions in a **key** will help you to identify them.

The descriptions on the key shown in Figure 3 are clues to identifying the animals found in leaf litter.

> Notice that the descriptions come as opposite statements.

FIGURE 2: A woodland floor.

> Choosing one statement leads you to the next statement, and so on.

> By working through the key in this way you arrive at a statement that identifies the animal in question.

Therefore, in biology, a key is a guide to a name. Different keys are used to identify different living things.

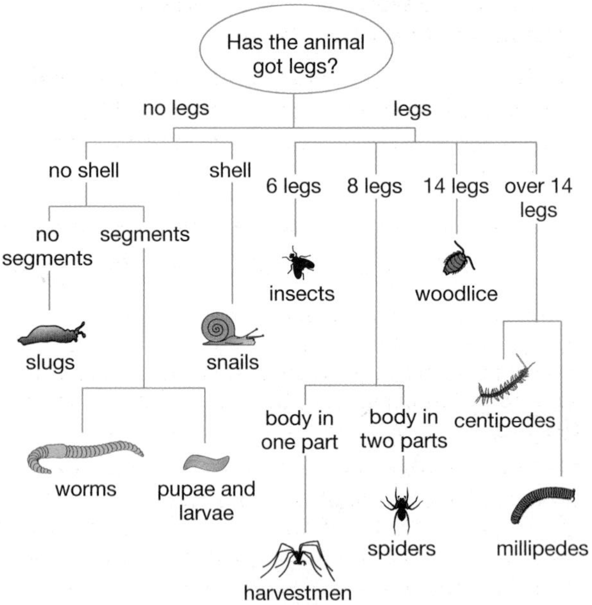

> Has the animal got legs?
> - no legs
>   - no shell
>   - no segments → slugs
>   - segments → snails
>   - worms
>   - pupae and larvae
>   - shell
> - legs
>   - 6 legs → insects
>   - 8 legs → woodlice
>   - body in one part → harvestmen
>   - body in two parts → spiders
>   - 14 legs → centipedes
>   - over 14 legs → millipedes

FIGURE 3: Using a key. You find an animal with eight legs. How do you identify what kind of animal it is?

QUESTIONS

1 Explain how you would use a key to identify an organism you don't recognise.

2 Look at the different fruits shown below. Make a key of opposite statements using descriptions of the fruits' appearance.

Variation within a species

Humans all belong to one species – *Homo sapiens*. However, people are different from one another. When you are next in a crowd look at the differences in the people near to you. The term **variation** refers to the differences in the particular characteristics of a species.

Continuous and discontinuous variation

The variation in some characteristics is spread over a range of values. We say that the characteristic shows **continuous variation**. Height of people is an example.

Q Biological keys   Human variation

A few people are either very short or very tall and there is a full range of 'in-betweens'.

Can you roll your tongue or not? Tongue rolling is a characteristic that shows **discontinuous variation**. There are no 'in-betweens' (intermediates). People can be put into distinctly different groups: people who can roll their tongue and people who cannot – there are no half-rollers! Try tongue rolling with a group of friends. Does the percentage of rollers and non-rollers agree with the percentages shown in Figure 4? If not, can you explain why (think about the size of your group)?

Different types of variation can be shown by using different types of graphs. Tongue rolling, an example of discontinuous variation, is more clearly shown by a bar graph (see Figure 4). Height, as an example of continuous variation, is best displayed by a line graph (see Figure 5).

The graph in Figure 5 is called a **normal distribution curve**. The 'middle' is the apex of the bell shape and is where the height of the largest percentage of the population is identified. The value in the 'middle' is called the **mean**. When comparing means it is useful to know by how much the data is 'spread out' around

each mean. You can form a living normal distribution curve by arranging a large group of people standing on a line into groups according to height. The few (probably) shortish people and tallish people should be on the left side and right side. Middle-height people (probably the majority) should be in the middle.

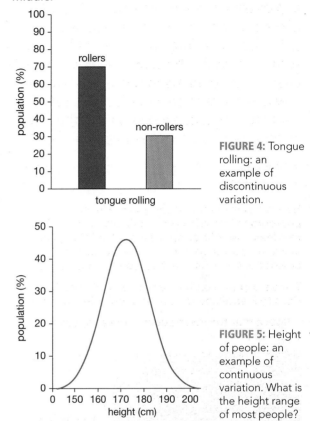

FIGURE 4: Tongue rolling: an example of discontinuous variation.

FIGURE 5: Height of people: an example of continuous variation. What is the height range of most people?

QUESTIONS

3 Define the word 'variation' and give examples of how people vary.

4 Explain what you can learn from the normal distribution curve shown in Figure 5. Why could you not make your interpretation from a bar chart?

Variations complicate identification (Higher tier only)

The characteristics of hybrids are usually a combination of those of the two parent species. Hybrid ducks are an example. The mixture results in variations that complicate their identification and so classification. Are the hybrids a new species?

Ring species refers to a chain of related species closely connected geographically. Differences between the species within the chain are not so great as to prevent the species from interbreeding and producing hybrid offspring. Again, are the hybrids new species or extreme variants? The differences between the species at each end of the chain are so great that interbreeding is prevented. They are distinct species in the strict sense of the term.

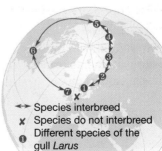

Species interbreed
Species do not interbreed
Different species of the gull *Larus*

FIGURE 6: *Larus* gulls illustrate the 'ring' idea: the geographical range of the *Larus* species forms a ring around the North Pole.

QUESTIONS

5 Explain how you would decide that variations in characteristics between different individuals are so great that they are separate species.

6 Suggest why ring species might be described as subspecies.

Adaptations

You will find out:
> why adaptations are important
> how organisms are adapted to extreme environments

Life is everywhere

Life can exist in the most unlikely and inhospitable places on Earth. From bacteria to polar bears, organisms have adapted to the most extreme environments.

FIGURE 1: Desert foxes are well suited to their extreme environment.

Surviving in extreme environments

The word **adaptation** refers to the characteristics of an organism that enable it to survive in a particular environment. Figure 1 shows a desert fox with its large ears that radiate heat and help to cool it. The fox's light-coloured fur helps reflect heat and provide camouflage. Fur and fat are examples of adaptations enabling polar bears and seals to survive in the extreme Arctic environment.

During the Arctic winter, the temperature may plunge to –50 °C or lower. Fur and fat help to reduce the rate of heat loss from the bodies of Arctic animals. These characteristics enable the animals to survive in the frozen landscape.

Remember!
Heat is transferred from hot to cooler environments until the temperature is the same throughout.

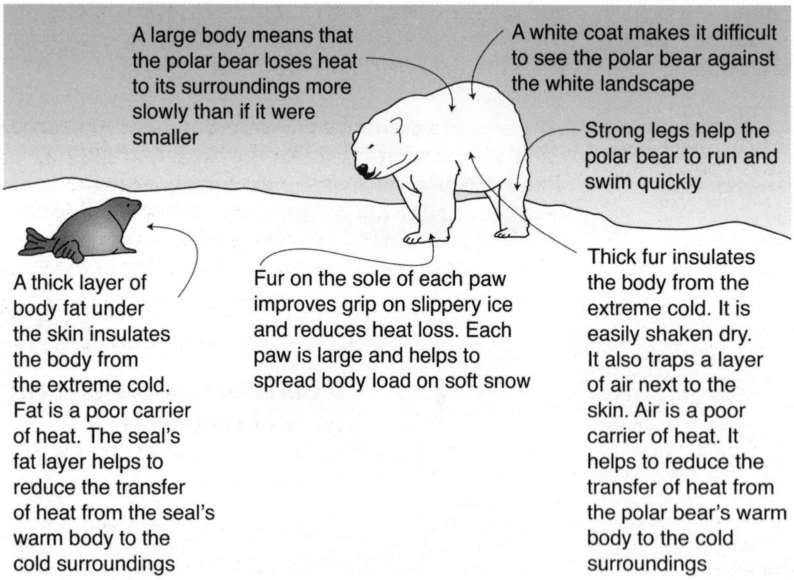

A large body means that the polar bear loses heat to its surroundings more slowly than if it were smaller

A white coat makes it difficult to see the polar bear against the white landscape

Strong legs help the polar bear to run and swim quickly

A thick layer of body fat under the skin insulates the body from the extreme cold. Fat is a poor carrier of heat. The seal's fat layer helps to reduce the transfer of heat from the seal's warm body to the cold surroundings

Fur on the sole of each paw improves grip on slippery ice and reduces heat loss. Each paw is large and helps to spread body load on soft snow

Thick fur insulates the body from the extreme cold. It is easily shaken dry. It also traps a layer of air next to the skin. Air is a poor carrier of heat. It helps to reduce the transfer of heat from the polar bear's warm body to the cold surroundings

FIGURE 2: Surviving Arctic conditions.

QUESTIONS

1 Explain why you may soon feel cold if you go swimming in an unheated pool.

2 List the adaptations of polar bears and seals that enable them to survive the cold of the Arctic environment.

3 The desert is another example of an extreme environment. Suggest how a camel has adapted to its environment.

Body size and surface area

Large bodies lose a smaller percentage of heat to their surroundings than smaller bodies. Why?

> Large bodies have a smaller surface area relative to their mass than smaller ones.

> Heat is lost from the body at its surface.

> The larger the body, therefore, proportionately less heat is lost from it. The smaller the body, proportionately more heat is lost from it.

> This probably explains why animals living in cold regions are usually larger than those living in warmer places in the world.

Penguin chicks are tiny. Figure 3 shows them in a huddled heap.

> **Huddling** has the effect of producing the equivalent of a large body.

> When huddled, the surface area of the heap of bodies relative to the heap's mass is proportionately less than one tiny body, on its own. As a result, the rate of heat loss from the huddle is proportionately less.

> Huddling is an adaptation of penguin chick behaviour that improves the chances of each chick surviving the extreme cold.

QUESTIONS

4 Suggest how humans are not adapted to survive in the Arctic.

5 Explain the advantage to penguin chicks of huddling together in a snow storm.

FIGURE 3: Huddling together helps penguin chicks to keep warm.

A world without light

Light is the source of energy that enables plants to produce food by photosynthesis. Plants are then eaten by animals, and so on, along the food chain. No light means no photosynthesis, which in turn means no food and therefore no organisms forming food chains.

The inky blackness of the ocean depths provides no light for photosynthesis, so how do communities of organisms flourish around cracks in the seabed called **hydrothermal vents**?

The cracks in the seabed lead down into the hot liquid rock below. Gases and superheated steam rise out of the cracks, raising the temperature of the nearby water to more than 90 °C. The extreme heat and pressure (due to the depth of water) create chemical reactions which produce hydrogen sulfide from the gases escaping from the vents.

Biochemical adaptations of different types of bacteria enable them to break down the hydrogen sulfide. These chemical reactions release the energy the bacteria need to make food from carbon dioxide (in solution) and water. The food produced supports the other organisms of the communities living in the vents.

QUESTIONS

6 Describe how the different types of bacteria in hydrothermal vents produce food in the absence of light.

7 Explain why scientists investigating new sources of enzymes useful to industry might be interested in the organisms of the communities living in hydrothermal vents.

FIGURE 4: Hydrothermal vents are called 'smokers', for obvious reasons.

Evolution

You will find out:
> about Darwin and his theory
> that natural selection is how evolution takes place
> about speciation

Charles Darwin 1809–82

Charles Darwin is best known as the first person to propose *how* evolution takes place. Natural selection was his big idea. He came to the theory in 1838, but did not publish until 1859.

FIGURE 1: Charles Darwin in 1838 soon after his return from the world voyage of HMS *Beagle*.

Darwin and his theory

Charles Darwin is best known as the naturalist who sailed the world (1831–6) in the survey ship HMS *Beagle*. He studied the wildlife of the countries he visited, particularly in South America and the Galapagos Islands off the coast of Ecuador.

Many people think that Darwin's experiences during the *Beagle* voyage prompted him to be the first to propose a theory of **evolution**. He wasn't, but he was the first to propose *how* evolution takes place through natural selection. Darwin described his ideas in a book titled *On the Origin of Species,* published in 1859.

Darwin's theory was a great shock to people who at the time had long-standing beliefs in the special place of humans in the natural world and of a benevolent creator or God.

Natural selection

Darwin's theory of **natural selection** includes a number of ideas which bring together his own observations and those of others. Alfred Russel Wallace (1823–1913) also came to the idea after Darwin but before the publication of Darwin's book.

QUESTIONS

1 Explain the importance of communicating scientific ideas to other people.
2 Describe how natural selection revolutionised our way of thinking about evolution.

Evolution in action

Darwin explained that natural selection occurred through a process of variation, competition, survival and inheritance.

Central to his theory of natural selection were the following concepts.

Variation

Variation in characteristics within a population provides a range of possibilities. For example, the characteristic 'length of leg' in a predator varies between individuals. Those with longer legs might be able to run down prey more easily than individuals with shorter legs.

FIGURE 2: The cheetah is the fastest runner on Earth. Its flexible spine and lever-like legs allow it run at over 110 km/h. How do these characteristics help it compete for resources?

Overproduction

Most organisms produce more offspring than will survive to adulthood.

Struggle for existence

Organisms need resources – such as food and living space – to survive. Supplies of resources are limited and so organisms must compete for them. The existence of competition is proven by the fact that populations do not generally increase rapidly in size even though organisms produce more offspring than will survive to adulthood.

Survival

Individuals who inherit advantageous variants of a characteristic – for example longer legs in predators – are said to be the best **adapted** to their environment. By being better adapted they are more likely to compete successfully for resources and, ultimately, to survive.

Advantageous characteristics inherited

As these individuals are more likely to survive, they are also more likely to reproduce. They will then be likely to pass on the gene controlling the advantageous trait to their offspring – and so on, generation to generation.

Gradual change over time

Over time the proportion of individuals in a population inheriting advantageous variants of characteristics will increase compared with less advantaged individuals. These individuals leave fewer offspring, so the poorly adapted characteristic may eventually be lost.

So according to Darwin's theory, by inheriting the most advantageous characteristics a species can change over time to become an entirely new species. The change is called evolution.

QUESTIONS

3 Explain the difference between evolution and natural selection.

4 The peppered moth exists in two forms: pale and dark. Birds eat both types. Percentages found in the countryside and a sooty, industrial area are:

Area	Pale moths	Dark moths
Countryside	22%	7%
Industrial	9%	26%

a Explain natural selection using the data.
b Explain why moth-eating birds are agents of natural selection.

Take owls and seagulls as an example. Owls and seagulls descended from a **common ancestor**. Individuals of this common ancestor adapted differently in order to successfully compete for resources – some adapted to catch fish and others mice. Both variants enabled the individuals to survive and reproduce, and over time they evolved into separate species that still survive today.

Other species descended from the same common ancestor as owls and seagulls, but not all were adapted for survival. An example is the dodo. Dodos become extinct in the seventeenth century because they had not developed characteristics – such as the ability to fly – that would enable them to escape predators, survive and reproduce.

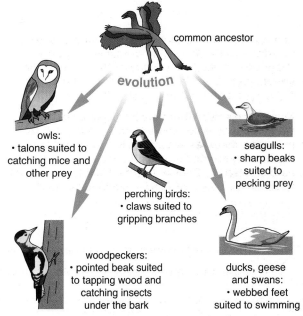

FIGURE 3: The evolution of birds.

Speciation (Higher tier only)

Speciation (the formation of new species) provides evidence for the natural selection of organisms. Geographical isolation is one way speciation occurs.

New species form when physical barriers, such as a sea, a river, a glacier or a mountain range, separate a population. For example, on one side of a newly formed mountain range the climate might be wetter and colder than on the other. Over many generations, one part of the population might change through natural selection to enable it to better withstand the harsher climate. Individuals with 'climate' genes are more likely to reproduce and pass on their genes (and therefore the advantageous characteristics).

Over time the proportion of individuals in the part population with the advantageous characteristics increases. This part of the population evolves compared with the other part populations. The characteristics of its individuals become different

compared with the individuals of the other part populations, forming a **subspecies**. Eventually, the difference in characteristics is so great that they become a new species. A new species has evolved where once there was only one.

The three-spined stickleback is an example of speciation. It was a marine fish that, after the Ice Age, became isolated in freshwater lakes and streams and evolved to live in its new environment.

QUESTIONS

5 Discuss the relationship between populations and species.

6 Use the internet to investigate the consequences of the movement of tectonic plates on speciation. Summarise your investigation using examples.

Causes of variation

You will find out:

> about chromosomes and genes
> what causes variation
> how Darwin's theory is supported
> how new evidence is validated

It's in your genes

From an earthworm to an elephant, the information that determines the characteristics of an individual organism is found in the genetic material stored on chromosomes.

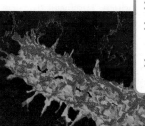

FIGURE 1: A human chromosome under a microscope. Magnification ×3500.

Variation

Characteristics vary

Laboradors are large dogs; corgis are smaller. Variation in the size between them is the result of differences in the genes that control the size characteristic of each breed. Size difference between the breeds is the result of genetic causes. However, variations in dog size within each breed may depend on environmental causes. For example, how fat or thin each dog is will depend on how much food and exercise it gets.

Genetic causes of variations in characteristics are inherited. Environmental causes are not. We say that these characteristics are **acquired characteristics**.

FIGURE 2: Fat or thin, corgis (left) will always be smaller than labradors (right) because of genetic causes.

QUESTIONS

1 Describe what a chromosome is made of.

2 Explain why acquired characteristics are not inherited. Use the internet to help you.

Did you know?

The shape of a protein molecule depends on the sequence of the amino acids that make it.

Chromosomes, genes and the nucleus

Chromosomes are found in the nucleus of most types of cell. Each one consists of a long-stranded molecule of a substance called deoxyribonucleic acid (**DNA**). The DNA is wound around a core of proteins. Each **gene** consists of a section of a DNA molecule.

Genes control characteristics

Most human cells have 46 chromosomes that carry about 25 000 genes. Other species' cells have fewer or more chromosomes (and fewer or more genes).

Each gene contains coded information that enables cells to make proteins. Characteristics, such as eye colour, length of leg, the enzymes that control chemical reactions in cells, are all the result of cells making proteins. That is why we say that genes control characteristics.

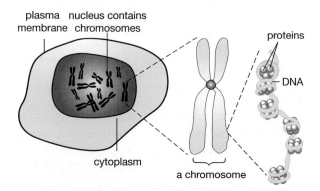

plasma membrane — nucleus contains chromosomes — proteins — DNA — cytoplasm — a chromosome

FIGURE 3: Chromosomes are found in the nucleus of most types of cell. Each gene is a section of a DNA molecule.

What causes genetic variation?

The offspring that develops from a fertilised egg inherits the chromosomes (and therefore the genes) from both parents (50:50). However, the reshuffling of the parents' chromosomes means that the combination of chromosomes (and therefore genes) in the offspring's cells is different to those of each parent. As a result, the characteristics of the offspring, although similar, vary compared with each parent.

These genetic causes of variation in the offspring are the result of different events taking place during sperm and egg formation in the parents. Genes are reshuffled because of:

> independent assortment of chromosomes (and therefore genes)

> crossing over, which exchanges bits of chromosomes (and the genes they carry) between chromosome pairs.

Mutations are another cause of genetic variation. The term refers to changes in the number of chromosomes (chromosome mutations) or in the genes (gene mutations) that chromosomes carry. Gene mutations in sperms and eggs are inherited and therefore are a cause of variations in offspring.

QUESTIONS

3 Discuss the evolutionary benefits of sexual reproduction.

Supporting Darwin's theory and validating evidence

Supporting Darwin's theory

> *DNA evidence.* Darwin lived before the time of genetic biology. However, new evidence from DNA research supports his theory of evolution. For example, comparing human DNA to that of perhaps our closest genetic relative, the chimpanzee, shows a 99% similarity, but human DNA is only 80% similar when compared to a horse. This illustrates how organisms have evolved over time, but share a common ancestry.

FIGURE 4: A chimpanzee: a member of the same family as gorillas, orangutans and humans.

> *Resistance.* Bacterial resistance to antibiotics is an example of evolution in action. Populations of bacteria always contain a few individuals with genes that give them resistance. These individuals survive antibiotic treatments and reproduce. The dosage of the antibiotic is gradually increased, but as resistance develops the dosage may reach a level which is poisonous to the patient. The resistance genes are passed on to the next generation. Resistance develops quickly, particularly in hospitals where the intensive use of antibiotics acts as a selection agent.

Validating evidence

Charles Darwin's *On the Origin of Species* is an example of how scientific knowledge was communicated to a wider audience. Through correspondence and presentations, Darwin discussed his theory both before and after his book's publication in 1859. Today, research results are first checked anonymously by other scientists who are expert in the field under investigation. This is called **peer review**. If **validated**, only then will the work be published in electronic and paper-based **scientific journals** available to the wider scientific community.

Scientific conferences are another way of communicating new ideas in a particular area of research. Scientists, expert in their area, gather from all over the world to meet and exchange ideas about their work and the work of other scientists in the subject under discussion.

QUESTIONS

4 Explain the meaning of the phrase 'intensive use of antibiotics acts as a selection agent'.

5 Explain the importance of validating new evidence from research through the process of peer review.

FIGURE 5: A scientific conference.

Genetic terms and pedigrees

It's all relative

The term 'genetics' was introduced in 1906. It refers to the study of the ways offspring inherit characteristics from their parents. Like any other branch of science, genetics has its own vocabulary. You need to know the meaning of some genetic terms.

FIGURE 1: He's so like his father. Which characteristics might the child have inherited?

Genes and alleles

Genes is a **genetic** term. It refers to a pair of **alleles** (different forms of a gene) which controls a particular characteristic. Different combinations of alleles lead to different characteristics.

Each allele of a pair occupies the same position on each of the pair of chromosomes carrying the alleles. The position of each allele on its chromosome is its **locus**.

Remember!
Offspring inherit their chromosomes equally from each parent. This means that the genes carried on the chromosomes are also inherited equally.

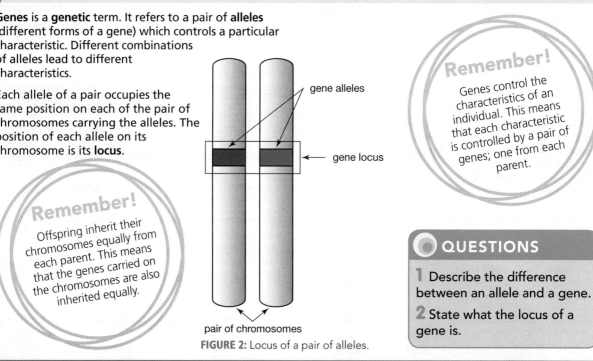

gene alleles

gene locus

pair of chromosomes

FIGURE 2: Locus of a pair of alleles.

Remember!
Genes control the characteristics of an individual. This means that each characteristic is controlled by a pair of genes; one from each parent.

QUESTIONS

1 Describe the difference between an allele and a gene.

2 State what the locus of a gene is.

Important genetic terms

Some characteristics are each controlled by a single pair of alleles. In simple terms, eye colour is an example. Height of people is controlled by several pairs of alleles working together.

If the alleles of a pair are the same, we say that the individual is **homozygous** for the characteristic controlled by that pair of alleles. If the alleles are different from one another, then we say that the individual is **heterozygous** for that characteristic.

A pure-breeding individual is homozygous for the characteristic in question. The characteristic does not change from one generation to the next.

If a person homozygous for brown eyes has children with a person who is homozygous for blue eyes, then almost certainly all of the children will have brown eyes because they are heterozygous for eye colour.

Each child carries the allele for blue eyes (remember that offspring inherit their parents' genes equally), but its effect is hidden by the allele for brown. We say that the brown allele is **dominant** and the blue allele **recessive**.

The term **expressed** refers to the activity of a gene. The allele for brown of the gene controlling eye colour is more actively expressed than the allele for blue. Therefore an individual heterozygous for eye colour will appear brown-eyed.

An individual's eye colour is visible while the enzymes produced by one of their cells are invisible. Seen or unseen, all of the characteristics of an individual are an individual's **phenotype**. All of the genes are the individual's **genotype**. Those actively expressing characteristics contribute to the individual's phenotype. However, the expression of a recessive allele of a gene is masked if its partner allele is dominant. The recessive allele does not contribute to the individual's phenotype.

QUESTIONS

3 Explain the difference between phenotype and genotype, giving examples.

4 Match the following terms with the correct definitions: i gene, ii recessive gene, iii dominant gene, iv pure-breeding individual:

a A gene which controls the development of a characteristic despite the presence of another allele of the gene.

b Section of DNA molecule which controls a specific characteristic such as height in pea plants.

c An individual whose characteristics do not change from generation to generation.

d A gene which does not control the development of a characteristic in the presence of another allele of the gene.

5 Write down the only possible genotype for blue eyes.

6 Create a similar matching question to question 4 (with answers) for the terms homozygous, heterozygous, pedigree and expressed.

Family pedigrees

The **pedigree** chart in Figure 3 begins with the grandparents of the children who are the latest generation of the two families represented. There are other ways of setting out a pedigree chart. For example, you can start with yourself as the author of the chart. After you come your parents, then grandparents and so on.

No matter how the chart is arranged, it shows the way characteristics of related individuals pass from one generation to the next.

Pedigree charts are usually produced for humans, horses and dogs. However, charts can be used for plants, cattle and other farm animals too. They provide helpful information about the purity of **lineage** of plants and animals important to farmers. In this instance 'purity of lineage' means the characteristics that make the plants and animals valuable to the agricultural industry, for example milk production in cows.

FIGURE 3: A family pedigree. Other than eye and hair colour, what other characteristics could the children inherit from their parents?

QUESTIONS

7 Explain one way of setting out a pedigree chart.

8 Explain the usefulness of pedigree charts for crops and livestock.

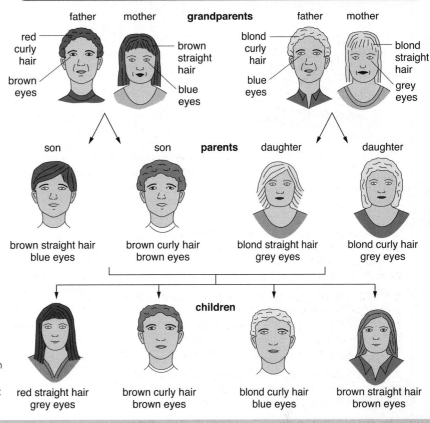

Monohybrid inheritance

You will find out:
> about patterns of monohybrid inheritance
> about Punnett squares
> about probabilities and outcomes of monohybrid crosses

Give peas a chance

Modern genetics began not in a science lab, but in a monastery garden. Gregor Mendel (1822–84) was a priest and studied mathematics and natural history at the University of Vienna. Later he studied inheritance in pea plants.

FIGURE 1: Pea plants.

Mendel's experiments

Mendel was interested in the way characteristics of pea plants such as flower colour are inherited by offspring from their parents. This inheritance of a single characteristic is called **monohybrid** inheritance. Mendel investigated the pattern of inheritance of other characteristics of pea plants. Following Mendel's way of thinking about his experiments will help you to understand genetics.

> Mendel started with pea plants which were all **pure-bred** for each characteristic he was studying. In the example here the characteristic is 'height of plant'.

> Mendel **cross-bred** pure-breeding short plants with pure-breeding tall plants. He collected and grew the plants' seeds. Their offspring were always tall. It seemed that the characteristic 'tallness' dominated the characteristic 'shortness'. Mendel called 'tallness' a **dominant characteristic**.

> Mendel then bred the next generation of pea plants from the offspring. He collected and grew the seeds produced. The characteristic shortness absent in the first generation turned up in the second generation. Mendel called 'shortness' a **recessive characteristic**.

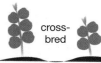

pure-bred parent plants:
1 tall, 1 short

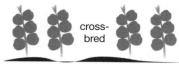

first-generation plants:
all tall

second-generation plants:
3 tall, 1 short

FIGURE 2: The genetic diagram shows three generations of pea plants. What do you notice about the second and third generations?

QUESTIONS

1 The table shows the results of breeding experiments with pea plants. The parental plants are pure-breeding. Explain how you can tell that: a tallness is dominant, b shortness is recessive.

Characteristic	Parental cross	First generation	Second generation
Height	Tall × short	All tall	780 tall; 270 short

How characteristics are inherited

We shall continue to follow Mendel's thinking but using the modern language of genetics. Mendel reasoned that sexually reproduced offspring receive the same number of genes from each parent and that the development of any particular characteristic, therefore, must be controlled by a pair of genes (one from each parent).

Mendel concluded that alleles must split when **gametes** (sex cells) form. We now know that alleles separate when cells divide, producing gametes, and that only one allele goes to each gamete. Mendel, however, did not know this.

Q Gregor Mendel   Punnett squares

Mendel used letters to symbolise alleles. For example, he used 'T' to show the allele which controls 'tallness' in pea plants and 't' to show the allele which controls 'shortness'.

The **Punnett squares** in Figure 3 summarise the results of Mendel's crosses between pure-breeding parent plants and first-generation plants.

Notice that the alleles controlling the height of the offspring of the pure-breeding parent plants are different (the parent plants are homozygous; the offspring are heterozygous). There is only one allele controlling the development of tallness (T), but its presence masks the effects of its partner allele (t). The allele T is dominant and the allele t is recessive. Also notice that the alleles of the short plant, which appear in the second-generation plants, are the same (the plant is homozygous).

FIGURE 3: The results of Mendel's experiments.

	Cross: **TT** × **tt**		Parent plants
Parental gametes	t	t	Pure-breeding recessive parent
Pure-breeding dominant parent T	Tt	Tt	First-generation plants
T	Tt	Tt	

	Cross: **Tt** × **Tt**		First-generation plants
First-generation gametes	T	t	
T	TT	Tt	Second-generation plants
t	Tt	tt	

QUESTIONS

2 The genetic diagram in Figure 4 shows the offspring of crosses between a pure-bred black bull and a pure-bred red cow. Coat colour is controlled by a single gene which has two forms (alleles): one for black and one for red coat colour.

a Give suitable letters to represent the two forms (alleles) of the gene.

b Which animals are definitely homozygous?

c Which animals are definitely heterozygous?

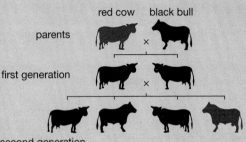

FIGURE 4: Cattle crosses.

3 Draw Punnett squares to show the possible first- and second-generation offspring where one parent has blue eyes and the other brown eyes. How does this compare with Mendel's findings?

Did you know?

The Cambridge geneticist Reginald Punnett (1875–1967) was the first to set out the results of a cross between parents as a table. We call these tables Punnett squares after him.

Probabilities

Using Punnett squares allows us to predict the probabilities of outcomes from crosses. Each first-generation plant shown in Figure 2 has two different alleles (heterozygous). However, all of the plants are tall because the T allele is dominant, masking the effect of the t allele, which is recessive.

However, not all of the second-generation plants have the same combination of alleles. Fifty per cent of the plants are heterozygous (Tt), 25% are pure-breeding tall (TT) (homozygous, dominant) and 25% are pure-breeding short (tt) (homozygous, recessive).

From the data you can predict that:

> The characteristic height of plants separates in the second generation in a ratio of three tall plants to one short plant.

> The phenotype 'tall' is expressed in either homozygous or heterozygous plants because the allele T is dominant.

> The phenotype 'short' is expressed *only* in homozygous plants because the allele t is recessive.

QUESTIONS

4 Look at the table in question 1:

a State the ratio of tall to short plants in the second generation.

b Calculate the probability and percentage of different phenotypes occurring in the second generation.

Genetic disorders

You will find out:
> about genetic disorders
> the symptoms of cystic fibrosis and sickle cell disease
> how to evaluate the risk of inheriting cystic fibrosis and sickle cell disease

Order and disorder

THE CAT SAT ON THE MAT makes sense. Lose the T of CAT and the sentence becomes THE CAS ATO NT HEM AT. Its information is scrambled. If the code of a gene alters, then its information, which enables a cell to make protein, may also be scrambled. Scrambled genetic information can result in genetic disorders.

FIGURE 1: Problems can happen when the coding gets mixed up.

Gene mutations

A change in a gene's DNA is called a **mutation**. Cell mutations can be the result of environmental factors, for example, exposure to cigarette smoke can cause mutation in lung cells and increase the risk of cancer. However, a mutation can also occur in genes. Remember that a gene's **code** enables cells to make protein. A mutation therefore may alter the type of protein produced, or no protein may be made at all.

Inheriting mutations

Mutations can occur in the genes of sperm and eggs. If either carries a mutation then any offspring will inherit the mutated gene.

Different **genetic disorders** are the result of inheriting different gene mutations.

QUESTIONS

1 Explain the effect of a mutation on a gene.

2 Describe how genetic disorders are inherited.

When things go wrong

Cystic fibrosis and **sickle cell disease** are examples of inherited recessive genetic disorders.

Cystic fibrosis

This disorder affects the movement of fluid in and out of cells. People with cystic fibrosis produce thick, sticky **mucus**, particularly in their lungs and in their digestive tract.

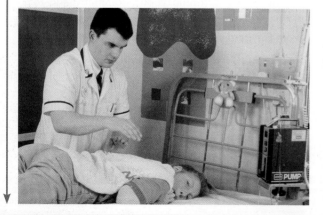

Major symptoms include:

> sticky mucus blocking the airways of the lungs, which makes breathing difficult

> lung infections which often are the result of bacteria becoming trapped in the sticky mucus

> problems digesting food, which can lead to malnutrition

> bone disease.

Treatments for cystic fibrosis include:

> physiotherapy and massage, to help clear mucus and fluid

> medication to help reduce fluid, dilate the airways, clear up infections and help digestion

> exercise to help develop the lungs and build strength

> a suitable and nourishing diet.

FIGURE 2: How does regular massaging help treat cystic fibrosis?

Sickle cell disease

Haemoglobin is a red pigment in our blood that absorbs oxygen. Sickle cell disease is caused by a mutation that alters the shape of haemoglobin molecules and causes them to absorb less oxygen. The red blood cells that carry the altered haemoglobin become sickle-shaped.

The symptoms of sickle cell disease vary from mild tiredness to extreme pain that requires hospital treatment. Generally, the symptoms include:

> feeling weak and tired

> sudden pain, known as a **sickle cell crisis**.

Crises happen when sickled red blood cells form clumps in the bloodstream. The clumps block the flow of blood to the body's organs. Pain and organ damage are the results.

Treatments for sickle cell disease include:

> medication for pain

> drinking plenty of fluids, or intravenous fluid drips if drinking is not possible, to help prevent a crisis

> blood transfusions for anaemia and to prevent stroke.

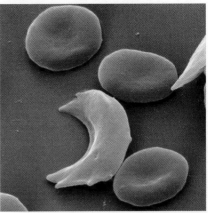

FIGURE 3: The disc-shaped cells carry normal haemoglobin. The cells shaped like the blade of a sickle contain sickle haemoglobin. Magnification ×7400.

QUESTIONS

3 Describe the difficulties faced by a person with cystic fibrosis and what might help them.

4 Explain why a person affected by sickle cell disease is likely to feel very tired and experience pain.

5 Explain why sickle cell disease sufferers are at risk of stroke.

Inheriting genetic disorders (Higher tier only)

Most of us carry some mutations. Fortunately most are recessive. Their effect is masked by the normal copy of the allele.

However, if a mutated allele is dominant, or a person inherits two copies of a mutated recessive allele, then the individual in question will be affected if the mutated allele is the cause of a genetic disorder. The risk of someone inheriting a particular disorder can be predicted using pedigree analysis.

Cystic fibrosis and sickle cell disease are two genetic disorders where screening by pedigree analysis can:

> consider the inheritance pattern of the disorder

> predict the risk of disease in future generations.

In Figure 4 three generations of a family are numbered from the top of the pedigree chart in Roman numerals, I, II, III and the individuals in each generation are numbered from the left as I-1, II-1, III-2, etc.

From the sample pedigree analysis in Figure 4 we can preduct the likely outcomes:

> I-1 and I-2 must be carriers of the disorder as one their children is affected

> II-4 and II-5 each has a one in four (25%) chance of carrying the disorder

> the probability that III-5 is a carrier of cystic fibrosis is one in four (25%) as they have a sibling with the disorder.

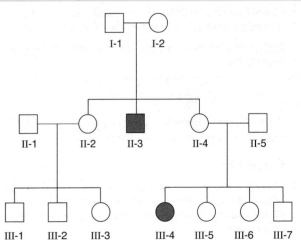

FIGURE 4: A sample pedigree analysis for cystic fibrosis. The squares are males and the circles females. A coloured shape indicates an affected individual.

QUESTIONS

6 Prepare a similar chart to Figure 4 for sickle cell disease.

7 If a carrier of cystic fibrosis and a person who does not have the cystic fibrosis allele decide to have a child, what is the probability of their child having the disorder?

Preparing for assessment: Applying your knowledge

To achieve a good grade in science, you not only have to know and understand scientific ideas, but you also need to be able to apply them to other situations. This task will support you in developing these skills.

✳ She has her grandfather's eyes

Ellie (16) has two brothers, Will (14) and Andy (11). All three are blond. Ellie's eyes are brown, but her brothers' are blue. Will has cystic fibrosis but Ellie and Andy are healthy. They all inherited these characteristics when the egg from which they developed was fertilised.

Body cells contain pairs of chromosomes, but each egg or sperm only contains one from each pair. The chromosomes carry genes, and these determine the characteristics we inherit. Some of Ellie's characteristics are easy to spot in her parents.

Ellie's father has blue eyes and blond hair but her mother has brown eyes and blond hair. Brown eyes are dominant to blue, so why don't Ellie's brothers have brown eyes too? It's because we all carry two copies of every gene. When the alleles differ, we have the characteristics the dominant gene produces. Parents pass one gene from each pair to their offspring, and it's just as likely to be the recessive one as the dominant one.

Ellie's father is homozygous for eye colour, but her mother is heterozygous. She passed a 'blue eye' gene to the boys and a 'brown eye' gene to Ellie. Brown hair is dominant over blond, but Ellie and her brothers are all blond. Neither of Will's parents have cystic fibrosis, but both his grandfathers had it.

✸ Task 1

Read the information opposite.

> Why do Ellie and her brothers resemble their parents?

> Explain how genetic information passes from parents to their offspring.

✸ Task 2

> Why are Ellie and her brothers so different even though their genes came from the same parents?

✸ Task 3

> Should Ellie's mother be surprised to have three blond children?

> Use a Punnett square to explain the reasoning behind your answer.

✸ Task 4

> Describe the main symptoms of cystic fibrosis.

> Explain how Will inherited this disease even though neither of his parents has it.

✸ Maximise your grade

These sentences show what you need to include in your work to achieve each grade.
Use them to improve your work and be more successful.

E
For grade E, your answers should show that you can:
> explain why offspring have some similarities to their parents
> understand that genes exist in different forms called alleles.

C
For grades D, C, in addition show that you can:
> describe how genes are passed on
> explain why offspring from the same parents can differ from one another
> use the terms: dominant, recessive, homozygous, heterozygous, phenotype and genotype correctly
> explain why a heterozygous individual does not show the characteristic their recessive allele codes for
> use a Punnett square
> describe the symptoms of cystic fibrosis.

A
For grades B, A, in addition show that you can:
> use a Punnett square to calculate the probability that offspring will inherit specific genes
> understand how cystic fibrosis is inherited.

Homeostasis

You will find out:
> about homeostasis
> that regulating body water content and temperature are examples of homeostasis
> about negative feedback

Keeping cosy

Imagine the room you are in is cold. If you turn up the heater control the room becomes warmer. This is because the control sends a signal to the boiler which warms the room's radiators. The control switches off at the temperature you chose. The room cools down. The control switches on again, and so on. Our bodies have controls that help us to maintain a constant temperature.

FIGURE 1: How does a spacesuit help an astronaut to maintain a constant temperature?

Constant conditions

Keeping conditions stable, or constant, is called **homeostasis**. For living things 'conditions' means the body's internal environment. The cells of the body work best when its internal environment is constant. Regulating body water content, body temperature and blood glucose are examples of keeping the body's internal environment constant so that optimum conditions are maintained.

Regulating body water

Regulating body water content involves:

> Sending signals to the brain carrying information about the water content of the blood.

> The brain processing the information and sending signals to the kidneys, regulating the amount of water in the urine produced by the kidneys.

The signal from the brain to kidneys is a **hormone** produced by the pituitary gland in the brain. The blood carries the hormone to the kidneys. Here it controls how much water the kidneys absorb and how much water the kidneys remove to maintain body water at an optimum level. The process is called **osmoregulation**.

Did you know?

An adult needs about 2.5 dm³ of water daily.

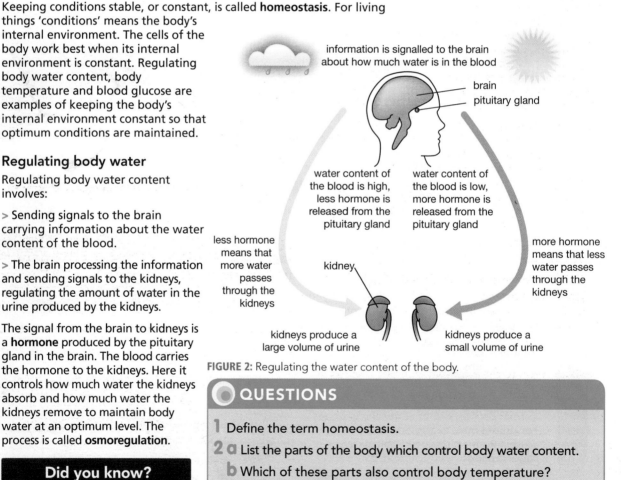

information is signalled to the brain about how much water is in the blood

brain
pituitary gland

water content of the blood is high, less hormone is released from the pituitary gland

water content of the blood is low, more hormone is released from the pituitary gland

less hormone means that more water passes through the kidneys

more hormone means that less water passes through the kidneys

kidney

kidneys produce a large volume of urine

kidneys produce a small volume of urine

FIGURE 2: Regulating the water content of the body.

QUESTIONS

1 Define the term homeostasis.

2 **a** List the parts of the body which control body water content.

   b Which of these parts also control body temperature?

3 Draw a simple diagram of the human body to show how body temperature is regulated.

Regulating body temperature

Wearing clothes help us to stay warm, but we're warm in the first place because the chemical reactions taking place in our cells release a lot of heat. This heat helps to warm our body at its centre to an optimum temperature of about 37 °C. The **enzymes** which control the chemical activity of our cells work best at this temperature.

> When the temperature outside the body changes, it also affects the temperature of the skin and blood.

> Information about these changes passes quickly to the brain and the brain sends signals to the skin.

> These signals trigger regulating mechanisms which either warm or cool the body depending on how cold or hot it is.

The process is called **thermoregulation**.

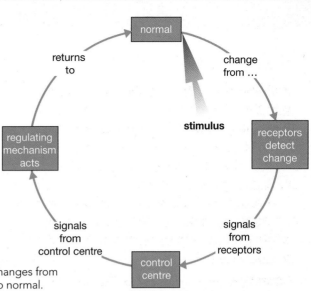

FIGURE 3: The features of a self-regulating system that enable changes from the normal values of the body's internal environment to return to normal.

How are conditions kept constant?

Keeping our body temperature at the optimum temperature of 37 °C is an example of homeostasis and is the result of self-regulating mechanisms. Self-regulating means that the body temperature adjusts itself automatically. All examples of homeostasis are self-regulating. Figure 4 summarises their features.

Notice that different stimuli are the trigger that starts the mechanism working. In the case of body temperature, the stimuli are the body becoming either too warm or too cold.

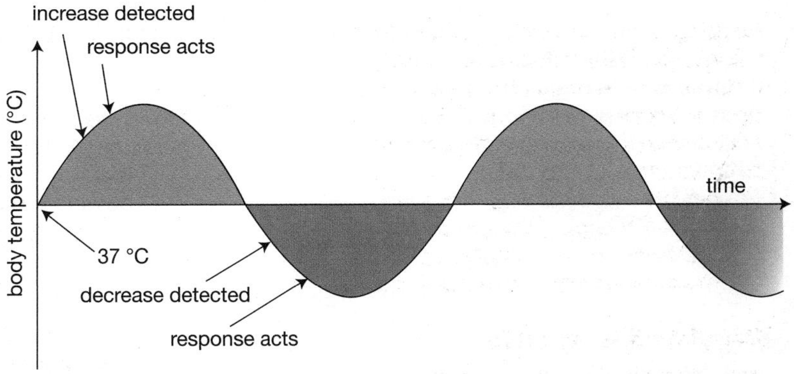

FIGURE 4: Self-regulation of body temperature. What trends do you notice?

QUESTIONS

4 List the features of a self-regulating mechanism.

5 Using an example, explain how stimuli trigger homeostasis.

Did you know?

The temperature at the centre of a camel's body can rise and fall by as much as 6 °C over 24 hours. If our body temperature changed like this we'd be dead!

Feedback (Higher tier only)

Feedback refers to the information about changes in a self-regulating mechanism that affect what happens in the future. For example, our being too hot or too cold is the information that brings about the changes that in time return the body temperature to normal. Because the information reverses any change away from normal back to normal, we say that the feedback is negative.

Negative feedback allows control mechanisms to fluctuate and self-adjust around a normal value, so keeping the body's internal environment constant.

QUESTIONS

6 Describe how negative feedback keeps the body's internal environment constant.

7 Explain the difference between negative feedback and positive feedback. Use your own research to help you to give examples that help your explanation.

Regulating body temperature

Steady now ...

Most animals attempt to keep their body temperature steady. The way they do this varies: a dog will pant when it is hot, a lizard lies in the sun to warm up, a hippo will wallow in the water to cool off.

You will find out:
> how the skin helps to control body temperature
> about vasoconstriction and vasodilation

FIGURE 1: What is the hippo trying to do?

Changes in the surroundings

Warming up

Running warms you up. The rate of chemical reactions in the cells of your muscles, brain and liver increases. More heat is released than when you are resting, so you feel hot. Probably your skin will be flushed red and wet with sweat. Any hair will probably lie flat against the skin. These changes in the skin help to prevent you from overheating.

> You're flushed red because more blood, warmed by body heat, is flowing through the blood vessels in the skin. More blood means that more heat is lost from the skin's surface to the outside. You cool down.

> You're sweaty because sweat glands in the skin produce sweat and release it on the skin's surface. Sweat is a very dilute solution of salts. Heat from the body evaporates the water in sweat, transferring heat away from the skin and cooling you down.

> Your body hair lying flat against the skin prevents a layer of air becoming trapped next to it. Air is a poor conductor of heat, insulating the body from heat loss. No air layer means more heat is lost from the skin's surface, cooling you down.

Cooling down

Stand outside in winter weather dressed in summer clothes and you'll soon feel cold. Any body hair will stand away from the skin which almost certainly will be paler. You're probably shivering as well.

> Your skin is pale because less blood is flowing through its blood vessels. Less blood means that less heat is lost from the skin's surface to the outside.

> You shiver because tiny muscles under the skin contract and relax very quickly (shivering). Chemical reactions in the muscle cells release energy that powers their contraction. The reactions also release heat, helping to keep you warm.

> Your body hair raised away from the skin traps a layer of air next to it. Air, being a poor conductor of heat, insulates the body from heat loss.

FIGURE 2: What mechanisms are working here?

FIGURE 3: What's helping to keep him warm?

QUESTIONS

1 List the changes you might notice in your body when you're hot and when you're cold.

2 Explain how sweating helps you to cool down.

3 Draw a diagram to illustrate the changes that occur in a cyclist's body during a cycle race.

Q Controlling body temperature   Shivering   Thermoregulatory centre

Thermoregulation

A part of the brain called the **hypothalamus** contains the **thermoregulatory** centre. This acts like a thermostat. It monitors and regulates body temperature – Figure 4 shows you how.

In the thermoregulatory centre, **receptors** detect the temperature of the blood flowing through it. The thermoregulatory centre processes the information and sends nerve impulses to the sweat glands and hair erector muscles that raise body hair away from the skin, and which control shivering and blood flow through the skin. A constant body temperature is the result of balancing these two mechanisms.

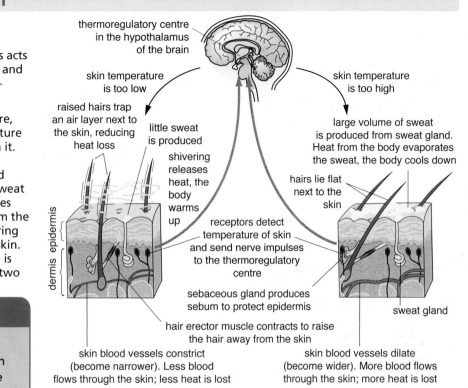

thermoregulatory centre in the hypothalamus of the brain

skin temperature is too low

raised hairs trap an air layer next to the skin, reducing heat loss

little sweat is produced

shivering releases heat, the body warms up

skin temperature is too high

large volume of sweat is produced from sweat gland. Heat from the body evaporates the sweat, the body cools down

hairs lie flat next to the skin

receptors detect temperature of skin and send nerve impulses to the thermoregulatory centre

sebaceous gland produces sebum to protect epidermis

sweat gland

hair erector muscle contracts to raise the hair away from the skin

skin blood vessels constrict (become narrower). Less blood flows through the skin; less heat is lost

skin blood vessels dilate (become wider). More blood flows through the skin; more heat is lost

dermis epidermis

FIGURE 4: Regulating body temperature.

QUESTIONS

4 Explain how the thermoregulatory centre in the brain helps to regulate body temperature.

Vasoconstriction and vasodilation (Higher tier only)

When we are too hot or too cold, self-regulating mechanisms bring about changes that return the body temperature to normal, in a process called negative feedback.

Heat loss from the body depends partly on the volume and flow rate of blood through the skin. The diameter of the vessels controls the volume and flow rate, thereby affecting the regulation of body temperature.

> **Vasoconstriction**: the blood vessels narrow. Blood vessel diameter reduces, so reducing the flow of blood through them. Therefore heat loss from the skin is decreased.

> **Vasodilation**: the blood vessels widen. Blood vessel diameter increases, so increasing the flow of blood through them. More heat is lost from the skin.

Nerve impulses, stimulating contraction of the muscles in the walls of blood vessels narrow the blood vessels. The impulses pass along the nerves from the thermoregulatory centre to the muscles. When the muscles relax the blood vessels widen.

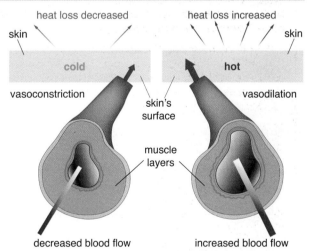

heat loss decreased

heat loss increased

skin

skin

cold

hot

vasoconstriction

vasodilation

skin's surface

muscle layers

decreased blood flow

increased blood flow

FIGURE 5: Vasodilation and vasoconstriction.

QUESTIONS

5 Explain how vasoconstriction and vasodilation help to regulate the body temperature of someone running followed by a cold shower.

6 Explain the roles of the systems involved in thermoregulation.

Did you know?

Sebum is an oily substance produced by the sebaceous glands of the skin. It keeps the skin waterproof and supple, and inhibits microorganisms from growing on the skin's surface.

Senses and the nervous system

You've got a nerve

We've all done it … chewed gum, rolled it into a ball between our front teeth and pulled it out into a thread: disgusting! But, what we've simply done is model a nerve cell. Under the microscope, nerve cells look strange. Each one consists of a cell body (the ball of gum) with fibres (the thread of gum) projecting from it.

You will find out:

> about nerve cells and the nervous system
> what receptors are
> how receptors work
> about dendrons and axons

FIGURE 1: Modelling a nerve cell or just plain disgusting?

Nerve cells and the nervous system

Neurones

A **neurone** is a nerve cell; its appearance is very different from other types of cell. Each neurone consists of a cell body and thin fibres which stretch out from it. Electrical impulses pass along the fibres.

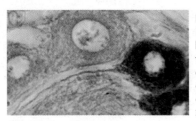

FIGURE 2: Nerve cells in the brain of a blowfly. You can see the long fibre extending from one of the purple-stained cells. Magnification ×1000.

Nerves and the nervous system

Bundles of neurones form nerves and nerves form the nervous system:

> The central nervous system consists of the brain and spinal cord.

> The peripheral nervous system consists of the nerves connecting the sense organs to the central nervous system, and the central nervous system to muscles and glands. There are different types. For example, cranial nerves connect to the brain and spinal nerves connect to the spinal cord.

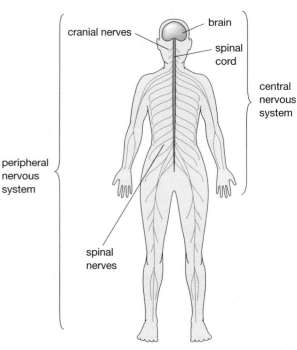

FIGURE 3: Plan of the human nervous system.

Different neurones

Nerves consist of different types of neurone which send electrical impulses in particular directions. For example:

> Sensory neurones form sensory nerves and send impulses from **receptors** in the sense organs to the central nervous system.

> Motor neurones form motor nerves and send impulses from the central nervous system to muscles and glands.

QUESTIONS

1 Name the sense organs.

2 Rearrange the following terms in order from simple to complex: nervous system, dendrite cell body and fibres, nerve, neurone.

Receptors

A **receptor** is the part of the fibre of a sensory neurone in the sense organs which detects stimuli. Receptors convert stimuli into electrical impulses and send them along neurones to muscles and glands. The electrical impulses are called **nerve impulses**. They carry information about stimuli from the sense organs along the neurones. Muscles and glands respond to nerve impulses.

Different types of receptor detect different types of stimulus. For example, photoreceptors detect light. Thermoreceptors detect changes in body temperature.

Some types of receptor are all over the body. For example, thermoreceptors are in the skin. Other types of receptor are concentrated in sense organs. For example, photoreceptors form a layer of cells in our eyes called the **retina**.

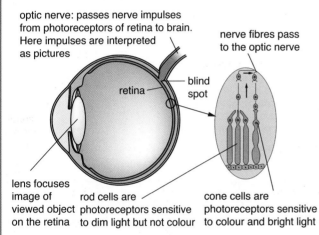

optic nerve: passes nerve impulses from photoreceptors of retina to brain. Here impulses are interpreted as pictures

nerve fibres pass to the optic nerve

retina — blind spot

lens focuses image of viewed object on the retina

rod cells are photoreceptors sensitive to dim light but not colour

cone cells are photoreceptors sensitive to colour and bright light

FIGURE 4: The different parts of the human eye.

Skin sensitivity

Sensitivity to touch depends on the force bearing down on an area of skin. It also depends on the number of touch receptors in the area. There are many touch receptors in the skin covering the tips of the fingers; far fewer are in the skin covering the thighs. Fingertips are very sensitive to touch; the thighs less so.

You can investigate the distribution of the touch receptors in the skin using a simple touch-tester (see Figure 5). Which areas of your skin are the most sensitive? Think how best to use a touch-tester to find out.

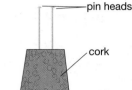

pin heads

cork

FIGURE 5: A simple touch-tester. Make sure you get the pins the correct way around.

QUESTIONS

3 Describe what a receptor does, using thermoreceptors as an example.

4 Explain why a fingertip is more sensitive than the outside surface of the thigh.

5 Outline the method that you would use to investigate human responses to external stimuli. Remember to include health and safety considerations in your plan.

Dendrons and axons

Figure 6 compares a sensory neurone with a motor neurone. Notice that the length of the fibre carrying electrical impulses *from* the cell body of each type of neurone is different. The fibre is called the **axon**. The difference in length of the axon helps you to tell which type of neurone is which. The fibre that carries electrical impulses *to* the cell body is called the **dendron**. Axons and dendrons end in fine branches called **dendrites**.

QUESTIONS

6 Give two differences between a sensory neurone and a motor neurone.

7 Using your own research, explain some of the symptoms of multiple sclerosis.

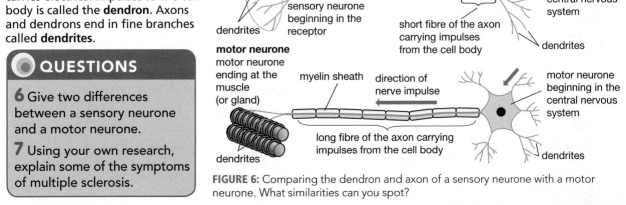

sensory neurone

cell body

direction of nerve impulse

sensory neurone ending in the central nervous system

dendrites

sensory neurone beginning in the receptor

short fibre of the axon carrying impulses from the cell body

dendrites

motor neurone

motor neurone ending at the muscle (or gland)

myelin sheath

direction of nerve impulse

motor neurone beginning in the central nervous system

dendrites

long fibre of the axon carrying impulses from the cell body

dendrites

FIGURE 6: Comparing the dendron and axon of a sensory neurone with a motor neurone. What similarities can you spot?

Responses and coordination

You will find out:
> about stimuli and responses
> how responses are coordinated
> about a simple reflex arc

Hmm, what should I do?

On seeing a fierce dog a man makes a quick getaway; the sight of the fleeing man prompts the dog to give chase. Who wins depends on who can run the faster, unless the man can think of an alternative escape plan. Reading on will help you to understand the biology behind the scene.

FIGURE 1: How might your body respond if you came across this dog?

Responding to stimuli

Imagine stepping on a pin. The sharp point pricking your skin is the **stimulus** causing the **response** of pulling your foot away. You don't think about it; it's an **involuntary response** to protect your foot from even more damage.

Imagine your mobile's ringing. What do you do: look to see who's ringing before answering it? Your response is **voluntary** because you thought about your action.

Different parts of the central nervous system coordinate different responses:

> The brain coordinates voluntary responses.

> The spinal cord coordinates involuntary responses.

voluntary response:
the brain decides whether to answer the ringing phone

involuntary response:
the spinal cord controls the automatic response bypassing the brain; you don't think about pulling your foot away

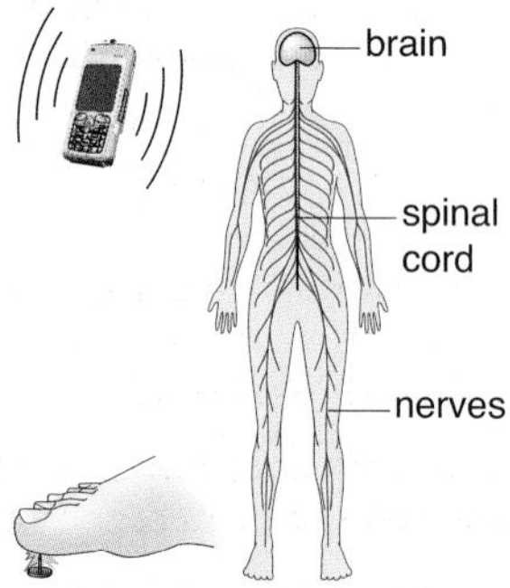

FIGURE 2: Conscious decision controls voluntary responses; involuntary responses are automatic.

QUESTIONS

1 Explain the differences between involuntary responses and voluntary responses.

2 You touch a hot iron and shout out in pain. State if shouting is a voluntary or an involuntary response.

3 You pick up a hot pan and drop it.

a Name the stimulus, effector and response.

b State the different parts of the body involved in the response.

Stimuli and response pathway

Stimuli (plural of stimulus) are changes in the environment (stepping on a pin is a simple example), which cause living things to take action. Responses are the action taken (jerking the foot away from the pin's point). The nervous system links stimuli and responses:

stimulus → receptor → sensory neurone →
central nervous system
response ← effector ← motor neurone ←

Nerve impulses are sent to the effectors. Muscles are effectors and the impulses cause them to contract (shorten). Glands like the salivary glands are also effectors. Impulses cause them to secrete substances.

The synapse

A chain of neurones links receptors with effectors. Tiny gaps separate the fibres at the end of one neurone from the beginning of the next neurone in the chain. The gap is called a **synapse**.

When nerve impulses reach the end of the fibre carrying them, a chemical is released from the fibre into the synapse. The chemical is called a **neurotransmitter**.

A neurotransmitter is a messenger that carries information about the nerve impulses across the synapse. When it reaches the next neurone, it triggers new impulses and so on across the synapses of the chain of neurones (see Figure 3).

Only the end of a neurone makes, stores and releases neurotransmitter into a synapse. This is why nerve impulses only travel one way along neurones.

Notice the myelin sheath in Figure 3. Myelin is a fatty substance that insulates the axons and speeds up the passage of nerve impulses along neurones.

chain of neurones

receptor — synapse — synapse — synapse — effector

neurone — neurone — neurone

① neurotransmitter stored here is released by the arrival of nerve impulses

③ neurotransmitter stimulates the next neurone in the chain, triggering new nerve impulses

ending of the neurone

beginning of the next neurone in the chain

② neurotransmitter is released into the gap of the synapse. It passes across the synapse

| direction of nerve impulses | myelin sheath wrapped around a dendron/axon | cell body of a neurone |

QUESTIONS

4 Draw a flow diagram showing the pathway from stimulus to response, for a scenario of your choosing.

5 Describe how information carried in nerve impulses passes across a synapse.

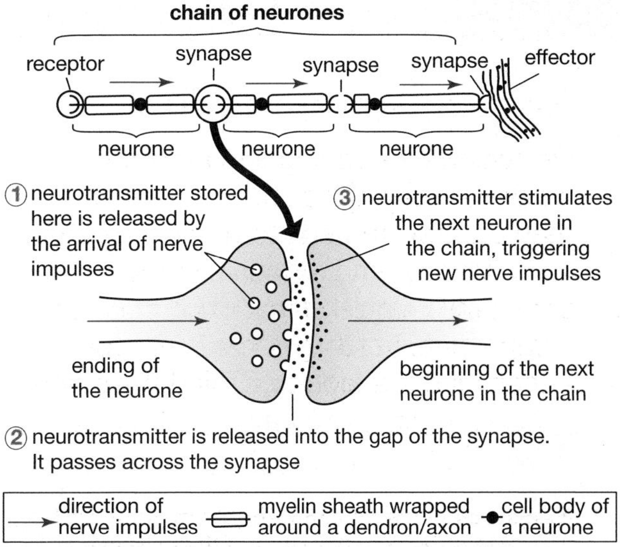

FIGURE 3: The synapse at work. It enables nerve impulses to pass from receptor to effector, helping to achieve a coordinated response to a stimulus.

The reflex arc

The involuntary behaviour of the person stepping on the pin is an example of a **reflex response**. It is automatic and quickly removes the foot from the pin.

Most reflex responses are fast, bypassing the brain, and help to protect the body from damage.

A reflex response is brought about by a chain of nerves called a **reflex arc**. In Figure 4 each nerve is represented by a single neurone. Receptor cells are represented by a single receptor:

> Sensory neurones send nerve impulses from receptor cells to the spinal cord.

> Motor neurones send nerve impulses from the spinal cord to effectors.

> Relay neurones in the spinal cord receive nerve impulses from sensory neurones and send them to motor neurones.

Figure 4 shows how the reflex arc works. The numbers indicate the path of the nerve impulses:

1 The pain receptor detects the stimulus of the pin and sends nerve impulses along the sensory neurone.

2 Nerve impulses travel along the sensory neurone from the receptor to the spinal cord in the central nervous system.

3 Nerve impulses from the sensory neurone cross the synapse and trigger new impulses in the relay neurone. The impulses travel along the relay neurone to the motor neurone.

4 Nerve impulses from the relay neurone cross the synapse and trigger new impulses in the motor neurone. The nerve impulses travel from the spinal cord to the effector.

5 There is another synapse where the motor neurone meets the muscle. Nerve impulses from the motor neurone cross the synapse and cause the muscle to contract.

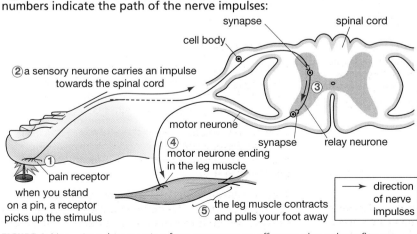

FIGURE 4: Nerve impulses passing from receptors to effectors along the reflex arc. What does this bring about?

QUESTIONS

6 Rearrange these parts of a reflex arc into their correct order: effector, sensory neurone, receptor, motor neurone, relay neurone.

7 Explain the difference between a reflex response and a reflex arc.

8 Describe the advantages of reflex responses to different stimuli.

Hormones at work

You will find out:

> that hormones are produced in endocrine glands

> that hormones are transported in the blood

> about target organs and tissues

> how blood glucose levels are regulated

Fright: flight or fight?

We've all been frightened at some time in our lives. Rapid breathing and a racing heart prime our body for flight or a fight. Extra glucose and oxygen carried in the bloodstream quickly reach our muscles, enabling them to work hard. The hormone adrenaline is responsible for our reaction to whatever is frightening us.

FIGURE 1: What happened for this response to occur?

Hormones

Hormones are chemicals produced by glands in the body and released into the blood. They circulate in the bloodstream and affect different tissues.

The glands that produce hormones are called **endocrine glands**. They are ductless glands, which is why hormones are released directly into the blood. The organs or tissues affected by hormones are their **target organs or tissues**. The sequence goes like this:

> the endocrine gland produces …

> a hormone, which circulates in …

> the blood, where the hormone affects …

> the target organ or tissue.

Hormones help to regulate the body's activities and keep the body's internal environment constant (**homeostasis**). Regulating body water content and blood glucose levels are examples.

Remember!

A duct is a tube. The substance produced by a gland passes through the duct to its destination. Ducted glands are called **exocrine glands**.

QUESTIONS

1 Outline how endocrine glands work.

2 How does the pancreas help to maintain the body's constant environment?

In Figure 2 you can see that the **pancreas** produces two hormones: **insulin** and **glucagon**. These hormones help to regulate blood glucose levels:

> Insulin *decreases* the level of blood glucose.

> Glucagon *increases* the level of blood glucose.

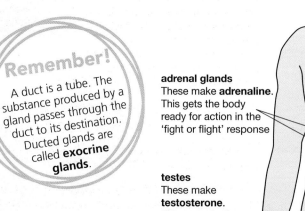

thyroid gland
This makes a hormone called **thyroxin**. This controls the rate of chemical reactions in the body

pituitary gland
This is sometimes called the master gland because it makes hormones that control other endocrine glands. It also makes **growth hormone**

pancreas
This makes hormones called **insulin** and **glucagon**. These regulate the amount of glucose in the blood

adrenal glands
These make **adrenaline**. This gets the body ready for action in the 'fight or flight' response

ovaries
These make the female hormones called **oestrogen** and **progesterone**. These cause the development of female characteristics during puberty and control the menstrual cycle

testes
These make **testosterone**. This controls the development of male characteristics in puberty

FIGURE 2: Endocrine glands produce hormones and release them into the blood.

Flight or fight   Adrenaline

Regulating blood glucose

The normal level of glucose in the blood is about 90 mg per 100 cm³ of blood; however, it rises or falls depending on circumstances:

> It *rises* following a meal as digested food is absorbed from the intestine into the bloodstream.

> It *falls* during exercise as vigorously contracting muscles use extra glucose as a source of energy.

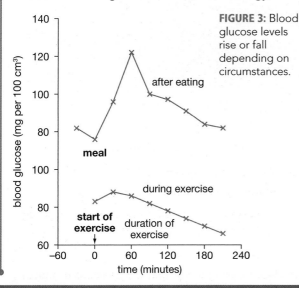

FIGURE 3: Blood glucose levels rise or fall depending on circumstances.

Returning blood glucose levels to normal is an example of a homeostatic mechanism in action, and the hormones insulin and glucagon are responsible:

> Insulin and glucagon are produced by the pancreas.

> The hormones are released from the pancreas into the bloodstream.

> The liver is the target tissue of glucagon; the muscles as well as the liver are the target tissues of insulin.

Insulin is released from the pancreas when the level of blood glucose is high. It promotes the conversion of glucose into another type of carbohydrate called **glycogen**. Glycogen is formed of many glucose units joined together. It is insoluble and is stored in liver and muscle tissue.

QUESTIONS

3 Explain why blood glucose levels change after a meal and during exercise.

4 Look at Figure 3. Explain why blood levels begin to fall an hour after a meal.

How glucagon regulates blood glucose levels (Higher tier only)

Glucagon is released from the pancreas when the level of blood glucose is low. It promotes the conversion of glycogen into glucose, which is then released into the bloodstream (see Figure 4).

The level of blood glucose is regulated at about 90 mg per 100 cm³ of blood as a result of the balance between the opposite effects of glucagon and insulin. The pancreas monitors this process by detecting the level of blood glucose in the first place and triggering the appropriate response.

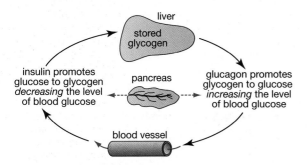

FIGURE 4: Regulating blood glucose levels.

Hormones and target tissues

Why does a particular hormone affect only a particular target organ or tissue? After all, hormones are released into the bloodstream and pass to all of the tissues of the body. The answer is in the **plasma membrane** of the cells of the target tissue in question.

It's rather like a lock and key. The shape of the molecules of a particular hormone means that they will only bind to the plasma membrane of the cells of its target tissue, and *not* to the plasma membrane of the cells of any other tissues. We say the hormone is **specific** to its target tissue.

Did you know?

Coordination by the nervous system is very rapid (milliseconds) but by endocrine glands is much longer (hours, days and even months). The exception is adrenaline.

QUESTIONS

5 Explain how insulin and glucagon maintain the body's internal stable environment.

6 Describe the differences between coordination by the nervous system and endocrine glands.

7 Explain why oestrogen will only affect the tissue lining the uterus (womb).

Diabetes

You will find out:

> about Type 1 diabetes and its treatment

> about Type 2 diabetes and its treatment

> the link between Type 2 diabetes and obesity

Insulin: genetic engineering in action

Until the discovery in the early twentieth century of the hormone insulin, in juice extracted from the pancreas, people wasted away from the effects of diabetes. The insulin injected by people with diabetes used to come from cows and pigs, but now bacteria have been genetically modified to produce the human form of insulin.

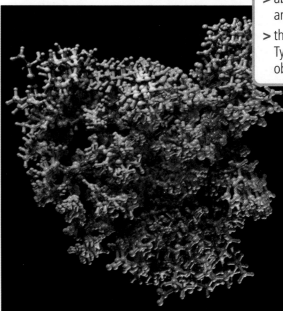

FIGURE 1: A model of a molecule of human insulin.

What is diabetes?

For some people, regulating their blood glucose levels is difficult. This condition is called **diabetes**. The blood glucose level of someone with diabetes becomes dangerously high and stays high because in many cases the pancreas is not producing enough insulin. Having a high blood glucose level for too long increases the risk of many serious health problems such as blindness, kidney failure, heart disease and even worse.

Symptoms

Tiredness and constant thirst despite drinking are **symptoms** of diabetes. A simple test helps to confirm the condition.

When a person's blood glucose levels remain high, the kidneys cannot absorb all of the excess glucose. The glucose appears in the person's urine. The test detects its presence (see Figure 2).

Causes

Diabetes resulting from the pancreas not producing enough insulin is called Type 1 diabetes. The condition generally occurs in younger people.

Some people can develop diabetes for other reasons when they're older. In these cases, the pancreas often produces some insulin but the liver and muscles (the target tissues for insulin) become **insensitive** to it. This condition is called Type 2 diabetes. Affected individuals are resistant to the effects of insulin. Obesity is probably the most important factor in the development of insulin resistance.

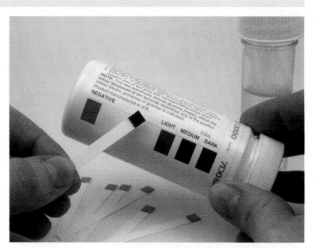

FIGURE 2: Here the dark colour on the Clinistix strip indicates a positive result for glucose in the urine. The person providing the sample may have diabetes. A lighter colour indicates a negative (normal) result.

QUESTIONS

1 List the symptoms and possible effects of diabetes.

2 Describe a test which indicates that a person might be developing diabetes.

3 State the link between blood glucose and diabetes.

Q Regulating blood glucose levels   Glycaemia   Diabetes types

Treatment

Treatment depends on the type of diabetes. Individuals with Type 1 diabetes usually need daily injections of insulin to reduce blood glucose levels. Even so, a healthy diet and regular exercise are still important.

> Exercise – exercise consumes glucose and reduces overall blood glucose level.

> Careful eating – cutting down on sugary food means a lower blood glucose level.

People with Type 1 diabetes are taught to inject themselves with insulin. The injection site is usually into fatty tissue, called **subcutaneous fat**, such as in the abdomen. Injection into fatty tissue reduces the risk of injecting insulin too close to a large blood vessel or nerve.

Getting the dose right is not always easy.

> If too little insulin is injected or too much sugary food eaten, blood glucose levels will remain too high resulting in many serious health problems.

> If too much insulin is injected, blood glucose levels might fall too low. If the person does a lot of exercise, that too might cause their blood glucose level to drop. The person might feel faint or even pass out; however, it is possible to learn to recognise the signals. To put things right they might eat something sweet which quickly boosts their blood glucose to the right level.

For those with Type 2 diabetes, careful eating, regular exercise and losing weight can successfully regulate blood glucose levels without the need for other treatment. However, after a time diet and exercise may not be enough and drugs to control blood glucose levels may be needed. Taking two or more different tablets in combination is the usual treatment.

QUESTIONS

4 Explain why a person with Type 1 diabetes might feel faint following an overdose of insulin.

5 Describe the similarities and differences between Type 1 diabetes and Type 2 diabetes.

Explaining the causes of diabetes

Type 1 diabetes is the result of either:

> An individual's immune system destroying the cells in the pancreas that produce insulin. This is an example of an **auto-immune disease**.

> A **mutation** of the gene encoding the production of insulin. The mutated gene no longer works properly. This is an example of a genetic disorder.

Type 2 diabetes is the result of:

> Insulin no longer being able to bind to liver cells and muscle cells (the target tissues). Therefore, the tissues do not respond to insulin even though it is being produced by the pancreas.

Obesity and diabetes: the link

An easy way to determine if someone is overweight is to measure their **body mass index (BMI)**. It is a measure of body fat based on height and mass (weight) that applies to normal-sized adult men and women.

This is the equation to calculate a person's BMI:

$$\text{BMI} = \frac{\text{mass (kg)}}{\text{height}^2 \ (\text{m}^2)} \ \text{kg/m}^2$$

Recent research, as shown in Figure 3, has indicated a strong correlation between obesity and the risk of developing Type 2 diabetes. However, the correlation is not straightforward. Studying the worked example on page 55 will help you evaluate the link.

QUESTIONS

6 Explain how diabetes is caused.

7 a Calculate the BMI for a man who is 1.65 m tall and weighs 96 kg.

b Does he risk developing Type 2 diabetes? If you found out that he was a professional rugby player how would that affect your answer?

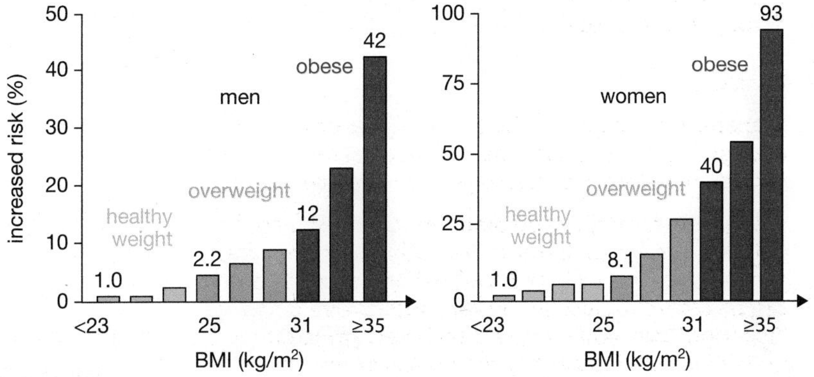

FIGURE 3: A graph showing the correlation between BMI and risk of developing diabetes. What kind of correlation is shown here?

Plant hormones

You will find out:
> that hormones enable plants to respond to stimuli
> how auxin brings about shoot curvature

Face the light

Do you keep plants at home? If so, you've probably noticed that their shoots bend towards the window. Light is the stimulus. The shoots respond by growing to where it's brightest (in this case the window). Roots grow away from light but towards the force of gravity.

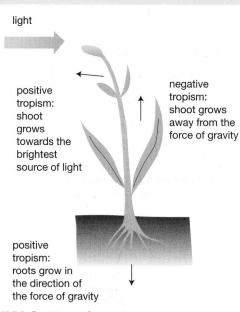

FIGURE 1: Why does this house plant grow to where the light is brightest?

Plant movements

Plants are never still. Shoots twist and turn and flowers and leaves move in daily rhythm.

Plant movements are the result of growth. They take longer than the fast-acting nervous systems and muscle movements of animals. Their movements can be seen using time-lapse photography.

Growth movements take place in response to gravity as well as light. When the movements are the result of stimuli coming mainly from one direction (a brightly lit window for example), then the response is called a **tropism**. The tropism is **positive** if plants grow towards the stimulus, **negative** if they grow away.

Positive and negative tropisms increase the survival chances of plants. For example, roots respond positively to the force of gravity. They grow downwards, firmly anchoring the plant into the soil. Shoots respond negatively to gravity, but positively to light. They grow towards the brightest source, maximising the rate of photosynthesis in their leaves.

light

positive tropism: shoot grows towards the brightest source of light

negative tropism: shoot grows away from the force of gravity

positive tropism: roots grow in the direction of the force of gravity

FIGURE 3: Positive and negative tropisms.

FIGURE 2: The leaves and flower heads of young sunflowers follow the sun. What does this tell you?

QUESTIONS

1 Describe the difference between a positive tropism and a negative tropism.

2 Explain the advantages of tropisms to plants.

3 Draw a flow chart to explain how tropism in shoots occurs.

Plant hormones

Tropisms are the result of differences in the growth rate of tissues on one side or the other of shoots and roots. Plant **hormones** are responsible for the different growth rates. The substance **auxin** is an example.

> The term **phototropism** refers to the response of plants to the stimulus of light. So positive phototropism means that plants grow towards the light.

> **Gravitropism** (or **geotropism**) refers to the response of plants to the stimulus of gravity. So positive gravitropism means that roots grow downwards.

Auxin affects plant responses to each stimulus. However, it seems that plant cells in stem tissue and root tissue are affected differently depending on the concentration of the hormone in the tissues.

Did you know?

Roots usually grow to where there is the most water in the soil. This is positive hydrotropism.

QUESTIONS

4 Describe three stimuli that affect the production of auxin.

5 Explain how the cells of shoot tissue and root tissue respond differently to auxin.

Action of auxin

Auxin seems to make the cellulose wall of plant cells more elastic. This means that the walls are more 'stretchy'. It is therefore easier for the cells to grow and rapidly enlarge.

Effects of auxin in shoots

In shoots, cell division takes place near the tip. The new cells then elongate (get longer). This is what makes the shoot grow. Auxin causes the cells to elongate.

Auxin is more concentrated in tissues on the side where light is least intense. The cells of the shaded tissues grow more *quickly*. On the more brightly lit side of the shoot the concentration of auxin is less. The cells here grow more slowly. As a result, the shoot grows towards light where it is brightest.

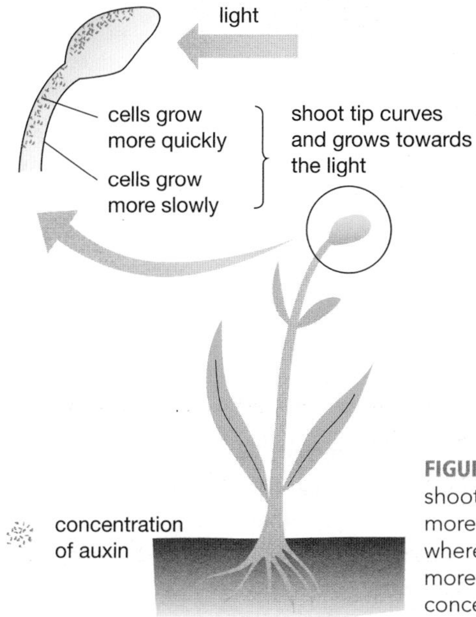

Effects of auxin in roots

In roots the opposite seems to be the case. Where the concentration of auxin is high, the cells of the tissues grow more *slowly*. Auxin is more concentrated on the underside of roots than the upperside. The cells of the tissues of the underside therefore grow more slowly than the cells of the tissues of the upperside. As a result the root grows down into the soil towards the force of gravity.

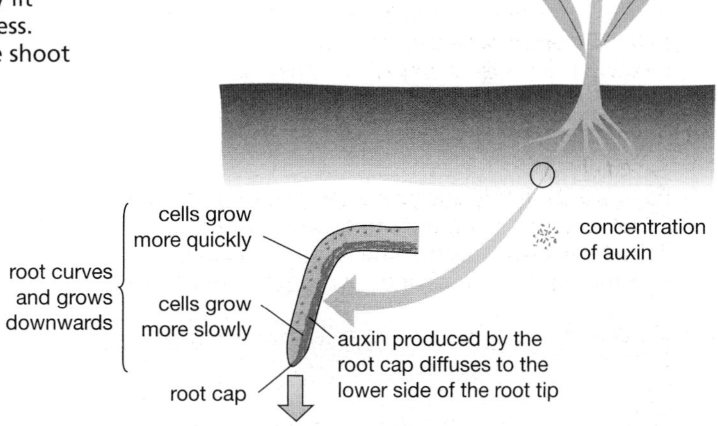

light

cells grow more quickly

cells grow more slowly

shoot tip curves and grows towards the light

concentration of auxin

FIGURE 4: The shoot grows more quickly where auxin is more concentrated.

cells grow more quickly

cells grow more slowly

root curves and grows downwards

root cap

auxin produced by the root cap diffuses to the lower side of the root tip

concentration of auxin

FIGURE 5: The root grows more quickly where auxin is less concentrated.

QUESTIONS

6 Define the word 'growth'.

7 Explain the effect of auxin on plant cells.

8 Predict how a plant will grow if you sow the seed on its side. Explain your answer.

Using plant hormones

You will find out:

> the commercial uses of plant hormones

> about selective weedkillers

> about rooting powder

> about fruit ripening

> how we get seedless fruit

Fallen leaves

Agent Orange is a synthetic plant hormone that was used during the Vietnam War in the 1970s. US planes sprayed large areas of forest to cause trees to lose their leaves, making it easier to spot enemy soldiers. The trees died and people were poisoned. Used wisely, plant hormones are very useful but we have to decide how to apply science – for our benefit or for destruction.

FIGURE 1: US planes spraying Agent Orange during the Vietnam War.

Plant hormones in food production (Higher tier only)

You will recall that the substance auxin is a plant hormone, which affects plant growth. Soon after its discovery in the 1920s other plant hormones were identified. Scientists quickly realised that the substances could be used to increase food production.

> **Weedkillers** are plant hormones used by farmers to kill unwanted plants (weeds). Killing weeds improves food production because the weeds compete with crops for growing space, water, soil nutrients and light. With weedkiller, yields improve and there is more food for us to eat. The farmers' extra sales offset their costs of buying and using weedkillers.

> Rooting powder contains plant hormones that in solution encourage cut stems to develop roots. Using rooting powder makes it possible to produce large numbers of new plants quickly. The new plants develop from **stem cuttings** taken from parent plants. Because the new plants are identical to the parent plants, growers can make sure that desirable qualities of the parent are kept in the new plants. Rooting powder therefore helps horticulturalists and farmers to grow new plants with guaranteed quality.

FIGURE 2: Although they look pretty, these poppies are a weed that has infested a wheat field.

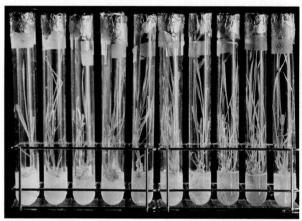

FIGURE 3: These cereal plants develop from tiny fragments of a parent plant growing in auxin-enriched gel. The technique allows mass production of identical plants and is an effective way of propagating any genes introduced into the parent plant.

> Fruit ripening and its control is another example of the commercial use of plant hormones. Supermarket staff must make sure that fresh food is ready when customers want it. It's not ideal to sell fruit that is not ripe or that is squashy and over-ripe. Controlling the ripening of bananas illustrates the point.

Bananas are picked under-ripe and exported to the UK. Below the decks of the container ships, ripening during the sea voyage is held back by reducing the level of oxygen in the air in the ship's hold. After docking, the bananas are unloaded into large warehouses. The levels of the gases in the atmosphere in the warehouses are carefully adjusted to control the time of ripening. The gas **ethene** is a plant hormone. It is released into the atmosphere just before the bananas are delivered to the shops for sale. The bananas ripen quickly and are ready for eating.

FIGURE 4: Not likely to be bought: if bananas arrived like this there would be little point shipping them across the oceans.

Selective weedkillers (Higher tier only)

The word **herbicide** is the technical term for weedkiller. Some types of herbicide stimulate the growth of plant stems. The plants became tall and spindly. However, the rate of root growth does not keep pace with the stem. The roots are not able to absorb enough water to support the growing plant. The plant dies.

When a farmer sprays a weed-infested field of wheat, why don't the wheat plants die as well as the weeds? The answer to the question is to do with the surface area of leaves.

Wheat plants are narrow-leaved; most weeds are broad-leaved. For a given mass of plants, broad-leaved weeds absorb more herbicide than narrow-leaved wheat plants.

Wheat plants are not affected by the herbicide at the concentrations that kill weeds. Farmers put this **selective** effect of herbicides to good use to keep their cereal crops free of weeds.

FIGURE 5: Selective herbicide controlling weeds in soya plants.

Seedless fruit (Higher tier only)

Seeds as well as shoots produce auxin. For example, a strawberry remains underdeveloped if all of the seeds which speckle its surface are removed. Removing the seeds removes the source of auxin which strawberries need for normal development.

If only some seeds are removed, then auxin is produced where the seeds remain, and that part of the strawberry develops normally. However, where the seeds have been removed, auxin is not produced. This part of the strawberry remains underdeveloped.

Fruits contain seeds when plants reproduce sexually. But consumers like some fruits to be seedless, and growers can produce seedless fruits by smearing the plants' female sex organs with auxin paste.

The auxin paste stimulates the development of the female sex organs and the fruit is produced. However, the egg cells within the female sex organs have not been fertilised and therefore seeds are not produced. The result is seedless fruits: seedless grapes, cucumbers and tomatoes are all produced in this way.

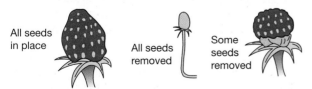

All seeds in place   All seeds removed   Some seeds removed

FIGURE 6: Which substances regulate the development of strawberries?

Interpreting data

You will find out:
> how to demonstrate an understanding of phototropism
> about analysing, interpreting and evaluating data

Being a scientist

Data is information about what is happening and has happened. Interpretation is working out its meaning. Imagine walking into the kitchen early one morning. The kettle is hot. Was someone up before you? Have they gone out or back to bed? You need more data to know the answers. Experiments are like this. They give answers but also raise more questions, which means more experiments, and so on.

FIGURE 1: Get the results and record the data.

Phototropism in cress seeds

Have you ever grown cress at home? If so, you probably sprinkled the seeds over damp tissue paper and then waited. If kept warm and well watered, the seeds will sprout shoots and roots after a few days.

You might have put the **seedlings** on a window shelf. If so, you would have soon noticed the developing plants growing towards the window. Auxin in the shoot tissue is at work and positive phototropism is the result.

Remember!
Comparing an experiment with its control helps you to decide whether any effects of the experiment are real or not.

FIGURE 2: What type of phototropism is shown in this cress seedling?

How would you set up an experiment to show that light affects the growth of cress? These questions will help you to find the answer:

> What do you think *might* happen (prediction) … and why?

> What *actually* happened in the experiment?

> What do you conclude from comparing what actually happened with your prediction (*might* happen)?

Working through the list will help you to find out what you need to know about phototropism in cress seedlings.

QUESTIONS

1 Explain why the shoots of cress seedlings placed on a window shelf grow towards the window panes.

2 Describe how you would set up an experiment to show that light affects the growth of cress seedlings.

Experiments with plant hormones

Investigating auxins

In the 1920s a Dutch biologist, Frits Went, investigated the development of cereal seedlings. He suggested that a substance regulated growth of the shoots. He called the substance auxin – the first plant hormone to be discovered. Went and other scientists carried out experiments to investigate the effects of auxin on shoot growth in response to light.

Table 1 summarises the **data** from the auxin experiments and the conclusions drawn.

Growing cress at home   Setting up an experiment   Frits Went

TABLE 1: The data from the experiments and conclusions.

Treatment	Response to light	Conclusion
Uncovered intact cereal seedling	✔	Control which shows that the tip is sensitive to light
Uncovered cereal seedling with its shoot tip removed	✘	Shows that the shoot tip contains a substance which controls the response of the shoot to light
Intact cereal seedling covered with aluminium foil which excludes light	✘	Shows that the shoot tip is sensitive to light
Cereal seedling with its tip cut off. The tip is placed on a slip of metal foil and replaced on the rest of the shoot. The metal slip prevents diffusion of chemicals from the shoot tip to the rest of the shoot	✘	Shows that a substance produced in the shoot tip diffuses to the region behind the shoot tip, where it controls the shoot's response to light
Cereal seedling with its tip removed. The tip is placed on an agar block and replaced on the rest of the shoot. The agar block allows diffusion of the substance produced in the shoot tip to the region behind the shoot tip	✔	Result confirms conclusion from the experiment with a slip of metal foil above
Cereal seedling with its tip removed. An agar block is placed on the rest of the shoot after it has been soaked in a solution of auxin	✔	Shows that the substance produced in the shoot tip controls the response of the shoot to light
Cereal seedling with its tip removed. An agar block is placed on the rest of the shoot after it has been soaked in a mash made of the shoot tip	✔	Shows that the substance produced in the shoot tip which controls the response of the shoot to light is probably auxin
Cereal seedling with its tip removed. An agar block is placed on the remaining part of the shoot	✘	A **control experiment** showing that auxin and not agar probably controls the response of the shoot to light

Investigating gibberellins

During the 1920s, Japanese scientists noticed that rice seedlings infected by the fungus *Gibberella fujikuroi* (now called *Fusarium*) grew very tall. In 1926, the scientists found that a substance produced by the fungus increased the distance along the shoot between leaves. The plant hormone **gibberellin** had been discovered.

> **QUESTIONS**
>
> **3** Explain the importance of control experiments.
>
> **4** Using the data from Table 1, analyse how auxin controls plant growth.

Analysing, interpreting and evaluating results from experiments

Analysis of the results of the auxin experiments suggested to Went that the tip of a growing cereal shoot acts as a light receptor, and that auxin:

> is produced in the shoot tip

> diffuses to the region behind the shoot tip

> stimulates growth so that the shoot bends towards the light shining mainly from one direction.

This led to the conclusion that bending of the shoot tip towards light happens when unequal distribution of auxin in the shoot causes unequal growth rates (see Figure 4 on page 43).

Soon after the discovery of gibberellin, a simple test to show the effect of different concentrations of it on shoot growth was developed. Figure 3 shows the results of this test.

FIGURE 3: Effect of gibberellin on shoot growth.

> **QUESTIONS**
>
> **5** Interpret the data shown in Figure 3 and comment on factors that might affect its quality.
>
> **6** Explain the difference between data and data interpretation.

Preparing for assessment: Planning an investigation

To achieve a good grade in science, you not only have to know and understand scientific ideas, but you also need to be able to apply them to other situations and investigations. This task will support you in developing these skills.

Investigating plant hormones

Top-quality lawns need to be kept weed-free. Synthetic auxins can be used to stop weeds germinating. A student wanted to find the minimum concentration of the synthetic auxin 2,4-D (2,4-dichlorophenoxyacetic acid) that she could use to treat her lawn at home. She looked on the internet to see if similar investigations had been done before, and found the method below.

Dissolve the auxin in 1% agar, allow the agar to set and place cress seeds on its surface; 20 cm^3 of agar will fill a petri dish. The seeds absorb water and auxin from the agar. Cress germinates quickly and can be used to judge the effect a synthetic auxin will have on other plants.

It is usually better to use a tried and tested method than to devise a new one. One place you can find methods is on the internet. However, not everything published on the internet is trustworthy. Check that a number of people have used the same technique.

Planning

1. State the student's hypothesis.

In other words, say what she expects to happen and why. Remember to state clearly the expectation and support this (using appropriate scientific terms) to gain Quality of Written Communication marks.

2. Identify the independent and dependent variables.

The independent variable is what she will change to test the hypothesis. The dependent variable is what she will measure to find the result.

3. 2,4-D is supplied as a solution in hot agar with a concentration of 1 cm^3 per litre. What values of the independent variable will you test and why? When will you measure the dependent variable?

Plants are usually sensitive to a very wide range of auxin concentrations. How could you make the concentration 10 times smaller for each test?

4. List two variables that you should control to make it a fair test. Suggest how you will control these variables to improve the quality of your results.

In your plan you should suggest values for these.

5. How will you make sure any differences are caused by the 2,4-D?

6. Write step-by-step instructions for carrying out the investigation. Explain how your method will test the hypothesis.

Show how the equipment will be used and state how many tests will be done. Be clear and logical in your instructions.

7. Identify any hazards and explain how the risks they pose can be minimised.

A hazard is something that could cause harm. A risk is the likelihood of being harmed.

✳ Processing evidence

1. In one experiment all the untreated seeds germinated. The seeds treated with 2,4-D gave these results. Display them on a line graph.

2,4-D concentration in cm³ per litre of agar	Germination (%)
0.0001	100
0.001	97
0.01	53
0.1	7
1	0

2. Describe the general trend in the results.

3. Illustrate the trend with examples from the graph.

4. Estimate the minimum concentration of 2,4-D needed to prevent weed germination.

Remember to put the independent variable on the *x*-axis of the line graph.

Make sure you start with the lowest concentration tested. There is no need to start at zero. When the values are too different to fit on a linear scale, each point on the scale can cover a power of 10.

Mark each value on your line graph with a simple pencil cross.

Decide whether a smooth curve or a straight line best fits the points. Never draw lines from point to point.

State what happens to the dependent variable as the value of the independent variable increases. You may need to state that this only applies between certain values.

Give one or two examples to illustrate how much difference it makes when the independent variable is changed.

If it falls between values state what they are.

✳ Connections

How Science Works

> Collecting and analysing data.

> Planning to solve a scientific problem.

> Collecting data from secondary sources including the internet.

> Working accurately and safely when collecting first-hand data.

> Evaluating methods of data collection and verifying information sources.

> Presenting information using appropriate language, conventions and symbols and tools.

Maths in Science

> Plot and draw graphs selecting appropriate scales for the axes.

> Translate information between graphical and numeric forms.

> Extract and interpret information from charts, graphs and tables.

B1 checklist (Topics 1 and 2)

To achieve your forecast grade in the exam you'll need to revise

Use this checklist to see what you can do now. Refer back to pages 10–47 if you're not sure.

Look across the rows to see how you could progress – *bold italic* means Higher tier only.

Remember you'll need to be able to use these ideas in various ways, such as:
> interpreting pictures, diagrams and graphs
> applying ideas to new situations
> explaining ethical implications
> suggesting some benefits and risks to society
> drawing conclusions from evidence you've been given.

Look at pages 270–92 for more information about exams and how you'll be assessed.

To aim for a grade E	To aim for a grade C	To aim for a grade A
recall that organisms can be classified into groups according to the characteristics they have in common, giving the backbone in vertebrates as an example	describe the characteristics of the five kingdoms describe the hierarchy of classification, from kingdom to species	understand the issues surrounding the classification of viruses and vertebrates explain that most classifications reflect the relatedness
define the meaning of the term species and state the limitations of this definition	explain why scientists use the binomial system to name and identify species	apply understanding of binomial classification to the conservation of species
construct keys that show how species can be identified	recall that the individuals of a species vary, and this variation can be continuous or discontinuous	*explain how variations such as hybridisation and ring species complicate classification*
explain that organisms are adapted to their environment, including extreme environments such as polar regions		apply understanding of adaptations to organisms near hydrothermal vents
recall that Charles Darwin was the first (with Alfred Russel Wallace) to explain that natural selection is the mechanism of evolution	explain Darwin's theory of natural selection in terms of variation, overproduction, competition, survival, inheritance and gradual change	*explain how speciation occurs as a result of geographic isolation*
understand that variation can be caused by genes or the environment	describe the causes of genetic variation	explain how genetics, including DNA evidence and bacterial resistance, can be used to support Darwin's theory

To aim for a grade E	To aim for a grade C	To aim for a grade A
state that the cell's nucleus contains chromosomes on which genes are located understand that a form of alleles leads to differences in inherited characteristics	explain the meanings of different genetic terms	accurately use genetic terms in extended writing
recall the meaning of the term monohybrid inheritance understand how to use Punnett squares and genetic diagrams	interpret monohybrid inheritance using Punnett squares, genetic diagrams and family pedigrees	analyse patterns of monohybrid inheritance, and calculate and analyse the outcomes of the crosses
recall that genetic disorders can be caused by gene mutations	describe the symptoms of sickle cell disease and cystic fibrosis	*evaluate pedigree analysis when screening for sickle cell disease and cystic fibrosis*
state that the term homeostasis refers to the maintenance of a stable internal environment describe thermoregulation and osmoregulation as examples of homeostasis	explain how body temperature and body water content are regulated	*apply understanding of the mechanisms of homeostasis to vasoconstriction and vasodilation* *explain vasoconstriction and vasodilation in terms of negative feedback*
recall that the central nervous system consists of the brain and spinal cord recall that nervous responses can be voluntary or involuntary	describe the function of the myelin sheath and neurotransmitter describe how stimulating receptors sends (transmits) electrical impulses along neurones	describe the function of dendrons and axons explain how different components work together to bring about a coordinated response, in the form of a simple reflex arc
recall that hormones are produced in endocrine glands and transported in the blood to their target organs	explain how blood glucose levels are regulated by insulin	*apply understanding of the effect of insulin to the role of glucagon regulating blood glucose levels*
state that lack of insulin causes Type 1 diabetes	explain that insulin injections control Type 1 diabetes and that dosage depends on the balance between exercise and diet	
state that insulin resistance causes Type 2 diabetes	explain that diet and exercise help to control Type 2 diabetes	understand and evaluate the correlation between obesity (including BMI calculations) and Type 2 diabetes
state that hormones enable plants to respond to stimuli	explain how hormones bring about plant responses and use data to support explanations	*understand the usefulness of plant hormones as weedkillers and substances that improve the growth of crop plants*

51

AO1 1 a The duck-billed platypus is a mammal that lives in water and is found only in Australia. It is oviparous and obtains oxygen through its lungs. State what is meant by the term oviparous. [1]

AO2 b Explain why the duck-billed platypus is difficult to classify as a mammal. [2]

AO2 c The binomial system of classification is the standard global method of identifying and naming species. The binomial name for the duck-billed platypus is *Ornithorynchus anatinus*.

State which part of the binomial is the species name. Explain your choice. [2]

d The spiny anteater is another mammal that lays eggs and lives in Australia. The anteater that lives in Africa is also a mammal but does not lay eggs.

AO2 i The Australian anteater and African anteater …

A are both poikilotherms
B are both homeotherms
C the Australian anteater is a poikilotherm and the African anteater is a homeotherm
D the Australian anteater is a homeotherm and the African anteater is a poikilotherm. [1]

AO2 ii Explain why it is better to describe each type of anteater using its binomial name rather than the name 'anteater'. [2]
[Total: 8]

2 The diagram shows a pedigree chart.

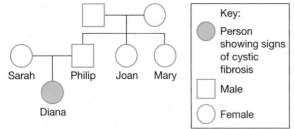

Key:
⬤ Person showing signs of cystic fibrosis
▢ Male
◯ Female

Sarah and Philip have been told that Diana, their baby daughter, has cystic fibrosis, which is an inherited disorder. As far as Sarah and Philip know, no one else in either of their families has the disorder.

AO1 a State one cause of different genetic disorders. [1]

AO1 b State which organs are affected by cystic fibrosis. [2]

AO2 c Suggest why you might think that the allele (gene) controlling cystic fibrosis is recessive. [2]

d Mary, Philip's younger sister, is concerned that she might develop the disease.

AO2 i Explain why this would not happen. [2]

AO2 ii State whether you think Mary might be a carrier of the disorder or not. [1]
[Total: 8]

3 The diagram represents the inside of the eye.

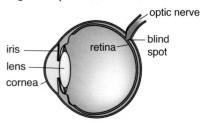

optic nerve
iris
lens
cornea
retina
blind spot

AO1 a State which part of the eye is sensitive to light. [1]

AO2 b Describe how nerve impulses pass from the eye to the brain. [3]

AO2 c Explain why it is difficult to see the colour of objects in dim light. [3]

AO3 d State one piece of evidence from the diagram that a part of the eye is not sensitive to light. [1]
[Total: 8]

4 The diagram shows the responses of a plant to different stimuli. The responses are called tropisms.

light

AO1 a What is the name given to the shoot's response to light? [1]

AO1 AO2 b Explain how the shoot responded to light. [3]

AO2 AO3 c Ibrahim cut off the tip of the shoot. He placed the tip on a thin piece of metal and reattached the tip, with the metal, onto the shoot. Ibrahim predicted the following: 'The shoot will *not* respond to bright light shining mainly from one direction.' Explain why Ibrahim's prediction was correct. [6]
[Total: 10]

✳ Worked example

AO1 a Complete the sentences below about regulating the body's internal environment. You may use the following words: regulate, reactions, control, hormone, nerve impulse, gene, homeostasis. [2]

Keeping the body's internal environment constant is called:

A homeostasis   C mutualism
B interdependence   D homozygous

A ✔

The signal from the pituitary gland of the brain to the kidneys regulating the volume of urine they produce is a:

A nerve impulse   C hormone
B self-regulating system   D enzyme

A ✘

AO1 b Blood glucose regulation is a homeostatic mechanism. The pancreas produces two hormones, insulin and glucagon, which help to regulate blood glucose levels. State the effect of insulin and glucagon on blood glucose levels. [2]

Insulin increases the level of blood glucose. Glucagon decreases the level of blood glucose. ✘ ✘

c Running has warmed this person up.
He is red in the face and sweaty.

AO2 i Explain why the person is red in the face. [2]

More blood is passing through the blood vessels. ✔ ✘

AO1 ii Describe how sweat helps to regulate body temperature. [2]

Sweat is like cold water. Splashing cold water on your face cools you down. ✘ ✔

AO1 d When the temperature outside the body changes, the temperature of the skin is affected. This triggers a process that regulates body temperature. Describe the process that regulates the body temperature. [3]

The process is called thermoregulation. Hormones are released by the brain into the blood and transported to the skin, which responds to the changes in temperature. ✔ ✘ ✘

This candidate scored 4 marks out of 11 which is below grade C. Overall, the candidate's answers demonstrate that the subject material is 'known about' but technical terms and process are not fully understood. By carefully checking the exact language used in the answer and ensuring the explanation is complete, the candidate could have raised his or her grade to a C.

How to raise your grade

Take note of the comments from examiners – these will help you to improve your grade.

The candidate has remembered the technical term homeostasis but has confused a hormone signal with a nervous response. The correct answer is hormone.

The candidate has muddled the effects of the hormones. Insulin decreases blood glucose levels; glucagon increases blood glucose levels. Revising and accurately using scientific terms can easily gain you more marks in the exam.

The candidate hasn't stated which part of the body the vessels supply blood to. The answer literally stares him or her 'in the face'... the red face!
'... cools you down' gains a mark but the candidate does not describe how this happens (evaporation of sweat draws heat from the body, cooling you down). The analogy of cold water gained no marks as it did not answer the question. An answer focused on a complete scientific explanation would have been more concise and improved the overall quality of written communication.

The candidate correctly names the process as thermoregulation but incorrectly describes how information passes between the brain and the skin. They should have mentioned nerve impulses. Using a flow chart can help you to revise thermoregulation.

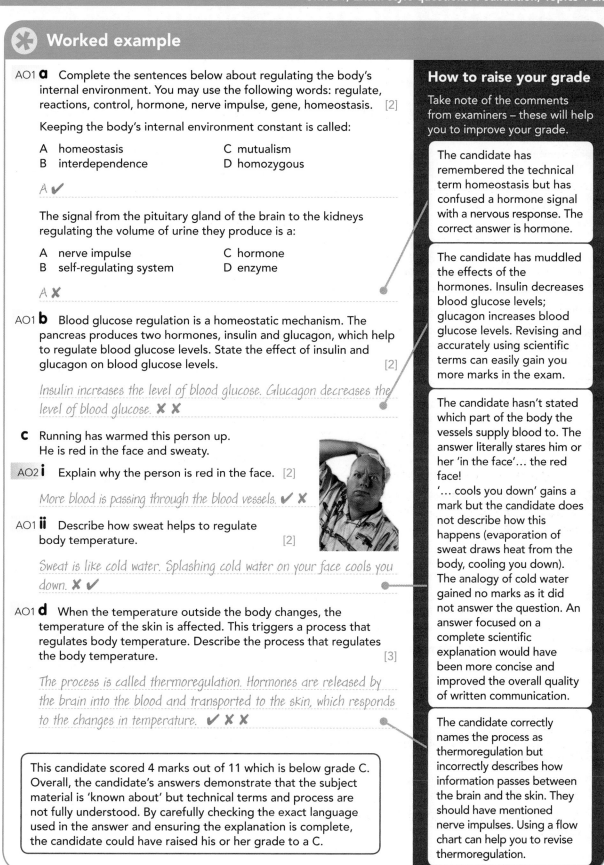

1 Closely related species of *Larus* gull form a ring around the North Pole. Adjacent species are closely related geographically.

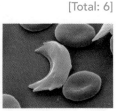

↔ Species interbreed
✗ Species do not interbreed
❶ Different species of the gull *Larus*

AO2 **a** The species of *Larus* gull are closely related because:

    A their genotypes are similar
    B feathers are a shared characteristic
    C they have wings and can fly
    D their phenotypes are similar. [1]

AO1 **b** Explain the difference between the terms genotype and phenotype. [2]

AO1 **c** Explain why ring species complicate classification. [3]

[Total: 6]

2 Sickle cell disease is a recessive genetic disorder that causes the haemoglobin in red blood cells to absorb less oxygen. The affected red blood cells are sickle shaped.

AO2 **a** Explain why feeling weak and tired is a common symptom of sickle cell disease. [2]

b The sickle cell trait refers to people heterozygous for sickle cell. The people are carriers but do not suffer from sickle cell disease. However, carriers are more resistant to malaria.

AO2 **i** Give **two** reasons why sickle cell trait is common in countries where malaria is prevalent. [2]

AO2 **ii** Explain why carriers are more resistant to malaria. [2]

AO2 **iii** A couple decide to have a child. The father has
AO3 sickle cell trait but the mother does not have the sickle cell allele. Calculate the probability and percentage likelihood of their offspring having sickle cell trait. Show your working, including a genetic diagram. [4]

[Total: 10]

3 The hormones insulin and glucagon regulate blood glucose levels at about 90 mg per 100 cm^3 of blood. The pancreas not producing enough insulin is one cause of diabetes.

AO1 **a** Explain why the pancreas is called an endocrine gland. [1]

AO1 **b** Explain the difference in the cause of Type 1 diabetes and Type 2 diabetes. [3]

c The graph shows the rise and fall of blood glucose levels in different circumstances.

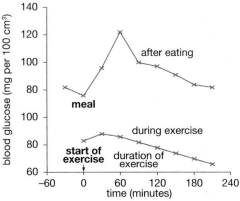

AO2 **i** Explain why blood glucose levels begin to fall 30 minutes after the start of exercise and 60 minutes after eating a meal. [2]

AO2 **ii** Indicate by extending the line on the graph what would happen to the blood glucose level of a person untreated for diabetes 60 minutes after eating a meal. [1]

[Total: 7]

4

AO1 **a** Animals respond to stimuli. Describe the difference between an involuntary response and a voluntary response. [2]

b The diagram shows a synapse separating one neurone from the next.

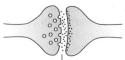

neurotransmitter is released into the gap of the synapse. It passes across the synapse

AO1 **i** State what a neurotransmitter is. [1]

AO1 **ii** Draw two arrows on the diagram indicating the direction of nerve impulses. [1]

AO2 **c** If a biological system that needs to maintain a constant level changes, explain the mechanism that regulates the system and returns it to its normal level. [6]

[Total: 10]

   AO1 recall the science   AO2 apply your knowledge   AO3 evaluate and analyse the evidence

✳ Worked example

Body mass index (BMI) is a measure of body fat based on a person's height and mass (weight). A person's BMI is calculated as follows:

$$BMI = \frac{mass\ (kg)}{height^2\ (m^2)}\ kg/m^2$$

Obesity is defined as a BMI greater than 30. There is a strong correlation between obesity and an increased risk of developing Type 2 diabetes.

AO2 **a** Explain why a BMI greater than 30 might not be a reliable indicator of obesity in a trained athlete. [2]

Probably an athlete's body is more muscular than average.
Muscle (protein) is more dense than fat giving a higher BMI value.
However the athlete is not obese. ✔ ✔

b The mass (weight) and height of three individuals are as follows:

Individual	Mass (kg)	Height (m)
A	51	1.70
B	109	1.80
C	64	1.60

AO2 **i** Calculate the BMI of individuals A to C. Show your working. [4]

A: 51/2.89 = 17.6. ✔

B: 109/1.80² = 33.6. ✔

C: 64/2.56 = 25. ✔ ✘

AO2 **ii** Identify which individual is most at risk of developing Type 2 diabetes. [1]

Individual B because the BMI value is more than 30 kg/m². ✔

AO2 **c** Explain how the claim that there is a correlation between obesity and increased risk of developing Type 2 diabetes might be validated by the scientific community. [4]

Scientists review other scientists' work and discuss it at scientific conferences. ✔ ✔ ✘ ✘

How to raise your grade

Take note of the comments from examiners – these will help you to improve your grade.

A clear answer that shows the candidate knows the difference between mass and density – an excellent start.

The candidate clearly knows how to apply the formula for calculating BMI. However, it is best to have a consistent pattern of working out for what is essentially an identical set of calculations (see individual B). Although all their calculations are correct, the candidate has left out the units (kg/m²) and so loses a mark.

The candidate's answer is correct and this time they have remembered to include units.

The candidate mentions the review process and scientific conferences. However being more specific, for example by explaining the peer-review process in validating evidence and the role of scientific journals and conferences in making research available to the wider scientific community, would have gained more marks.

This candidate scored 8 out of 11 marks which is grade B. The answers were competent and showed a clear understanding of content and ability to apply knowledge. The loss of 1 mark in part **bi** might have been avoided if the candidate had compared his or her answer to the equation given – where the units are clearly shown.

B1 Influences on life (Topic 3)

What you should know

Microbes and diseases

Microbes can cause diseases.

The body defends itself against disease.

Immunisation and antibiotics help the body to defend itself against disease.

● List three ways the body defends itself against disease.

Fit and healthy

Diet, smoking, alcohol and other drugs affect the body's organs in the short and long term.

● Explain why smoking harms your health.

Ecology and ecological relationships

Organisms interact with their environment and each other.

Energy is transferred along food chains.

Organisms influence one another and are affected by the environment.

● Give an example of a food chain.

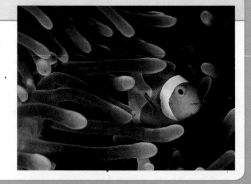

Survival

Adaptations to the environment help survival.

The abundance and distribution of organisms are related to available resources.

Feeding relationships can be modelled quantitatively as pyramids of numbers.

● Explain how energy is transferred along a food chain.

You will find out about

> pathogens, how they are spread and the diseases they cause

> how animals and plants defend themselves against pathogens

> using antiseptics and antibiotics to prevent the spread of infection

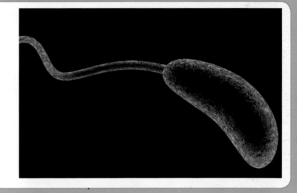

> drugs and their effects on the nervous system and organs

> the ethics of organ transplants

> interdependency between organisms

> the relationship between energy transfer between trophic levels and the shape of a biomass pyramid

> how survival depends on the relationship between species, including parasitism and mutualism

> human population data and the impact of the human population on the environment

> indicator species

> recycling carbon and nitrogen

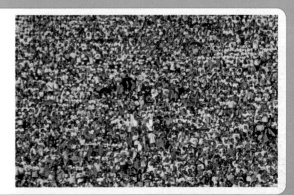

Drugs

You will find out:
> what a drug is
> about the general effects of drugs
> how to investigate reaction times

It's a miserable life

Drug addiction seems to be part of modern life and creates misery for everyone involved. The addict has an expensive, life-altering and unhealthy habit to feed. The addict's family see their loved one destroying his or her life. The police spend time tracking dealers and arresting addicts who often turn to a life of crime to be able to afford their habit. Why does all this happen?

FIGURE 1: The hopelessness of addicts.

What are drugs?

A **drug** is a substance from outside the body which affects chemical reactions *inside* the body. The results are effects on the central nervous system that produce physical changes, such as in heart rate, and psychological effects that can lead to addiction.

Painkillers

Painkillers are drugs that affect the nervous system. They deaden pain or affect the way we think about it.

Painful stimuli are detected by pain receptors. Nerve impulses pass from the receptors to the brain, which interprets the stimuli as painful.

Legal use of powerful painkillers is by **prescription** issued by a doctor. Morphine is an example of a prescription-only painkiller. It is produced from opium which is a substance found in poppy plants. It blocks nerve impulses: no impulses, no pain. Its **narcotic** effects cause drowsiness.

Hallucinogens

Hallucinogens are another group of drugs that affect the nervous system. Cannabis (marijuana) and lysergic acid diethylamide (LSD) are examples. They can produce sensations of false reality (hallucinations, hence the name), and cause changes in **psychological behaviour**, for example, people using them illegally may think that they can jump out of high windows without injuring themselves.

Sniffing the volatile solvents in glues, paints, nail varnish and cleaning fluids also produces dangerous disorientation. The solvents slow down bodily functions affecting, for example, the nervous system which controls breathing and heart rate.

Stimulants and depressants

Caffeine is a non-prescription, legal drug. It is a **stimulant** found in tea, coffee, chocolate and cola. The stimulant increases the speed of our reactions.

FIGURE 2: Sniffing solvents.

We respond to stimuli more quickly because caffeine increases the speed of neurotransmission and so the rate at which nerve impulses pass along neurones.

Alcohol in beer, wines and spirits is also a non-prescription legal drug. It is a **depressant**; that slows down the activity of the brain and our reactions. We respond to stimuli more slowly because alcohol decreases the rate at which nerve impulses pass along neurones.

Remember!

The chemical name for the alcohol in beer, wines and spirits is ethanol.

QUESTIONS

1 Define the term drug.

2 Describe the difference between a stimulant and a depressant.

Drug dependence and addiction

Drugs taken under doctor's orders to fight disease and control pain are a medical success story. With medical guidance, drugs issued by doctors can effectively control or cure illness. However, there is a danger in taking legal painkillers and other illegal drugs that affect the nervous system. They may alter a person's mood, and give a false sense of well-being. These effects make a person crave the drug. Without medical guidance the body gets used to the changes taking place within its tissues. The person comes to depend on the drug and dependence leads to **addiction**.

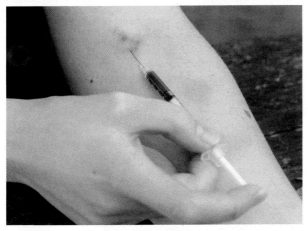

FIGURE 3: An addict injects herself with heroin. The bruises are caused by repeated injection.

Addiction is expensive because many drugs are illegal or illegal to obtain without a doctor's prescription. An **addict** (a person addicted to drugs) can only buy supplies from drug dealers who can exploit the addicts to make a lot of money. The addict's life is usually one of ill-health and often short unless the drug habit is kicked. **Abuse** is a word often used to refer to the non-medical use of drugs.

Did you know?

Self-injecting drugs using dirty (non-sterile) needles shared between users increases the risk of spreading blood-borne diseases such as hepatitis B and AIDS. The viruses causing the diseases spread from person to person because they are in the blood contaminating the needles.

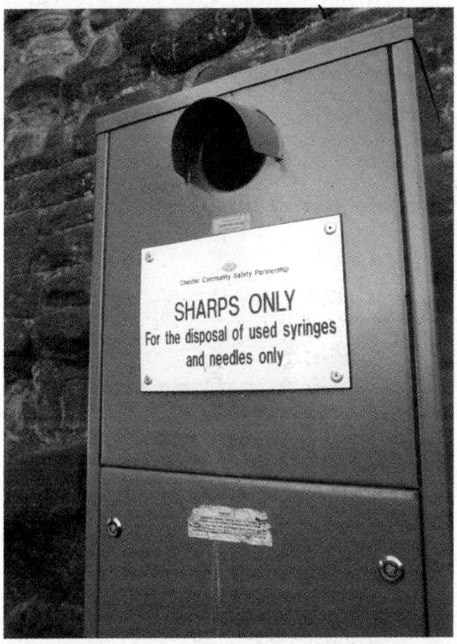

FIGURE 4: This bin in Cheshire is for the collection of used syringes which could infect street cleaners and members of the public with blood-borne diseases if discarded thoughtlessly.

QUESTIONS

3 Explain what is meant by drug abuse.

4 Discuss how injecting illegal drugs increases the risk of spreading disease.

5 Assess the social and physical effects of drugs.

Painkillers and their actions

Painkillers block the release of neurotransmitter into the synapses which separate the neurones (see pages 36–7). Stimulants enhance the release of neurotransmitter. **Reaction time** depends on how quickly and how much neurotransmitter is released. The term refers to the time it takes for a person to respond to a stimulus. Stimulants and depressants affect reaction times.

Remember!
A neurotransmitter carries information about nerve impulses across synapses.

Measuring reaction times

You can measure your reaction times using simple methods such as:

> how long it takes to press a button in response to a flashing light

> how far a ruler falls before you catch it.

QUESTIONS

6 Describe how you would test the hypothesis 'Reaction times decrease with caffeine intake'.

7 Explain the action of painkillers. Support your explanation with a diagram.

8 Suggest the effect of coffee on nerve impulses.

Smoking and alcohol abuse

You will find out:

> the harmful effects of chemicals in cigarette smoke

> about the correlation between smoking and its negative effects on health

> about the harmful effects of alcohol abuse

Smoke gets in your eyes

Smoking cigarettes was very fashionable early in the twentieth century. It was the thing to do and film stars glamorised it. Doctors even recommended smoking as a cure for depression. How times change!

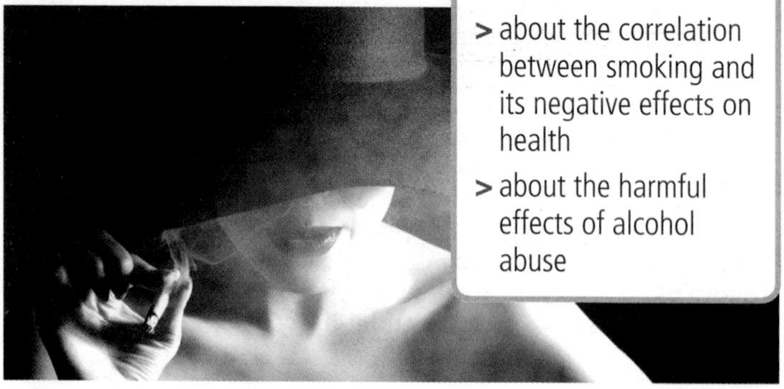

FIGURE 1: Is it glamorous to smell like an ashtray?

Legal drugs

Tobacco

Why do people smoke even though smoking is harmful to health?

> Chemicals in tobacco smoke give smokers a sense of well-being.

> Nicotine is one of the chemicals. By stimulating the brain, it gives a buzz and helps to relieve tension.

> Nicotine is addictive, which is why people continue to smoke, even though they know it's harmful.

Tar and carbon monoxide are other substances in tobacco smoke that are also harmful to health.

Figure 2 summarises the dangers: smokers are more likely to suffer from heart disease, lung cancer, emphysema and other lung diseases than non-smokers.

- Carbon monoxide is a gas that combines with haemoglobin in red blood cells. It reduces the oxygen-carrying capacity of the blood

- Nicotine is an addictive drug. It is a powerful poison and increases heart rate and blood pressure. Raised blood pressure increases the risk of heart disease

- Tar contains over a thousand chemicals. Some of them are carcinogens (substances that cause cancer). Tar collects in the lungs as tobacco smoke cools

FIGURE 2: Substances in tobacco smoke.

QUESTIONS

1 Name three diseases linked with smoking.

2 Describe the effects of drinking alcohol on behaviour.

Passive smoking (breathing in someone else's tobacco smoke) also increases risks to health.

Alcohol

Ethanol is the substance in beer, wines and spirits we call alcohol. In the short term, drinking alcohol lowers inhibitions, which is why alcoholic drinks at parties are popular.

Alcohol affects the brain even in small amounts. Responses to stimuli slow down, so reaction times are longer. More alcohol affects the part of the brain controlling arm and leg movements. Vision may be blurred. Even more and the person may pass out. Because drinking alcohol lengthens reaction times, the risk of driving unsafely increases sharply. This is why it is illegal to drink and drive. Figure 3 summarises some of the short-term effects of alcohol.

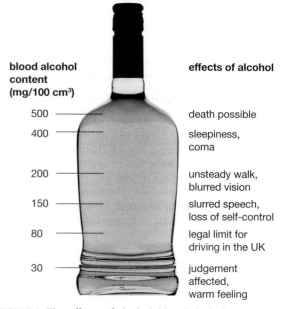

blood alcohol content (mg/100 cm³)	effects of alcohol
500	death possible
400	sleepiness, coma
200	unsteady walk, blurred vision
150	slurred speech, loss of self-control
80	legal limit for driving in the UK
30	judgement affected, warm feeling

FIGURE 3: The effects of alcohol: blood alcohol content is the amount of alcohol present in the blood measured in mg of alcohol per 100 cm³ of blood.

Alcohol abuse

Long-term effects of too much alcohol

Alcohol abuse usually refers to heavy drinking over a long period, leading to physical dependence. However, sometimes abuse is used to describe drinking large volumes of alcohol in a short time – so-called **binge drinking**. Long-term alcohol abuse can cause liver cirrhosis, brain damage, heart disease, cancer and raised blood pressure.

Figure 4 presents some data on alcohol-related liver disease.

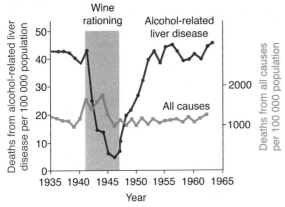

FIGURE 4: Deaths from all causes and from alcohol-related liver disease in Paris, 1935–65. Deaths from liver disease fell by 80% when wine was rationed during the second world war (1939–45). Death levels rose quickly when rationing ended. What conclusions can be drawn from these figures?

How much alcohol is too much?

Sex, age, body mass and how quickly the body's cells break down alcohol affect how much an individual can drink safely. For example, 'safe drinking' for a woman is about two-thirds that for a man of the same body mass. Also, different drinks contain different amounts of alcohol. A pregnant woman who drinks alcohol regularly increases the risk of her baby developing abnormally.

Drinking four units of alcohol a day for men and three units for women is reckoned to be safe, but opinions vary. All doctors agree that alcohol abuse damages health.

FIGURE 5: One unit of alcohol (average measure): after drinking one unit, the level of alcohol in the blood rises to 20 mg/100 cm^3.

> ## ◉ QUESTIONS
>
> **3** Calculate how many glasses of wine contain the same amount of alcohol as $1\frac{1}{2}$ pints of beer.
>
> **4** Evaluate the graph in Figure 4, considering what you can learn from, and the limitations of, the evidence.

Smoking and disease

Making the link

Research data collected over the decades between 1940 and 1980 established the link between smoking and disease. For the time period shown in Figure 6, deaths from lung cancer increased sharply, whereas deaths from other types of lung disease fell.

Further studies compared the risk of dying of lung cancer and other smoking-related diseases with the number of cigarettes smoked. Figure 7 summarises the evidence and shows that there is a correlation.

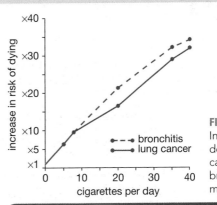

FIGURE 7: Increased risk of death from lung cancer or bronchitis for male smokers.

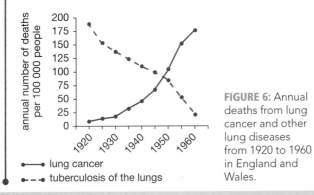

FIGURE 6: Annual deaths from lung cancer and other lung diseases from 1920 to 1960 in England and Wales.

> ## ◉ QUESTIONS
>
> **5** Evaluate the data shown in Figures 6 and 7. What can you learn from these graphs?
>
> **6** Explain how research made the link between smoking and increased risk of disease.
>
> **7** Comment on why deaths from lung disease other than cancer fell during the twentieth century.

Ethics of transplants

The ultimate gift

National Health Service records show that over 17 million people in the UK have registered to donate their organs after death. Even so, with 8000 patients on transplant waiting lists in the UK, every year 400 people die while waiting for an organ to become available. The demand for organs far outstrips supply.

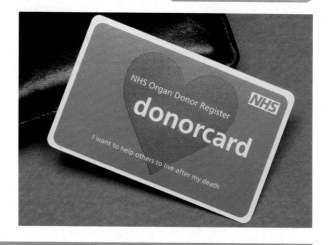

FIGURE 1: People who have given permission for their organs to be transplanted might carry a donor card.

Transplanting organs

Transplant surgery aims to replace a diseased organ with a healthy one. A **donor** is the person supplying the healthy organ. The person receiving it is the **recipient**.

Most organ donors are dead victims of accidents. Previously, they had given permission for their organs to be transplanted in the event of their deaths. However, some living donors donate tissues such as bone marrow or even an organ where there are two doing the same job, for example a kidney.

One kidney is enough to do the job of filtering waste from the blood, leaving the other available for transplantation. In these cases, donor and recipient are often members of the same family. Because donor and recipient are closely related, there is less risk of the organ being **rejected**. Globally, kidneys are the most commonly transplanted organs.

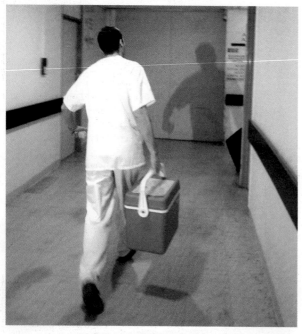

FIGURE 2: The heart begins to deteriorate minutes after the death of the donor. Success depends on fast organ transfer and speedy surgery.

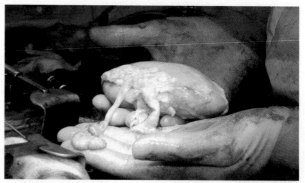

FIGURE 3: A donor kidney about to be transplanted into the recipient patient. How can doctors tell it will be accepted?

QUESTIONS

1 Describe the aim of transplant surgery.

2 Explain one reason why human donor organs are in short supply.

3 Design a leaflet aimed at encouraging people to become donors.

Transplantation surgery   Problems of rejection of transplanted organs

Supply and demand

The demand for human organs for transplantation far outstrips supply. With organ donation remaining voluntary and there being a lack of donors, there is a search for alternative sources of organs.

> Animal donors as an alternative source of organs are an active research area. An animal donor was first used in 1963 when American surgeons transplanted a kidney from a chimpanzee into a patient. The transplant was quickly rejected by the recipient.

> **Genetic engineering** has opened the way to using **genetically modified (GM)** animals as organ donors. These new technologies are not yet used routinely. However, the possibility offers powerful alternative treatments of disease. The term **xenotransplantation** refers to the potential of transplanting animal organs into humans.

GM animals are effective donors if their organs can be modified to protect them from the risk of rejection by the recipient. Pigs are the preferred animal as their organs are a similar size to those of humans.

> **Transplantation tourism** arises because of the gap between supply and demand. Some wealthy people needing a transplant are prepared to pay for organs. Legal or not, poor people in developing countries are often prepared to donate for the money. For example, in rural Pakistan up to half of village residents may have only one kidney.

QUESTIONS

4 Explain the difference between morals and ethics using the supply and demand for organs for transplantation to illustrate your answer.

5 State how the gap between supply and demand of organs can be reduced.

6 'Animals have the same rights as humans to health, safety and well-being.' Discuss.

Morals and ethics: issues for discussion

Is it right to use animals as a source of organs for transplants? Most of us benefit from modern medicine at some time in our lives. For some people the benefits are not the issue. For them it is a question of **morals** (what is right or wrong) and **ethics** (the action we take as a result of our moral judgement). They think that using animals to source organs is cruel and wrong.

Is it right that money drives transplantation tourism and is the incentive for poor people in developing countries to sell their organs? The increased risk of transplanting diseased organs into recipients because poor donors do not receive regular health care is one issue. Another is that the deal exploits poor people and violates their human rights. These are ethical concerns and arise because of the potential risk to the health of both recipient and donor. Enthusiasm for increasing the supply of organs in developed countries also puts pressure on the ethics for the right to life.

FIGURE 4: Pakistani men reveal scars after their kidneys were removed in 2007. Pakistan is known to have numerous secret groups involved in paying poor people for their kidneys. Suggest arguments for and against transplant tourism.

Choosing who

Organs are in short supply. Is it right therefore that anyone needing a transplant should have one? Especially if the transplant is needed because the person in question has brought the problem on themselves. For example, should a liver transplant for an alcoholic or a heart transplant for someone who is obese have the same priority as a life-saving transplant for someone suddenly taken ill? Is the chance of success better for the individual with an unhealthy lifestyle than for the person at death's door through no fault of their own?

Today, modern medicine can achieve amazing outcomes but it is expensive and resources are limited, including organs for transplant. This raises ethical concerns. How do we **prioritise** transplants? Who most 'deserves' the chance to live? Should 'deserve' even come into the equation? These are difficult questions. There are no easy answers.

QUESTIONS

7 Give your definition of an unhealthy lifestyle.

8 Discuss the prioritising of treatments and patients from different viewpoints.

Infectious diseases

You will find out:

- that different pathogens cause different infectious diseases
- that pathogens are spread in various ways
- about some infectious diseases

Natural disasters

The spread of infectious diseases often follows natural disasters. The normal infrastructure of a country may be destroyed and large numbers of people end up in insanitary conditions. Governments and aid agencies work hard to put in place clean water, latrines and proper food-handling techniques to try to prevent the spread of disease.

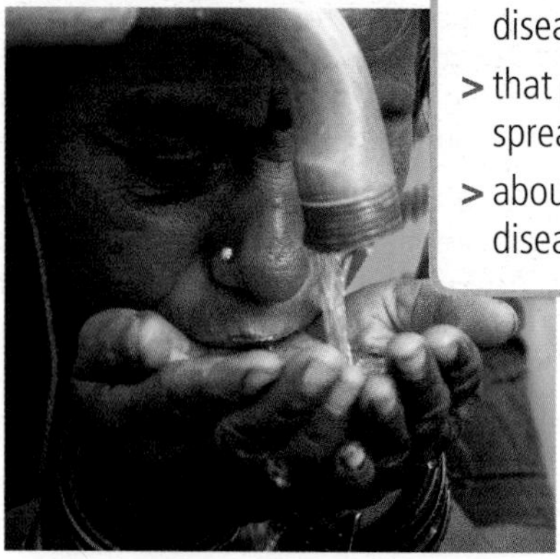

FIGURE 1: Why is having clean water to drink essential in preventing disease?

What causes disease?

For most of us the word 'disease' conjures up ideas of feeling unwell. We blame **bacteria** and **viruses** for most of our illnesses. However, **fungi** and **protists** are culprits as well.

Organisms that cause infectious disease are called **pathogens**. We often call pathogens microbes (microorganisms) because most of them are only visible under a microscope.

Our body is warm and moist, which makes it an ideal environment where pathogens can multiply. Different pathogens spread from person to person in various ways.

The term **infectious** refers to diseases caused by pathogens that spread from person to person.

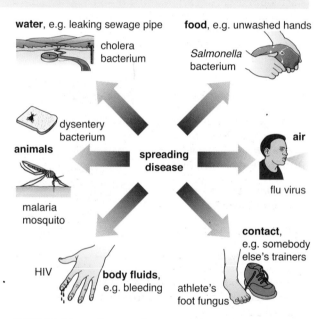

water, e.g. leaking sewage pipe
cholera bacterium
food, e.g. unwashed hands
Salmonella bacterium
dysentery bacterium
animals
spreading disease
air
flu virus
malaria mosquito
contact, e.g. somebody else's trainers
HIV
body fluids, e.g. bleeding
athlete's foot fungus

FIGURE 2: How infectious diseases are spread.

QUESTIONS

1 Define the term pathogen. Give some examples of pathogens.

2 Explain why the human body is an ideal environment where pathogens can multiply.

Infectious diseases

Cholera

Cholera bacteria are found in water contaminated with sewage. Vomiting, stomach cramps and diarrhoea are **symptoms** of the disease. Victims pass large volumes of liquid faeces and unless treated quickly to replace the lost water they may die. The disease spreads rapidly where there is overcrowding and insanitary conditions.

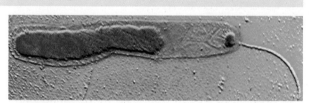

FIGURE 3: Cholera bacterium *Vibrio cholerae*. Magnification ×16 500.

Colds and flu

A sneeze produces a jet of moisture droplets that shoot out of the nose and mouth. The airborne viruses and bacteria infecting the lining of the airways are carried in the droplets and spread to people nearby. This is how the viruses that cause colds and influenza (flu) pass from person to person. Infection rates are particularly high in crowded places like schools and hospitals.

FIGURE 4: Give her a tissue! A jet of droplets erupts from a woman's nose and mouth when she sneezes. What do these droplets contain?

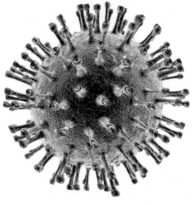

FIGURE 5: A computer model of the human immunodeficiency virus (HIV). The knobs are proteins which bind the virus to a particular type of white blood cell which helps to defend the body against disease.

Salmonella infection

Salmonella bacteria are found in the gut of most chickens. After the chickens are slaughtered the bacterium may contaminate the carcasses before they are cooked. Someone who then eats food contaminated with *Salmonella* develops food poisoning. Symptoms include fever, pain and diarrhoea. Most victims of food poisoning recover quickly.

Cooking chicken at 68 °C or higher kills *Salmonella* bacteria. Particular attention to personal hygiene is also important; not washing hands after handling raw chicken and then preparing other foods increases the risk of *Salmonella* food poisoning.

Did you know?

When preparing chicken from frozen it should be completely thawed, otherwise the centre of the carcass may not reach the safe cooking temperature.

HIV

HIV stands for **human immunodeficiency virus**; this is the virus that causes **acquired immunodeficiency syndrome (AIDS)**. The virus destroys some of the white blood cells which help to defend the body against pathogens.

Normally a person's white blood cells destroy the pathogens before they can cause disease. An infected (HIV-positive) person is less well protected. Pathogens gain a foothold and cause the diseases associated with AIDS, which are a particular type of skin cancer and pneumonia. The word 'syndrome' refers to a group of diseases rather than a particular disease.

HIV's main route of spreading is in body fluids from person to person by unprotected sexual contact or by drug abusers sharing syringes and needles.

Athlete's foot

Sweaty feet are an ideal environment for fungi and toes are particularly vulnerable to infection by the fungus causing athlete's foot. Inflamed skin and intense itching are symptoms of the problem.

Contact between people spreads the athlete's foot fungus, so borrowing other people's footwear is not a good idea. Washing and drying carefully between your toes helps to reduce the risk of infection.

QUESTIONS

3 Explain the difference between infectious diseases and non-infectious diseases.

4 Match the cause of each disease in the list to bacterium, fungus or virus: cholera, AIDS, flu, athlete's foot, food poisoning.

Diarrhoea

The different bacteria causing diarrhoea invade the cells lining the small intestine, where they multiply and produce **endotoxins** (poisons) which inflame the tissue, causing pain and fever.

The endotoxins stimulate the wall of the small intestine to contract violently and more frequently than normal. Absorption of digested food and water through the intestinal wall is prevented. As a result, faeces is liquid (diarrhoea), the victim loses a lot of water and the body quickly dehydrates. Children and elderly people are particularly vulnerable to dehydration and may die unless treated promptly.

QUESTIONS

5 Explain why the symptoms of diarrhoea associated with food poisoning are a serious risk to health.

6 Explain the difference between the term syndrome and disease.

7 Compare the symptoms and causes of *Salmonella* infection and foot and mouth disease. You may carry out your own research to help you.

Q Food hygiene   HIV infection   Diarrhoea

Animal vectors

You will find out:
> that *Anopheles* mosquitoes spread the malarial protozoan
> how houseflies spread the dysentery bacterium

Anything to declare?

Every year about 1500 travellers return to the UK with malaria, but this is only a small number compared with the whole world. Over 280 million people are infected with malarial protozoa, more than 100 million people develop the disease each year and two million people die from malaria each year.

FIGURE 1: A mosquito feeding; notice the blood in its abdomen.

Insect-borne disease

The term animal **vector** refers to animals that spread **pathogens** (disease-causing organisms).

Fly-borne diseases

Houseflies are a health hazard. They leave behind bacteria wherever they walk and feed. When they walk on food, they may leave behind bacteria that make us ill. This makes them one example of a vector.

The food route is how houseflies can pass on dysentery bacteria to people. In the UK, dysentery is usually caused by the *Shingella* bacterium. The more serious amoebic dysentery, caused by an amoebic parasite, is mainly found in tropical areas. Like cholera, victims suffer from diarrhoea and pass large amounts of liquid faeces. Children and elderly people living in insanitary conditions like refugee camps are particularly vulnerable to the loss of water from the body and are at risk unless treated promptly.

Treating diarrhoea

In countries where clean drinking water is hard to come by, diarrhoea-type diseases are a serious problem. Giving a solution of table salt and sugar to

victims of diarrhoea saves many lives daily. The treatment is called **oral rehydration therapy** (ORT).

The salt and sugar help the body to absorb water from the intestines. This replaces the water lost in the liquid faeces. A sachet of the mixture costs only a few pence and victims recover rapidly.

Malaria

The single-celled protozoan parasite that causes malaria is passed from person to person by mosquitoes. Although there are many types of mosquito, only female *Anopheles* mosquitoes spread malaria. The mosquitoes are the vectors and people are the parasite's **host**.

The mouthparts of female mosquitoes are ideally suited to sucking up blood. Long and sharply pointed, they pierce the victim's skin until a blood vessel is reached. A food tube is then pushed in; saliva is pumped down it and the victim's blood sucked up.

If an *Anopheles* female feeds on a person already infected with the malarial protozoan she will suck in thousands of the parasites with the victim's blood. The parasites are passed on when she feeds on another person.

> ### QUESTIONS
>
> **1** State why houseflies are a health hazard.
>
> **2** Describe how *Anopheles* mosquitoes pass malaria parasites from person to person.

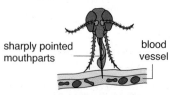

sharply pointed mouthparts   blood vessel

FIGURE 2: The head of a female *Anopheles* mosquito.

Pathogens

Plasmodium

The malarial protozoan is called *Plasmodium*. It infects liver cells and red blood cells. Once the protozoan is in the bloodstream, flu-like symptoms are followed later by high fever, cold chills and heavy sweating. The pattern of the symptoms depends on the species of *Plasmodium* causing the problems.

FIGURE 3: Global distribution of malaria.

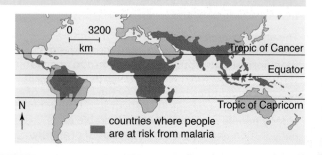

0   3200 km

Tropic of Cancer

Equator

Tropic of Capricorn

N

countries where people are at risk from malaria

Plasmodium flourishes in the warmer regions of the world, which is why malaria is a medical problem in tropical countries. Some countries find the problem particularly difficult to manage, as they are short of expert help and find it hard to finance treatment and prevention.

Figure 3 shows the global distribution of malaria.

Fighting malaria depends on destroying the mosquito vector or the *Plasmodium* parasite, or preventing contact between the vector and people. Bed nets are an effective way of preventing contact. They allow people to sleep at night without being bitten by mosquitoes.

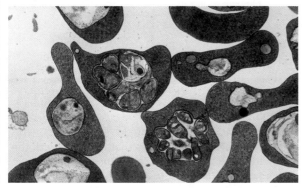

FIGURE 4: How can you tell that these human red blood cells are infected with malaria parasite *Plasmodium*? Its toxins (poisons) cause the symptoms of malaria. Magnification ×4400.

Houseflies: the problem

Houseflies feed on almost any organic material, including faeces. We are at risk of being infected with bacteria like dysentery bacteria that flies leave behind when they feed on our food. Covering food up stops houseflies from feeding on it, and helps to prevent the spread of infectious diseases.

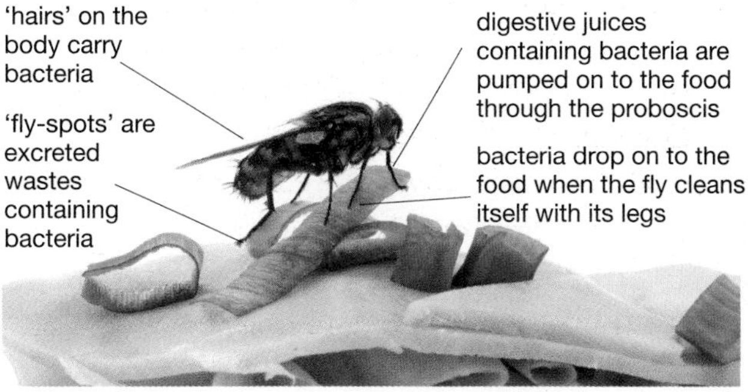

'hairs' on the body carry bacteria

'fly-spots' are excreted wastes containing bacteria

digestive juices containing bacteria are pumped on to the food through the proboscis

bacteria drop on to the food when the fly cleans itself with its legs

FIGURE 5: Houseflies pass on pathogens. Walking on uncovered food leaves a trail of bacteria.

QUESTIONS

3 Explain the difference between a disease vector and a host.

4 Explain how *Plasmodium* causes the symptoms of malaria.

Malaria: the cycle of infection

Malaria is the result of the interaction between three components: the malarial protozoan *Plasmodium*, *Anopheles* mosquitoes and people.

Treatment/prevention aims to break the chain of infection:

> Draining the water in habitats where *Anopheles* mosquitoes breed destroys its juvenile stages.

> Insecticides sprayed on the water's surface kill *Anopheles* juvenile stages.

> Drugs prevent the *Plasmodium* parasite from reproducing in the human host.

> Bed nets prevent contact between the mosquito vector and human host.

> Vaccines which inhibit different stages in the *Plasmodium* life cycle are in development.

QUESTIONS

5 Explain how knowledge of the life cycle of the mosquito helps to control malaria.

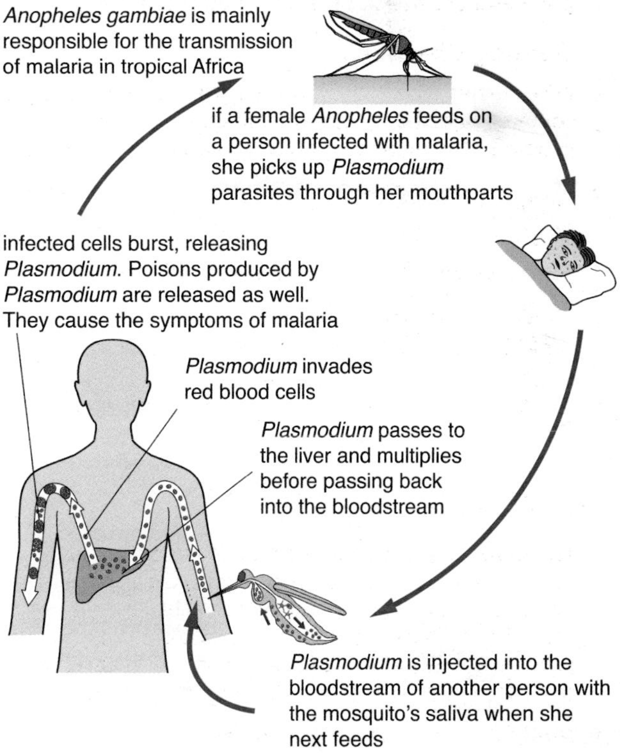

Anopheles gambiae is mainly responsible for the transmission of malaria in tropical Africa

if a female *Anopheles* feeds on a person infected with malaria, she picks up *Plasmodium* parasites through her mouthparts

infected cells burst, releasing *Plasmodium*. Poisons produced by *Plasmodium* are released as well. They cause the symptoms of malaria

Plasmodium invades red blood cells

Plasmodium passes to the liver and multiplies before passing back into the bloodstream

Plasmodium is injected into the bloodstream of another person with the mosquito's saliva when she next feeds

FIGURE 6: Passing on the malarial protozoan.

Infection: prevention and control

Always do the washing up

Alexander Fleming was a biologist working in St Mary's Hospital in London. He went on holiday in the summer of 1928 and left his laboratory untidy. When he returned, he found mould on the culture plates on which bacteria were growing. The mould was *Penicillium notatum*. No bacteria were growing near to the mould. Something the mould produced was stopping them. Fleming called the 'something' penicillin.

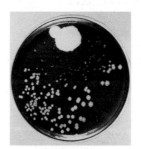

FIGURE 1: The dish in which Fleming found mould growing. Notice that bacteria are not growing near to the mould.

You will find out:

- > how antiseptics prevent the spread of infection
- > how antibiotics and antifungals control infection
- > about the effects of antiseptics and antibiotics on bacterial cultures
- > about resistant bacteria

Stopping the spread of infection

Antiseptics

Antiseptics are chemicals used to attack microbes which might otherwise cause diseases. They stop microbes from multiplying. We use antiseptics to swab a wound or clean skin to stop infection.

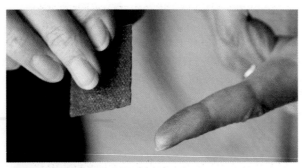

FIGURE 2: An antiseptic is used to clean cuts and scratches.

Antibacterials

Antibacterials are substances that interfere with the growth of bacteria and so can be used to treat bacterial infection. Antiseptics are antibacterials; so too are antibiotic drugs. However, the term is more often used to describe substances in health care and cleaning products than medicines.

QUESTIONS

1 Explain the difference between antibacterials and antibiotics.

2 Name three commonly used antiseptics.

3 Suggest why a doctor would not give you antibiotics if you had flu.

How effective are antiseptics and antibiotics?

Figure 3 illustrates a simple way of finding out how effective antiseptics are.

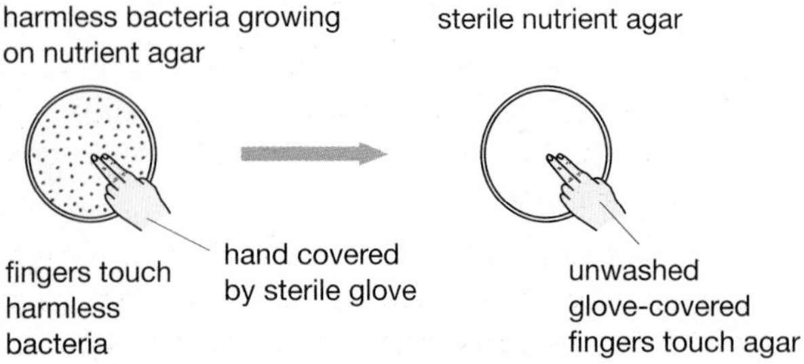

harmless bacteria growing on nutrient agar
sterile nutrient agar
fingers touch harmless bacteria
hand covered by sterile glove
unwashed glove-covered fingers touch agar

FIGURE 3: How clean are our hands after washing them? This is an experiment for finding out. Repeat the experiment after washing your fingers with ordinary soap and then again with antiseptic soap. What would you expect to find after 3 days?

You can test the effects of antibiotics on cultures of harmless bacteria. Figure 4 shows you how.

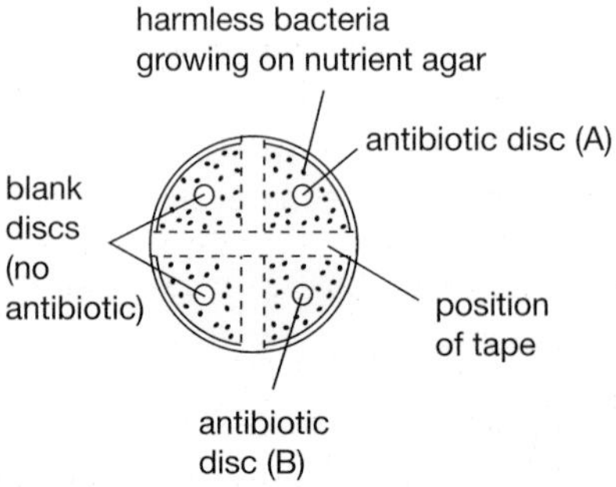

harmless bacteria growing on nutrient agar
antibiotic disc (A)
blank discs (no antibiotic)
position of tape
antibiotic disc (B)

FIGURE 4: This is a test of the effects of antibiotics on cultures of harmless bacteria. Leave for 3 days at 25°C. What might you expect to see?

Alexander Fleming Using antiseptic Antibacterial soaps Fungi infecting humans

Antibiotics

We use **antibiotic** drugs to control infection. Before their discovery, infectious diseases were major killers. Now most infections caused by bacteria can be controlled thanks to antibiotics. Antibiotics are *not* an effective treatment for diseases caused by viruses.

The different antibiotics affect bacteria differently. **Bactericides** such as penicillin kill bacteria. **Bacteristats** such as tetracycline prevent bacteria multiplying.

QUESTIONS

4 Write a plan for the experiments shown in Figures 3 and 4. Suggest how you will make the experiments fair and safe. Predict what the results might be.

5 Explain why antifungal drugs might cause unpleasant side-effects.

Antifungals

Antifungal drugs are used to treat fungal infections such as athlete's foot. They work because of differences between human (animal) cells and fungal cells. For example, there are many differences in chemistry between human cells and fungal cells. Antifungals target the differences, killing the fungal cells but not the human cells.

However, there are also many similarities between human cells and fungal cells. This means that people using antifungals may suffer unpleasant side-effects if the drugs are not used properly.

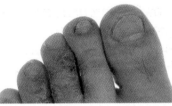

FIGURE 5: Athlete's foot is treated with antifungal agents.

Resistance in bacteria and antibiotic misuse (Higher tier only)

Resistance

Widespread use of antibiotics has led to the development of **resistance** among certain strains of bacteria. This means the antibiotic in question becomes less effective for treating bacterial infections.

Resistance arises as a result of the high mutation rates of bacterial genes and the ongoing exposure of bacteria to antibiotics. Populations of bacteria always contain individuals with resistance genes. These individuals survive antibiotic treatment, reproduce and spread quickly. Since the first-choice antibiotic becomes ineffective, a different antibiotic is used to treat the resistant bacteria and again mutations result in bacteria resistant to the new antibiotic. These bacteria are now resistant to both antibiotics. Using yet another antibiotic repeats the cycle, eventually leading to bacteria resistant to most antibiotics, for example, **MRSA**.

Infections caused by MRSA are very difficult to treat, with potentially serious consequences. For example, MRSA infection may result in fatal blood poisoning.

Bacterial resistance is often the result of antibiotic misuse:

> In some countries over-the-counter sales of antibiotics without prescription makes them widely available for people to treat their infections without medical advice.

> Although antibiotics are ineffective against viral infections, more than 30% of people use them.

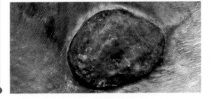

FIGURE 6: A skin abscess caused by an MRSA infection as a complication after surgery.

> Up to 40% of people do not finish their course of antibiotics because they 'feel better' even though they are still infected. The risk of failure to complete treatment is increased where people have to buy their own medicines and may try to save money.

> Antibiotics sold over the counter might be diluted to the point where they are no longer effective.

> In many countries, antibiotics are added to animal feed and so can enter the human food chain.

These different examples illustrate the link between emergence of resistant strains of bacteria and the misuse of antibiotics. Since 2006, European Union regulations banning the addition of antibiotics to animal feeds have been in force. Since then the scale of the problem of resistant bacteria seems to be declining slowly.

QUESTIONS

6 Using your own research, explain how scientists have collected evidence that antibiotic use allows resistant bacteria to evolve.

7 Explain which aspects of their experimental design ensured that they could draw valid conclusions from the results and the limitations of the evidence.

8 Draw a population of bacteria. They are very sensitive to an antibiotic. Colour one bacterium red. It is very resistant to the antibiotic. Use the diagram to suggest how the population will change if **i** antibiotics are given, **ii** the patient stops taking the antibiotics before all the bacteria have been destroyed.

Animal and plant defences

Mmmm, tasty

The cinnabar moth caterpillar is vividly coloured, alerting birds to the fact that it has a very unpleasant taste. This taste comes from alkaloid poisons that are in the plants that it feeds on. The moth itself is unaffected by the poisons.

FIGURE 1: Why is the cinnabar moth caterpillar so brightly coloured?

Physical barriers

Human skin is like a soft suit of armour. It covers the body with an outer layer, forming a physical barrier between the body's insides and the pathogens (disease-causing organisms) outside. So long as the skin is undamaged, even the pathogens that live on it cannot get inside.

New skin cells replace old, worn-out cells every 10 days or so. The old cells flake off. Their flakiness protects us from the pathogens attached to them. The pathogens fall off with the old cells.

FIGURE 2: A coloured electron micrograph of household dust. This contains shed skin cells, dust mites, hairs and fabric threads, soil and earth, pollen grains, fungal spores and particles of food.

Cilia and mucus, as well as the skin, are a physical barrier to pathogens. They help keep the airways and lungs free of bacteria and other particles.

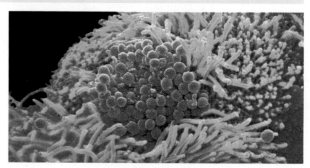

FIGURE 3: A coloured electron micrograph with *Staphylococcus* bacteria (coloured red) trapped on the hair-like cilia lining the windpipe.

The surfaces covering plants are a physical barrier to pathogens as well. However, they are also a defence against plant-chewing animals. Vicious thorns skewer and stab; hair-like structures secrete sticky substances that trap the unwary would-be plant eater.

FIGURE 4: A fly trapped on the sticky leaf surface of the carnivorous butterwort plant.

Did you know?

The skin is the body's largest organ. On average it covers an area of 2 m^2 and about one million bacteria cover each cm^2.

QUESTIONS

1 Describe how the replacement of old skin cells with new skin cells helps to protect us from pathogens.

2 State two ways plants protect themselves from plant-eating animals.

The body's chemical defences

The body's chemical defences against attack by pathogens help keep us healthy for most of the time. The body's natural defences, physical and chemical, are shown in Figure 5.

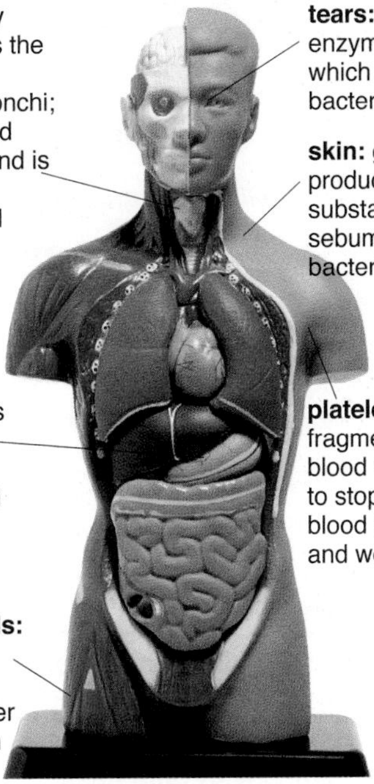

mucus: made by goblet cells, lines the surfaces of the windpipe and bronchi; traps bacteria and other particles, and is swept away by hair-like cilia until it reaches the throat when it is swallowed

tears: contain the enzyme lysozyme which destroys bacteria

skin: glands produce an oily substance called sebum which kills bacteria and fungi

stomach: glands in the stomach wall produce hydrochloric acid which kills bacteria on food

platelets: cell-like fragments in the blood which help to stop the loss of blood from cuts and wounds

white blood cells: produced in the bones; destroy bacteria and other pathogens which infect the body

FIGURE 5: The body's physical and chemical defences protect us from pathogens.

White blood cells protect the body

The surfaces of pathogens carry substances which the body does not recognise as its own. The substances stimulate some types of white blood cell to bind to the pathogens carrying them. The pathogens are destroyed. Other types of white blood cell are stimulated to produce proteins called **antibodies** which also bind to the pathogens, destroying them.

If pathogens enter the body through cuts or scratches, then white blood cells, called phagocytes, pass from the blood through the tissues to the site of infection. Their activities cause an **inflammatory response** as they destroy the invaders.

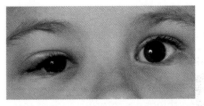

FIGURE 6: What are the swelling, redness and heat signs of?

QUESTIONS

3 Smoking damages the cilia lining the airways to the lungs. Suggest why smokers often develop a cough.

4 Explain how blood cells protect the body from infectious pathogens, using a flow chart.

New medicines

Plants' chemical defences

Although plants cannot move away from unwelcome attention, they respond vigorously to attack using chemicals as their defence. For example, **alkaloids** are bitter-tasting plant chemicals. They trigger vomiting. A bitter taste is often a warning signal not to swallow the plant material we're chewing. In general, animals avoid bitter-tasting plants and prey. Bitterness is a defence against would-be predators.

Bacterial attack is often a signal to the plants to produce antibacterial chemicals. These kill bacteria and therefore limit disease and the damage it causes to plant tissues. So effective are these antibacterials that disease in plants caused by bacterial infections is very rare.

Antibacterials enabling plants to combat their natural bacterial pathogens are also effective against bacterial pathogens that infect humans. For example, lemon balm, garlic and tea tree are sources of antibacterials effective against a variety of bacterial pathogens.

A substance called SPE 1 is another example of a plant antibacterial. It is effective against *Salmonella* bacteria which cause food poisoning. Adding it to

animal feed potentially allows farmers to produce *Salmonella*-free livestock reared for meat. The idea is particularly interesting following the European Union's ban on adding antibiotics to animal feed.

New medicines

Fewer than 10% of plants have been investigated for their potential as new medicines. However, teams of scientists are searching the world for likely plants. Rainforests seem to be where particularly promising plants with antibacterial possibilities are growing. Discovering them has added importance as bacterial pathogens are developing resistance to the antibiotic drugs currently used to treat infectious diseases.

QUESTIONS

5 Explain the potential importance of plants as a source of antibacterial medicines.

6 Explain how plants help us to combat infectious diseases caused by bacteria.

Interdependency

You will find out:
> about interdependency between organisms
> how a species' survival depends on other species

What's the point of wasps?

Wasps are probably our least favourite garden companion. Their behaviour is erratic and they can sting – very painfully! Although wasps occasionally attack us, they more often attack the insect pests that can spoil the garden's plants and ruin the crops we eat. So next time they bother you, don't squash them, shoo them away carefully.

FIGURE 1: We depend on wasps for pest control.

Depending on one another

Saying that all living things are interdependent refers to the dynamic relationship between living things (including us) that ensures survival. The interdependency between plants and insects is a good example.

> Many types of flower depend on insects as pollen carriers.

> Insects depend on flowers as a source of food.

> Plants' male sex cells are inside pollen grains.

> If insects did not carry pollen to the female parts of flowers then there would be no new generations of plants for the insects to feed on.

> Plants and insects depend on one another to survive.

QUESTIONS

1 Draw a diagram to show that plants and insects are interdependent.

Mutualism and parasitism

Mutualism

The survival of some species depends on particular links with another species. For example, oxpecker birds feed on blood-sucking ticks that cling to the backs of wildebeest in east Africa.

The oxpeckers benefit from the supply of food; the wildebeest from the removal of parasites. The term **mutualism** refers to a relationship where both species benefit.

Cleaner fish provide another example of mutualism. When they feed on the dead skin and external parasites of other fish species this benefits the host by keeping them clean and free from health-threatening parasites.

Parasitism

Parasitism is a one-sided relationship between two species. A parasite obtains food at the other species' expense. The parasite benefits, but the other species, the **host**, is usually injured and may die.

Fleas and headlice are insect parasites. They are called **ectoparasites** because they cling to the body's surfaces. They both have a flattened shape to help them cling to the host. Claws on their legs allow them to grip tightly.

FIGURE 2: Oxpeckers perching on a wildebeest. Some species of oxpecker drink the blood of the animals on which they perch. This raises the question: are they parasites?

Endoparasites live inside the body. An example is a tapeworm which feeds from the host's digested meal. The products of the digested meal are absorbed through the surface of the tapeworm's body.

Muscular contractions of the intestine move food through it. The head of a tapeworm is adapted; enabling it to resist the movement. Suckers and hooks attach the tapeworm to the wall of the intestine as food moves through.

Mistletoe is a plant parasite. It is a poisonous plant that takes water and mineral salts from the host tree on which it grows. Its leaves produce sugars by photosynthesis. However, some types of mistletoe depend on the host plant for sugars as well.

FIGURE 4: Hooks and suckers surround the head end of a tapeworm. Magnification ×20. What function do they perform?

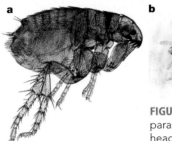

FIGURE 3: What kind of parasites are the flea (**a**) and headlouse (**b**)?

QUESTIONS

2 Explain the difference between mutualism and parasitism.

3 Explain how fleas and headlice are adapted to being parasites.

4 State why interdependency between most living things ultimately depends on the link between photosynthesis and respiration.

Useful bacteria (Higher tier only)

Nitrogen-fixing bacteria

Peas, beans and clover are examples of **leguminous** plants. Their roots have swellings on them called root nodules. These contain **nitrogen-fixing bacteria**. The bacteria convert nitrogen from the air into compounds which the plants use to make proteins:

$$\text{nitrogen} + \text{hydrogen} \rightarrow \begin{array}{c}\text{nitrogen-}\\\text{containing}\\\text{compounds}\end{array} \xrightarrow{\text{absorbed by plants}} \text{proteins}$$

In return, the bacteria obtain sugars from the plant's roots. Their mutualism benefits both partners.

Chemosynthetic bacteria

Photosynthesis produces food and supports communities on land and in sunlit waters. In the inky blackness of hydrothermal deep-sea vents, the substances released by the underwater volcanic activity of the vents are the raw materials for another process, called **chemosynthesis**:

$$\begin{array}{c}\text{carbon}\\\text{dioxide}\end{array} + \begin{array}{c}\text{hydrogen}\\\text{sulfide}\end{array} \rightarrow \text{sugars} + \text{sulfur}$$

Using chemosynthesis different types of bacteria produce the food which supports the vent communities (see page 17).

Many invertebrate animal species are in partnership with chemosynthetic bacteria. Giant tube worms are the best example. The bacteria that live in the body of the worms depend on oxygen. The worms absorb oxygen from the water enabling the bacteria to make food that the worm needs. Both the worm and its bacteria benefit: an example of mutualism in action.

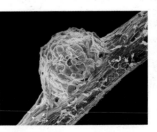

FIGURE 5: Nitrogen-fixing bacteria inside a root nodule.

FIGURE 6: Giant tube worms on the seabed by a hydrothermal deep-sea vent.

QUESTIONS

5 Suggest what would be the effects of removing nodules from the roots of leguminous plants.

6 Explain how organisms living in deep-sea vents survive in the absence of photosynthesis.

Energy and biomass

You will find out:
> about energy transfer along a food chain
> about a pyramid of biomass

The Sun: our provider

Sunlight underpins life on Earth. Without sunlight and the photosynthesis that depends on it, most communities of organisms would cease to exist.

FIGURE 1: Plants trap light energy, converting it into the chemical energy of food.

Food chains

Animals need food:

> Herbivores consume plants.

> Carnivores consume other animals.

> Omnivores consume plants and other animals (most human beings are omnivorous).

Most carnivores are **predators**. They catch and eat other animals. The animals caught are their **prey** and are often herbivores.

Scavengers are carnivores that feed on the remains of prey left by predators or on the bodies of animals that have died because of disease or old age.

A food chain shows the links between plants, prey, predators and scavengers.

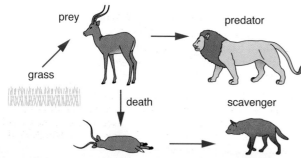

Producers and consumers

Plants, algae and some bacteria are called **producers** because they produce food by photosynthesis. This is why food chains always begin with producers. Animals use this food when they eat producers.

Even when they eat other animals, predators depend on producers indirectly since somewhere along the line the prey has been a herbivore. Because they take in food, animals are called **consumers**.

QUESTIONS

1 Arrange the organisms: grass, rabbits, fox, into a food chain. Label the herbivores, carnivores, predator, prey and producer.

2 Explain why all food chains begin with plants.

FIGURE 2: A food chain shows the links between the eaten and the eaters. Arrows represent the transfer of food (and therefore food energy) between different organisms. Feeding transfers food (energy) from one organism to the next in the food chain. The number of links in the food chain is limited.

Energy flow

Food chains form a **food web**. This is usually a more accurate description of feeding relationships between plants, prey, predators and scavengers. Why? Most animals eat more than one type of plant or other animal.

Plants convert light energy into the chemical energy of food using photosynthesis. A food chain represents one pathway of food energy through a community of organisms. A food web represents many pathways.

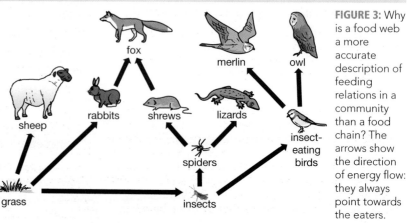

FIGURE 3: Why is a food web a more accurate description of feeding relations in a community than a food chain? The arrows show the direction of energy flow: they always point towards the eaters.

At each link in a food chain, energy is lost in the waste products produced by organisms. Energy is also lost as a result of **metabolism** in the form of heat.

In Figure 4 the loss of energy at each link in the food chain means that the food energy available at each link is less than that at the previous link. Eventually the food energy available dwindles to zero: no energy available means no further links in the food chain. Now you know why there is only a limited number of links in a food chain.

QUESTIONS

3 Suggest why less energy is lost in the transfer of energy from prey to predator than from plant to herbivore.

4 Explain why there is a limited number of links in a food chain.

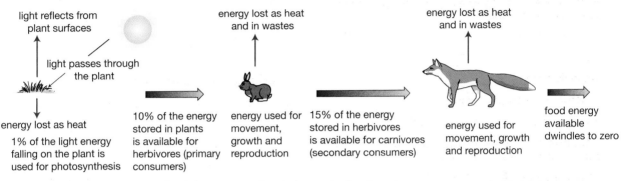

light reflects from plant surfaces

light passes through the plant

energy lost as heat

1% of the light energy falling on the plant is used for photosynthesis

10% of the energy stored in plants is available for herbivores (primary consumers)

energy lost as heat and in wastes

energy used for movement, growth and reproduction

15% of the energy stored in herbivores is available for carnivores (secondary consumers)

energy lost as heat and in wastes

energy used for movement, growth and reproduction

food energy available dwindles to zero

FIGURE 4: Energy flowing along a food chain. Energy flow is the result of eating.

Biomass

Respiration is part of the metabolism of cells. During respiration, sugars are oxidised, releasing energy. The energy released enables cells to make large molecules from smaller ones. The molecules form the materials that make up plant and animal tissues. We refer to the amount of materials as **biomass**.

Pyramids of biomass

Food chains do not tell us about the biomass of producers and consumers, **pyramids of biomass** do. They can be used to describe the food chains that make up a food web in terms of the amounts of food and energy that pass between their links.

Different **trophic** (feeding) levels make up the pyramid. Each trophic level consists of organisms that have the same type of food:

> Producers form the trophic base of the pyramid.

> Consumers form the trophic levels in the order:
1) herbivores, which feed on the producers,
2) primary carnivores, which feed on herbivores, and
3) secondary carnivores, which feed on primary carnivores.

Why is there less biomass in each trophic level than the one below it? Only a proportion of biomass of a trophic level is food (and therefore energy) for the consumers of the trophic level above it. Energy is lost at each link in a food chain of a food web, and each link is part of a trophic level. Energy, therefore, is lost from each trophic level. As a result, each consumer trophic level has less biomass than the one below it.

Now you know why there is only a limited number of trophic levels in a pyramid of biomass.

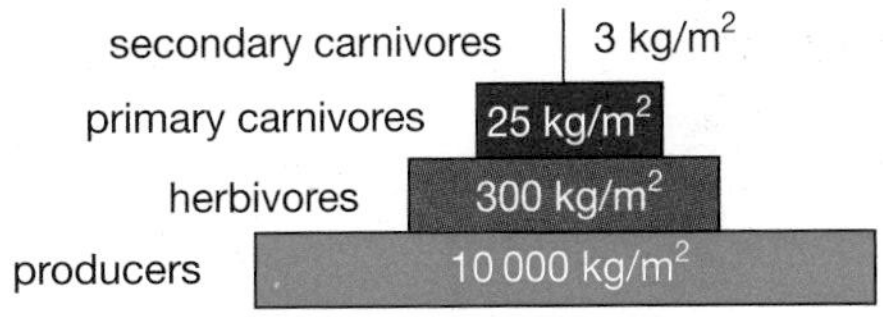

secondary carnivores	3 kg/m²
primary carnivores	25 kg/m²
herbivores	300 kg/m²
producers	10 000 kg/m²

FIGURE 5: Plants trap light energy, converting it into the chemical energy of food. Data is expressed as kilograms of biomass per square metre (kg/m²). Usually mass is measured as **dry mass** rather than fresh mass because each individual contains a different percentage of water.

QUESTIONS

5 A cow consumes 913 kJ. It uses 37 kJ growing and 305 kJ in respiration, and loses 571 kJ in urine and faeces:

a Calculate the percentage of energy intake present in the cow's faeces and urine.

b Calculate the percentage of energy intake used up in respiration.

6 Cows spend a lot of time eating grass. Use your answers to question 5 and explain why this is so.

Population pressures and recycling

Buy, bye

Today, more people live in cities than in the countryside. Industry and technology offer improved living standards and leisure time. However, when people are richer they consume more: all this consumption can have a bad effect on the environment. It's important that we use natural resources carefully: recycling can help.

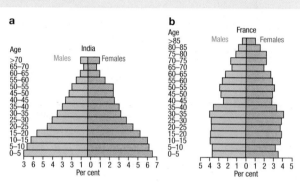

FIGURE 1: Recycling to use natural resources fully.

You will find out:

> that the human population is increasing

> how recycling reduces the demand for resources

World population

About 12 million people lived in the world 10 000 years ago; about 6.7 billion people live in the world today. Estimates suggest that more than 10 billion people will be alive before the end of the century.

Figure 2 shows that the populations of developed nations are levelling off, but that the populations of developing nations are still growing.

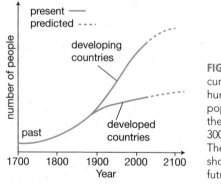

FIGURE 2: Growth curves of the human population over the past 300 years or so. The dotted lines show possible future trends.

Age profile of populations

The rate of human population growth is affected by the number of young people, particularly women of child-bearing age, in the population. Young people are a larger proportion of the population of many developing countries than of developed countries. Comparing age population pyramids makes the point.

The base of each pyramid represents the percentage of children in each country's population. Each top represents the percentage of each country's oldest inhabitants. The other age groups are represented in five-year steps in between.

Countries with broad-base pyramids like India's have populations with high birth rates, low life expectancy (most will die before old age) and improving health care which reduces child mortality. More children therefore will survive to be adults who will have their

FIGURE 3: Describe the differences in age profile of the populations of **a** India and **b** France.

own children. The populations of countries with age population pyramids like India's will continue to grow in the foreseeable futures as Figure 2 suggests.

Countries with narrow-base pyramids like France's have populations with low birth rates and high life expectancy (most will achieve old age) as a result of well-developed health care and living conditions. The populations of countries with age population pyramids like France's (for example, the UK) are stable and may even decline unless immigration compensates.

Did you know?

Developed and 'developing' usually refer to economies, life expectancy and poverty rates of the people.

QUESTIONS

1 State the differences between developing and developed countries shown in Figure 2.

2 Look at Figure 3. Explain how this information assists in predicting the future global population profile.

Resources: supply and demand

Human population growth and improving standards of living mean that resources are in constant demand. Some of them are at risk of being used up.

The term **resources** refers to the raw materials we take from the environment to run industry and our homes. These include the ores we use to extract metals and the oil we use to produce plastics. Both ores and oil are **non-renewable resources**. They cannot be replaced. But even renewable resources, like the wood for making paper, can be used at an unsustainable rate.

Plastic and paper

There is a big demand for plastic and paper. For example, plastic is used to produce shopping bags and drinks bottles, and paper is used in cardboard boxes and printing. This creates two problems:

> Industrial methods used to manufacture paper and plastics use non-renewable resources such as fossil fuels (needed to generate electricity).

> Most plastics and some papers are not biodegradable: they will not rot away.

Packaging crazy

Packaging fuels demand for paper, plastic and metal. In the USA 35% of waste is packaging. Packaging accounts for 75% of glass, 40% of paper, 29% of plastic and 14% of aluminium used in the UK.

Metals

Many industries, including building and manufacturing industries, rely on having a constant supply of metals. However, the Earth contains a limited amount of metal ore and the supply will eventually run out (see Table 1).

TABLE 1: Annual use and estimated reserves of some metal ores. How long will reserves last at the current rate of use?

Metal ore	Annual use (million tonnes)	Reserves (million tonnes)
Iron	1000	800 000
Copper	10	1600
Tin	0.23	12

> ## QUESTIONS
>
> **3** Explain the term 'non-renewable resources'.

Waste: recycle or dump?

Waste disposal

Waste that isn't recycled needs to be incinerated or put into landfill. However, we are running out of landfill sites and they need careful management to stop them polluting water supplies or releasing methane.

When paper and plastics are incinerated, some of the energy produced can be used as heat for industrial processes and to warm homes. However, the process is controversial because it can release pollutant gases.

Recycling

Too often we just throw away things that are out of fashion or no longer useful. Recycling paper, plastic and metals saves the energy used to make them (see Table 2), avoids having to use raw materials and solves the problem of disposal. It reduces the demand for raw materials while ensuring demand for paper, plastics and metals is met.

TABLE 2: Energy saved by recycling materials as an approximate percentage of the energy needed to make them in the first instance. Which material is it most efficient to recycle?

Material	Steel	Aluminium	Plastic bags	Paper
Percentage	75	95	60	50

Paper recycling: is it worth it?

Making 1 kg of paper requires 2.2 kg of wood, 445 dm^3 of water and 7 kW h of energy. Recycling paper makes sense: less wood, water and energy are needed.

Some products are made of 100% waste paper. Others are a mix of waste with new wood pulp. Recycled paper is used to make newspaper, card, envelopes, writing paper and tissues.

> ## QUESTIONS
>
> **4** The table shows the proportion of waste dumped in landfill, recycled and burnt in England for 2004–5 and 2009–10.
>
> | Waste disposal | 2004–5 (%) | 2009–10 (%) |
> |---|---|---|
> | Landfill | 84 | 78 |
> | Recycled | 7 | 12 |
> | Burnt | 8 | 9 |
> | Other | 1 | 1 |
> | Total (million tonnes) | 24.6 | 28.2 |
>
> **a** Explain what is meant by recycling waste.
>
> **b** Calculate how much the proportion of recycled waste has increased between 2004–5 and 2009–10, expressed as a percentage proportion of all waste.

Water pollution

You will find out:
> how nitrates and phosphates affect the environment
> about eutrophication
> about water-quality indicator species

Water: it's vital

The Thames is England's longest river. In medieval times it was home to salmon, but over the years, as London grew, the river became polluted and the salmon disappeared. Salmon were not seen in the Thames for 150 years. However, in recent times the river has been cleaned up and the fish have returned once again.

FIGURE 1: Environment Agency scientists monitoring the water quality of the Thames in London.

Pollutants

Producing food and manufacturing goods for an ever-increasing population uses more and more chemicals and produces in turn more and more chemical wastes. The wastes may be released into the environment. They can be harmful to our health and to wildlife. We call harmful chemicals **pollutants**. Their release causes **pollution**.

Nitrates and phosphates

Nitrates and phosphates are pollutants found in fertiliser. Figure 2 shows a farmer spraying liquid fertiliser containing nitrates and phosphates.

FIGURE 2: Applying liquid manure as a fertiliser.

> Each year more than 140 million tonnes of fertiliser are used in the world.

> Crops absorb the fertiliser in solution and use the nitrogen and phosphates it contains to make proteins, increasing growth.

> The crop yield increases, so there is more food for the growing population and the farmers make more money.

Problems can occur, however, when any fertiliser, and the nitrates and phosphates it contains, not absorbed by crops runs into groundwater (water underground), ponds and rivers. The nitrates and phosphates pollute the water. Groundwater provides one-third of Britain's drinking water. Nitrate and phosphate concentrations in drinking water above the recommended safety level are a health hazard.

QUESTIONS

1 Explain how the concentration of nitrates in groundwater increases.

2 List the sources of phosphates that pollute drinking water.

Eutrophication

Nitrate- and phosphate-rich water washed from the fertiliser on the land into ponds, lakes and rivers stimulates the growth of algae and water plants. This growth of vegetation clogs the water. When the vegetation dies, bacteria decompose the organic material using up the dissolved oxygen in the water. Ammonia and other poisonous substances are also released. Wildlife living in the water dies through lack of oxygen or poisoning. The process is called **eutrophication**.

Sewage also contains nitrates and phosphates. Treated or untreated, it eventually runs into rivers and the sea. Sewage running into water adds to the problems caused by eutrophication.

Q Pollutants and pollution   NPK fertilisers   Phosphate detergents

Process of eutrophication

> Bacteria that need a high concentration of oxygen decompose the accumulating dead organic material. Oxygen dissolved in the water is used up.

> Ammonia and other poisons are released. Aquatic wildlife dies through lack of oxygen and poisoning, adding to the dead organic material. Decomposition continues, and with so much dead organic material available the bacteria quickly multiply, speeding up the eutrophication process

> Bacteria that need little oxygen take over the process of decomposing the dead organic matter.

> The water turns black and foul-smelling gases like hydrogen sulfide are given off. Only species like bloodworms and sludgeworms can survive these conditions. So, the amount of wildlife and biodiversity of the water drops.

FIGURE 3: The Shropshire Union Canal in Cheshire, in 2005. The canal has been clogged with weed and algae due to fertiliser runoff.

QUESTIONS

3 Explain why the concentration of oxygen decreases in fertiliser-enriched water.

4 Draw a flow diagram to explain the process of eutrophication.

Indicator species

When a river is polluted with sewage, the wildlife is affected. The more the water is polluted with sewage, the less oxygen there is in solution because of eutrophication. Fewer species therefore survive in the polluted parts of the river.

The presence or absence of different species indicates how polluted (and therefore how eutrophic) the water is. These species are called **indicator species**. Indicator species can be used by scientists as evidence to assess the level of pollution.

In Figure 4 the number of species and types of species at sites 2 and 3 are less than at sites 1 and 4. At site 4 the dilution of sewage means that water quality is no longer affected. The species found at site 4 are the same as those in the unpolluted water at site 1.

The species found at sites 1 and 4 include stonefly and shrimps. These species are very sensitive to the water's oxygen concentration. They are clean-water indicators because they cannot survive in polluted water where the concentration of oxygen is low. Their absence indicates reduced oxygen levels, suggesting that pollution with sewage is causing eutrophication.

Few species are found at site 2. Those present include bloodworms and sludgeworms. These species are polluted-water indicators. They are pollution tolerant because they can survive at low levels of oxygen. Other less tolerant species cannot.

QUESTIONS

5 Explain the effect of heavily polluted water on species that are intolerant to low levels of oxygen.

6 Explain how bloodworms survive in water with low levels of oxygen.

The absence of species intolerant to low levels of oxygen reduces competition, enabling tolerant species like bloodworms to flourish. Their presence in large numbers indicates heavily polluted water.

Bloodworms are the larvae of non-biting midges. The blood-red colour of a bloodworm is the result of its body containing haemoglobin. This pigment also colours our blood red. It absorbs oxygen.

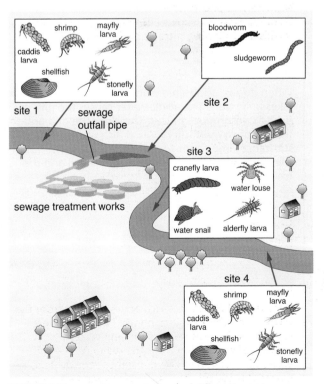

FIGURE 4: The presence or absence of different species indicates how polluted water is with organic wastes.

Pollution in the air

You will find out:
> how acid rain affects the environment
> about air-quality indicator species
> how to investigate the effect of sulfur dioxide on plants

Exporting pollution

Despite the photograph showing an idyllic scene, this lake in Sweden has seen a 100-fold increase in acidity over the past 40 years. Only the very hardiest plants and animals now survive in the lake's water. The acidification of the lake is due to acid rain.

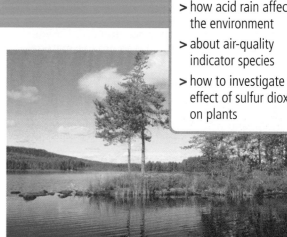

FIGURE 1: Lake Gardsjon in Sweden. What caused its acidification?

Where sulfur dioxide comes from

The increasing human population means that we use more resources for heating, cooking, transport and so on. Here 'using more resources' means burning more fossil fuels, which releases gases such as sulfur dioxide. This is where most of the sulfur dioxide in the air comes from.

$$\text{sulfur} + \text{oxygen} \rightarrow \text{sulfur dioxide}$$
$$\text{(from fossil fuel)} \quad \text{(from air)} \quad \text{(gas)}$$

Pollution with sulfur dioxide reduces air quality. It adds to other gases polluting the air.

Some gases (including sulfur dioxide) in the air dissolve in water vapour and fall as **acid rain** or acid snow.

QUESTIONS

1 Describe how burning fossil fuels produces sulfur dioxide.

2 Outline how acid rain forms.

3 Suggest one way to reduce the amount of sulfur dioxide in the air.

Effects of sulfur dioxide pollution

Acid rain

When it falls, acid rain or snow eventually passes into lakes and rivers. The acidic water causes the gills of fish to overproduce mucus. This clogs the gills and the fish die of oxygen starvation. It also washes substances important for healthy tree growth out of the soil. Poisons are released from the soil and the trees die.

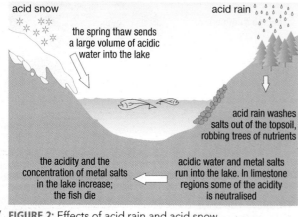

acid snow

the spring thaw sends a large volume of acidic water into the lake

acid rain

acid rain washes salts out of the topsoil, robbing trees of nutrients

the acidity and the concentration of metal salts in the lake increase; the fish die

acidic water and metal salts run into the lake. In limestone regions some of the acidity is neutralised

FIGURE 2: Effects of acid rain and acid snow.

Indicator species

Lichens are a mutualistic combination of a fungus and green alga. They grow on trees, stones and roof-tops. There are different types: shrubby, leafy and slightly leafy.

The tolerance of each type of lichen to the level of sulfur dioxide in the air is different. Their presence or absence is an indicator of air quality. Table 1 sets out the differences.

TABLE 1: Types of lichen and their tolerance to sulfur dioxide.

Lichen	Tolerance to sulfur dioxide
Shrubby	Little tolerance
Leafy	Medium tolerance
Slightly leafy	High tolerance

Different surveys show that the number of lichen species varies according to the level of sulfur dioxide in the air. A greater variety of lichen species is observed where sulfur dioxide pollution is low, that is away from city centres.

Burning fossil fuels   Acid rain formation   Lichens – an example of mutualism

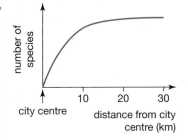

FIGURE 3: Lichens are an indicator species. When the level of sulfur dioxide pollution decreases, the variety of lichen species increases.

Black spot is a fungal disease that covers rose leaves. Its presence is an indicator of *good* air quality.

FIGURE 4: Black spot fungus, shown here on a rose leaf, is an indicator species.

Black spot fungus is sensitive to sulfur dioxide, so high levels of the pollutant in the air reduce the extent of the disease – a rare example of the benefits of pollution, at least for roses!

Do pollutants affect plant growth?

Pollutants are chemicals harmful to our health and to wildlife. Sulfur dioxide is a pollutant. We have seen, however, that roses can tolerate and even benefit from it. This raises the question: is sulfur dioxide harmful to plants and does it affect plant growth?

You can answer the question by planning a simple experiment. Figure 5 shows you how you might investigate whether or not cress seeds germinate and grow better in clean air or in air polluted with sulfur dioxide.

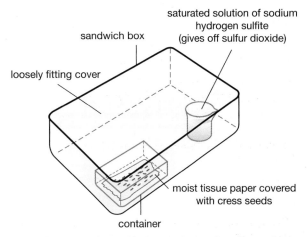

FIGURE 5: An experiment for investigating the effects of sulfur dioxide on seed germination and growth.

QUESTIONS

4 Suggest why shrubby lichens are less tolerant to sulfur dioxide pollution than leafy lichens.

5 Plan the investigation outlined in Figure 5. Remember to explain the importance of a control experiment.

Why is acid rain an international problem?

For much of the year the prevailing wind blows from the west/south-west to the east/north-east across Europe. These prevailing winds carry acid water vapour from the UK, France and other countries west/south-west of Norway and Sweden. This is why acid rain or acid snow falls on Norway and Sweden, many hundreds of kilometres away from the source of the pollution.

Figure 6 shows the percentage contributions of acid gases produced by power stations and vehicles of different European countries to the problem of acid rain or snow falling on Norway and Sweden.

QUESTIONS

6 Draw a flow diagram to explain the formation of acid rain.

7 Explain why Norway and Sweden are particularly affected by acid rain.

8 Explain why trees exposed to acid rain die.

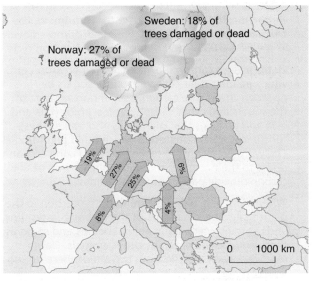

FIGURE 6: Some contributions of acid gases from selected European countries to the acid rain and acid snow falling in Norway and Sweden.

Recycling carbon and nitrogen

What are we made of?

We are made of star stuff. Forged in the fiery heat of stars, elements and the compounds they form make the living matter of cells.

You will find out:
> how carbon is recycled
> how nitrogen is recycled

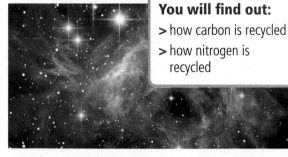

FIGURE 1: Is this where we were born?

Decomposition

Fungi and bacteria are everywhere: in soil, air and water. Their food comes from dead bodies and other dead organic materials. Decay and **decomposition** are the result of their activities. This is why they are called **decomposers**. The compounds released because of their activities are **nutrients**, which are released into the environment.

The nutrients are absorbed in solution by plants and pass to animals as the result of feeding. Carbon, nitrogen and the compounds they form are examples of nutrients.

> ### QUESTIONS
>
> 1 Explain why fungi and bacteria are called decomposers.
>
> 2 State why decomposers are important for the growth of new plants.

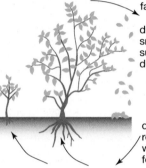

falling leaves

dead leaves break up into small pieces, exposing a larger surface area to attack by decomposers

decomposers feed on the leaf remains, releasing compounds which are the nutrients needed for new plant growth

FIGURE 2: Decomposers feeding release nutrients into the environment.

The carbon cycle

Respiration and **photosynthesis** recycle carbon as carbon dioxide (CO_2) between the environment, the dead and the living. The percentage of carbon dioxide in the air is 0.035% and the result of the carbon cycle.

Plants absorb carbon dioxide from the environment, which enables their cells to produce sugars by photosynthesis. The carbon is an important part of the sugars and other carbohydrates, lipids (fats and oils) and proteins that plant cells also make. These substances are the materials which build plant bodies. The word fix means 'to make part of'. Fixing carbon refers to the processes that make the carbon of carbon dioxide part of other molecules.

When plants are eaten by animals, the carbon in the plant tissues becomes part of the carbohydrates, lipids and proteins which build animal bodies and so on as these animals are eaten by other animals. Plants remove carbon dioxide from the atmosphere during

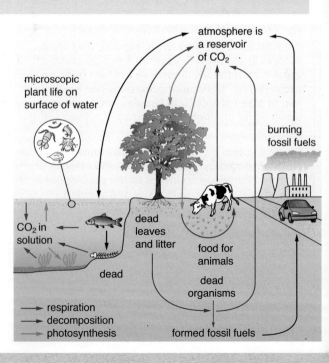

atmosphere is a reservoir of CO_2

microscopic plant life on surface of water

burning fossil fuels

CO_2 in solution

dead leaves and litter

food for animals

dead

dead organisms

→ respiration
→ decomposition
→ photosynthesis

formed fossil fuels

FIGURE 3: The carbon cycle. How is CO_2 removed from the atmosphere?

Q Decay and decomposition   Fixing carbon   Fixing nitrogen photosynthesis; plants and animals release carbon dioxide into the atmosphere during respiration.

The respiration of decomposers also releases carbon dioxide into the atmosphere, as does our burning of fossil fuels (coal, gas and oil). The fuels are formed from the fossilised remains of plants that lived hundreds of millions of years ago. The carbon dioxide released is the carbon fixed during photosynthesis by those ancient plants all that time ago.

Chalk is formed from the fossilised remains of aquatic microscopic organisms settling into layers on the sea bed millions of years ago. Later geological upheavals have raised the chalk layers, forming the hills and cliffs that, for example, guard England's south-east shore. Exposed to rain (which is slightly acid), the chalk dissolves and more carbon dioxide is released into the atmosphere.

QUESTIONS

3 Explain the relationship between respiration and photosynthesis in maintaining the concentration of carbon dioxide in the atmosphere at 0.035%.

4 State how animals obtain carbon-containing compounds.

The nitrogen cycle (Higher tier only)

The atmosphere is a vast reservoir of nitrogen gas (78% by volume) and this element is an essential part of proteins. Proteins build bodies. Unfortunately most living things cannot make direct use of gaseous nitrogen. However, **nitrogen-fixing bacteria** living in the root nodules of leguminous plants or in the soil can (see page 73). They 'fix' (to make part of) gaseous nitrogen as ammonia (NH_3), which forms ammonium compounds. These compounds are very soluble. Plants absorb them in solution from the soil through their roots, enabling them to make proteins and grow. Animals obtain the nitrogen they need for making proteins from the food they eat and so the nitrogen compounds pass along the food chain.

Proteins (nitrogen-containing compounds) are a major part of the remains of dead animals and plants. Animal wastes (faeces and urine) also contain nitrogen: for example, urine contains urea ($CO(NH_2)_2$). Decomposers, including soil bacteria, break down dead and waste matter, converting proteins and urea into ammonia. **Nitrifying bacteria** convert this ammonia to nitrates.

Like ammonium compounds, nitrates are very soluble. Plants absorb them in solution from the soil through their roots. Chemical reactions in plant cells convert nitrates into ammonium compounds which the cells use to make protein, enabling plants to grow.

Lightning plays a part in the cycle. Its energy breaks apart nitrogen molecules in the atmosphere. The nitrogen atoms react with atmospheric oxygen forming nitrogen oxides which dissolve in rain drops.

Nitric acid (HNO_3) and nitrous acid (HNO_2) are produced. Reaching the ground, the acids react with compounds in the soil, forming nitrates. Industrial processes and vehicle engines also release nitrogen oxides into the atmosphere, and are eventually converted into nitrates.

Nitrates not absorbed by plants are converted by **denitrifying bacteria** in the soils to nitrogen gas which is released to the atmosphere. Overall the different processes recycle nitrogen between the environment, the dead and the living:

nitrogen fixation → nitrification → denitrification.

QUESTIONS

5 Explain why fields are sown with leguminous crops (such as peas and beans) in 'rotation' with other crops.

6 Explain the differences in the roles of nitrogen-fixing bacteria, denitrifying bacteria and nitrifying bacteria in the nitrogen cycle.

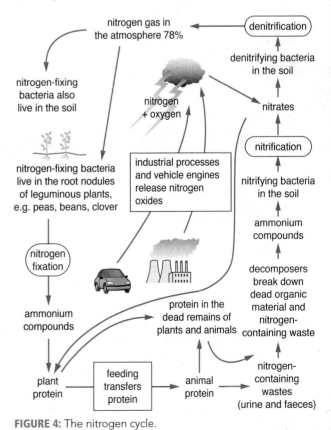

FIGURE 4: The nitrogen cycle.

Preparing for assessment: Applying your knowledge

To achieve a good grade in science, you not only have to know and understand scientific ideas, but you also need to be able to apply them to other situations. This task will support you in developing these skills.

Our day at the seaside

Andy and Barney are drawing a food web for this rock pool. They notice that nothing seems to be eating the seaweed.

All the food chains must start with the microscopic algae on the surface of the rocks, plankton in the water or the bits of dead seaweed that litter the area.

There are several different crabs in the pool. Some are difficult to spot. Their shells are covered in barnacles and anemones.

Shrimps eat plankton and detritus, which means bits of dead seaweed or dead animals. Barnacles and mussels filter food out of the water so they consume a mixture of plankton and detritus.

Task 1

The organisms in the rock pool have a dynamic relationship. When one population becomes more common, those that feed on it can increase their numbers and vice versa. What word describes the way living things interact with each other like this?

Task 2

Andy and Barney's food web shows the feeding relationships in the rock pool. If pollution causes shrimp numbers to fall, how will other animals in the food web be affected?

Task 3

Hermit crabs feed on dead seaweed or dead animals. The barnacles and anemones on their shells catch the bits that break off as they feed.

> Do these animals benefit the crabs in any way?

> What name is given to this sort of relationship?

✴ Maximise your grade

These sentences show what you need to include in your work to achieve each grade. Use them to improve your work and be more successful.

E

For grade E, your answers should show that you can:
> explain how populations affect each other
> use the term 'interdependence' correctly
> explain how one species can depend on another.

C

For grades D, C, in addition show that you can:
> explain why food chains rarely involve more than four organisms.

A

For grades B, A, in addition show that you can:
> show that you understand why pyramids of biomass can have different shapes
> explain with particular clarity and detail why pyramids of biomass can have different shapes.

✴ Task 4

In the rock pool, there are 8 g of herbivores and 1 g of carnivores for every 100 g of producers.

> Draw a pyramid of biomass for the rock pool.

> Explain why rock pool food chains rarely have more than four tropic levels.

> Shrimp farms add synthetic feeds to the water. It is found that 100 kg of feed produces about 65 kg of shrimps. That's a lot. Mammals like sheep only make 1 kg of extra meat when they eat the same amount of feed. Suggest reasons for this difference.

Preparing for assessment: Analysis and conclusions

To achieve a good grade in science, you not only have to know and understand scientific ideas, but you also need to be able to apply them to other situations and investigations. This task will support you in developing these skills.

✸ Task

> Test the hypothesis that caffeine makes drivers less likely to have an accident because it reduces their reaction times.

✸ Context

A driver's reaction time is the time they take to respond when they spot a hazard.

Caffeine is a popular legal drug found in tea, coffee, cola and energy drinks. It is a stimulant. Since it makes users more alert, it might cut their reaction times.

✸ Method and results

Two drivers were tested on a driving simulator. A computer measured the time they took to react to 10 different hazards in milliseconds (ms) and calculated an average. Then the two drivers drank a cup of coffee containing 60 mg of caffeine. They repeated the reaction time test at 3, 10, 30 and 60 minutes after drinking it. The results are shown in the table below.

Time after consuming caffeine (min)	Average reaction time (ms)	
	Driver 1 male (30 years)	Driver 2 female (22 years)
0	267	252
3	254	250
10	239	255
30	235	250
60	250	255

✴ Processing the evidence

1. Display the results on a graph.

2. Add lines of best fit to each set of results.

> Remember to put the independent variable on the x-axis.
>
> Choose a suitable scale for each axis – there is no need to start at zero.
>
> Make it easy to compare caffeine's effect on the two drivers.

> You will need to decide whether each line of best fit should be straight or curved.

✴ Stating conclusions

1. For each driver, explain in detail the effect the caffeine had.

2. Do the results support the hypothesis? If they do, use scientific and mathematical ideas to explain why you would expect the results you got.

3. Are there any anomalies to consider?

> If the pattern is different in different parts of the graph, split your explanation into two parts.
>
> Use numbers from the graphs to illustrate your answer.

> If the results do not support the hypothesis, consider whether the test method is faulty or the hypothesis is either wrong, or only correct in certain circumstances.
>
> Be sure to use correct scientific vocabulary to gain Quality of Written Communication marks.

> Results usually show some scatter due to random errors, but an anomalous result is completely different from the others.

✴ Evaluating the method and conclusions

1. State what was good about the test method.

2. Make a list of variables that may not have been controlled in this investigation.

3. How could the method be improved?

4. How would you reword your hypothesis in light of the results obtained?

> You should consider whether the method was reliable, repeat measurements, whether the conclusions are valid, whether a fair test was carried out.

> Do we know anything about the two drivers?

> Give reasons why the changes are needed and explain why they would improve the quality of the evidence.

> Consider the hypothesis itself and the scientific language.

✴ Connections

How Science Works

> Collecting and analysing data.

> Collecting data from secondary sources.

> Working accurately and safely when collecting first-hand data.

> Evaluating methods of data collection and verifying information sources.

> Using both qualitative and quantitative approaches.

> Presenting information using appropriate language, conventions and symbols and tools.

Maths in Science

> Calculate arithmetic means.

> Plot and draw graphs selecting appropriate scales for the axes.

> Translate information between graphical and numeric forms.

> Extract and interpret information from charts, graphs and tables.

B1 checklist (Topic 3)

To achieve your forecast grade in the exam you'll need to revise

Use this checklist to see what you can do now. Refer back to pages 58–83 if you're not sure.

Look across the rows to see how you could progress – **bold italic** means Higher tier only.

Remember you'll need to be able to use these ideas in various ways, such as:
> interpreting pictures, diagrams and graphs
> applying ideas to new situations
> explaining ethical implications
> suggesting some benefits and risks to society
> drawing conclusions from evidence you've been given.

Look at pages 270–92 for more information about exams and how you'll be assessed.

To aim for a grade E	To aim for a grade C	To aim for a grade A
define what a drug is and explain the physical and psychological effects of different drugs	describe how drug abuse can lead to drug addiction	understand that drugs that affect the nervous system mostly have their effect at the synapse
recall the effects of some chemicals in cigarette smoke	explain the effects of some chemicals in cigarette smoke	evaluate data that establishes the correlation between smoking and ill-health
recall the harmful effects of alcohol abuse	evaluate some of the harmful effects of alcohol abuse	
recall that organs can be transplanted	describe how the demand for organs can be supplied	discuss the ethical issues of organ transplants
recall that infectious diseases are caused by pathogens, including animal vectors	describe how different pathogens are spread	apply understanding of animal vectors of disease
state that animals and plants are able to defend themselves against pathogens	explain how animals and plants are able to defend themselves against pathogens by physical and chemical means	understand that antibacterials produced by plants may be useful to humans
know that antiseptics help to prevent the spread of infection	understand that antibiotics are used to treat and control infections	*evaluate evidence that resistant strains of pathogenic bacteria (including MRSA) can arise from the misuse of antibiotics*

To aim for a grade E　　To aim for a grade C　　To aim for a grade A

To aim for a grade E	To aim for a grade C	To aim for a grade A
recall that living things are interdependent	understand why living things are interdependent, giving mutualism and parasitism as examples	apply understanding to include mutualism in *nitrogen-fixing bacteria in legumes and chemosynthetic bacteria in tube worms*
state that energy is transferred along food chains and between trophic levels	explain and apply understanding to the transfer of energy along food chains and between trophic levels in a pyramid of biomass	
describe global population change	explain and use data to show how the increase in human population has an impact on the environment and how the impact can be reduced by recycling	
describe the sources of pollution, including sulfur dioxide, and nitrates and phosphates	explain the processes of eutrophication and acid rain formation explain how scientists can use indicator species to assess the impact of these phenomena	apply understanding of indicator species
state that decomposers recycle dead organic matter	understand how carbon is recycled	*understand how nitrogen is recycled*

AO1 **1 a** LSD is a drug. It is a …

    A depressant   C stimulant

    B painkiller   D hallucinogen.   [1]

AO1 **b** Describe the effect of a painkilling drug on the nervous system.   [2]

    c It is illegal to obtain addictive drugs without a doctor's prescription.

AO2 **i** Suggest why drug addiction can be an expensive habit.   [1]

AO1 **ii** Define the meaning of 'drug abuse'.   [1]

AO1 **d** Caffeine is a stimulant; alcohol is a depressant.
AO2   Explain why the effects of caffeine and alcohol on a person are different.   [3]

    [Total: 8]

2

AO1 **a** *Anopheles* mosquitoes are vectors of disease. Explain the meaning of the word vector.   [2]

AO1 **b** State two ways houseflies can spread infectious diseases.   [2]

    c Houseflies can pass on dysentery bacteria to people. People with dysentery pass large amounts of liquid faeces.

AO1 **i** State why dysentery is a serious risk to health.   [1]

AO2 **ii** Explain how oral rehydration therapy (ORT) can help to save the lives of people with dysentery.   [3]

    [Total: 8]

3 The diagram represents a food chain.

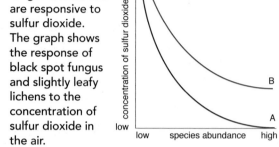

AO2 **a** Identify the producers.

    A a   B a, b   C c   D b, c   [1]

    b The arrows represent the transfer of energy between organisms along the food chain.

AO2 **i** Which arrow represents the most efficient transfer?   [1]

AO2 **ii** Suggest two ways that energy is lost between a and b   [2]

AO2 **c** Explain why not all of the light falling on plant surfaces is used for photosynthesis.   [2]

AO1 **d** Explain why there is only a limited number of links in a food chain.   [2]

    [Total: 8]

4 The disease black spot is caused by a fungus that covers rose leaves. Lichens are a mutualistic combination of a fungus and green algae.

AO2 **a** Explain the meaning of 'mutualistic combination'.   [2]

    b Black spot fungus and lichens are responsive to sulfur dioxide. The graph shows the response of black spot fungus and slightly leafy lichens to the concentration of sulfur dioxide in the air.

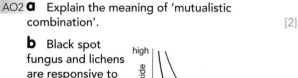

AO3 **i** Describe the main trends shown in the graph.   [1]

AO2 **ii** Identify which line, A or B, represents black spot.   [1]

AO3 **iii** An area has high occurrence of black spot. Use the graph to state what this shows about the level of pollution in the area.   [1]

AO3 **c** Rosie set out to investigate the effects of sulfur dioxide on seed germination and growth.

In five sandwich boxes Rosie placed 24 cress seeds on damp filter paper plus a beaker of saturated solution of sodium hydrogen sulfite, which gives off sulfur dioxide. In another five sandwich boxes, Rosie placed an equal number of seeds on damp filter paper with a beaker of distilled water. The table below shows her results.

Number of seeds that germinated	
With water	With sodium hydrogen sulfite
18	7
16	10
16	6
18	10
19	11

Rosie wrote a prediction before carrying out this experiment: 'More seeds will germinate in cleaner air'. Explain whether Rosie's prediction was correct. Include the results for all boxes in your explanation.   [6]

    [Total: 11]

✴ Worked example

AO1 **a** Complete the sentences below about infectious diseases using the following words:

A bacterium   D pathogen
B fungus,   E virus
C protist.   [2]

An organism that causes disease is called a …

D Pathogen. ✔

The type of organism that causes athlete's foot is a …

A bacterium   D pathogen
B fungus,   E virus
C protist.

B Fungus. ✔

AO1 **b** State two ways infectious diseases are spread.   [2]

Food and air. ✔ ✔

AO1 **c** **i** State which cells in the body are infected by human immunodeficiency virus (HIV).   [1]

Red blood cells. ✘

ii Explain why human immunodeficiency virus (HIV) causes AIDS.   [2]

It reduces the amount of oxygen carried in the blood. ✘

iii State which bacterium causing food poisoning might infect a person eating under-cooked chicken.   [1]

Cholera bacterium. ✘

AO1 **d** The terms bactericide and bacteriostat refer to the actions of different antibiotic drugs. Explain the meaning of the terms.   [3]

Antibiotics are drug used to treat bacterial infections. Bactericides destroy bacteria. Bacteriostats also destroy them. ✔ ✔ ✘

This candidate scored 6 marks out of 11 which is a grade C. Complete revision of basic topic material in part **c** would have lifted performance beyond grade C.

How to raise your grade

Take note of the comments from examiners – these will help you to improve your grade.

> The candidate has not been put off by the available options, showing clear understanding of technical terms.

> Nothing more is needed to gain full marks in this part of the question. Always be clear and precise.

> The candidate has identified that blood cells are infected by HIV but has confused the type of cell. The correct answer is a type of white blood cell.

> AIDS is a syndrome of diseases characteristic of HIV. The candidate has carried forward the error from **ci**. The correct answer to **cii** does not depend on the answer to **ci**.

> The candidate's knowledge of pathogens is incomplete. The answer is the *Salmonella* bacterium.

> The candidate correctly identifies that the action of antibiotics is against bacteria; and that bactericides destroy them. However, they do not recognise that two different terms suggest two different actions of antibiotics. Bacteriostats prevent bacteria from multiplying.

1 **a** The diagram shows how different antibiotic drugs attack bacterial cells.

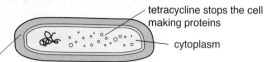

tetracycline stops the cell making proteins

cytoplasm

penicillin and cephalosporin weaken the cell wall

AO1 **i** Name the type of cell structure affected by tetracycline. [1]

AO1
AO2 **ii** Explain why antibiotics are not an effective treatment for diseases caused by viruses. [2]

b Antifungals are drugs used to treat fungal infections such as athlete's foot.

AO1 **i** Why are antifungals effective drugs? [1]

AO2 **ii** Suggest why antifungals may cause unpleasant side-effects. [1]

AO2 **c** Bacteria develop resistance to antibiotics. Describe the development of bacterial resistance to antibiotics as an example of evolution in action. [6]
[Total: 11]

2 Peas, beans and clover are examples of leguminous plants which have nodules on their roots that contain bacteria.

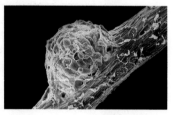

AO1 **a** **i** Which one of the following is the name given to these bacteria:

A *Escherichia coli*
B Nitrogen fixing
C Chlorophyll
D Sulfur fixing [1]

AO1 **ii** Describe the role of bacteria contained in the root nodules in the survival of legumes. [2]

b Chemosynthetic bacteria and giant tube worms live near to hydrothermal deep-sea vents. The bacteria can live in the body of the giant tube worms.

AO1 **i** Explain why the relationship between the giant tube worm and the chemosynthetic bacteria living in its body is an example of mutualism. [2]

AO2 **ii** Compare the processes of chemosynthesis and photosynthesis. [3]
[Total: 8]

3 The graph shows the link between the increase in the risk of males dying from bronchitis and lung cancer, and the number of cigarettes smoked daily.

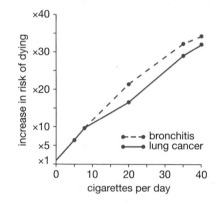

increase in risk of dying

×40
×30
×20
×10
×5
×1

- - - bronchitis
—— lung cancer

0   10   20   30   40
cigarettes per day

AO3 **a** Describe the main trend shown in the graph. [2]

AO3 **b** Discuss why the graph cannot establish cause and effect. [3]

AO3 **c** A man decides to reduce the number of cigarettes he smokes per day from 40 to 20.

i How has he changed his risk of dying from bronchitis and cancer? [1]

ii Are there other factors that need to be taken into account? [2]
[Total: 8]

4 Most organisms cannot use the elemental gas nitrogen directly. The nitrogen cycle is a natural process that gives organisms access to nitrogen.

AO1 **a** Suggest why organisms need nitrogen. [2]

AO2 **b** Explain two characteristics of a cycle. [2]

AO1
AO2 **c** Explain the role of different types of bacteria in recycling nitrogen gas into useful, accessible forms. [6]
[Total: 10]

AO1 **recall the science**   AO2 **apply your knowledge**   AO3 **evaluate and analyse the evidence**

✳ Worked example

A group of students carried out surveys at along their local river along points A–E.

Diagram 1
Direction of flow ⟶   Factory discharging warm water into the river ▉

A   B   C   D   E
Pig farm   1 km

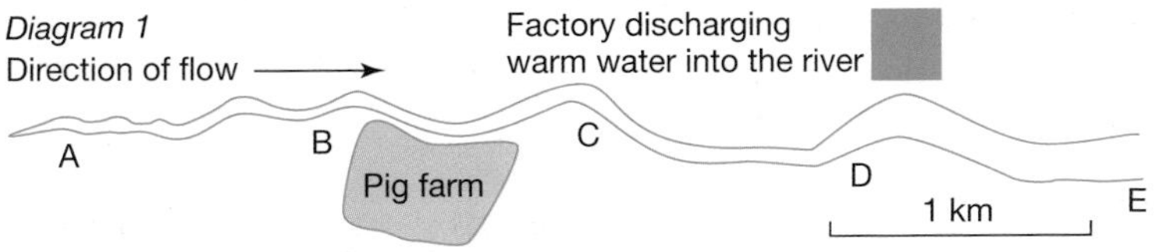

They presented their results as a bar graph.

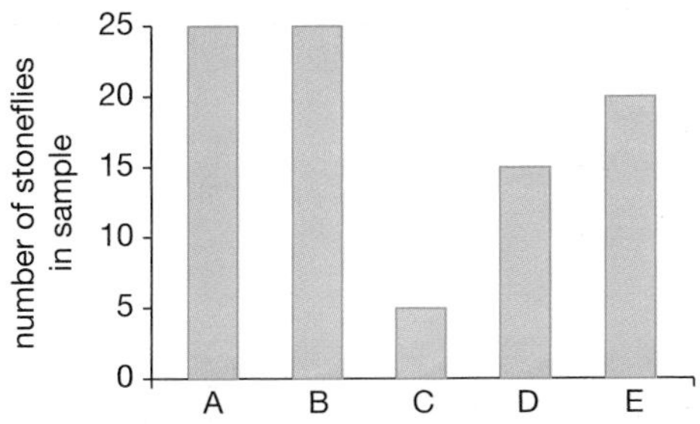

number of stoneflies in sample (y-axis: 0, 5, 10, 15, 20, 25)
A: 25, B: 25, C: 5, D: 15, E: 20

AO3 a i Describe the main trends shown in the data. [3]

The number of stoneflies falls between B and C and goes up again between C and D. ✔ ✔ ✘

AO3 ii Explain what the bar graph shows about the concentration of oxygen at point B along the river. [1]

The number of stonefly is high, indicating a high concentration of oxygen. ✔

AO3 iii At which point along the river is the water most polluted? [1]

At point C, because the number of stoneflies is lowest at this point. ✔

b Trout are fish that feed on caddis flies, which in turn feed on stoneflies.

AO2 i Explain how the change in the water's oxygen concentration between points B and C will affect trout numbers. [1]

Trout numbers would decrease. ✔

AO2 ii Oxygen is less soluble in warm water than in cold water. Use this information to estimate the likely number of trout at E. [1]

There would be no trout here. ✘

AO2 c Explain how a leak of liquid waste from the pig farm into the river could cause a change in the number of stonefly in the river. [4]

Animal waste enriches the water with nitrogen-containing compounds, causing bacteria numbers to increase. These bacteria use up more dissolved oxygen in respiration. So, the oxygen concentration of the water decreases. ✔ ✔ ✔ ✘

This candidate scored 8 marks out of 11 which is on the grade A/B border. Checking all answers for completeness would have raised performance to a grade A, or A*.

How to raise your grade

Take note of the comments from examiners – these will help you to improve your grade.

There are three parts of the graph to comment on – the constant number at points A and B; the drop in numbers at C; and the increase in numbers at D. As the candidate has only commented on two of the three, only 2 marks are given.

The candidate has applied their understanding of stonefly as clean water indicators, to the data provided to gain full marks.

The candidate has given the correct answer – point C – and gained the mark. Their explanation is correct but it gains no additional marks as only 1 mark is available for this question. Remember, don't write more than the question asks for – your time could be better spent on another question.

A clear, succinct answer.

The candidate clearly understands the principle as shown in part **i**. However, they have failed to apply that understanding here.

This question requires the candidate to give four facts in a logical order to score full marks. The candidate has given a logical answer but has not shown what will happen to stonefly numbers (they will decrease). Always check your answer to ensure you have fully answered the question.

C1 Chemistry in our world (Topics 1–3)

What you should know

The changing Earth

Active volcanoes usually appear at plate boundaries and produce gases, some of which are poisonous.

Human activities such as burning fossil fuels and natural factors such as volcanoes affect the atmosphere.

Smog and soot are visible signs of air pollution.

- Name two gases produced by a volcano.

Rocks and their uses

There are three types of rock – igneous, sedimentary and metamorphic – that are formed in the course of the rock cycle.

The rock cycle involves the processes of volcanic eruption, weathering, erosion, sedimentation and compression.

Each type of rock has its own properties and uses.

- List the properties and uses of one type of rock.

Chemical reactions

Chemical reactions can be described in words and equations using symbols to represent elements and compounds.

Chemical reactions can be recognised by changes that occur during the chemical reaction, including changing pH and the production of gas.

The rate of chemical reactions is affected by temperature, concentration and surface area.

Acids and alkalis produce salt and water. This is called a neutralisation reaction.

- Give the chemical formulae for two different compounds.

You will find out about

> the composition of the early atmosphere and the atmosphere today

> how chemistry helps scientists to understand the changes to the Earth's atmosphere since it formed

> the formation of oceans

> how igneous, sedimentary and metamorphic rocks are formed

> the many uses of limestone, a type of sedimentary rock

> the advantages and disadvantages of quarrying limestone

> the smallest particles of matter that can be observed using chemistry being atoms and how they behave in reactions

> thermal decomposition of compounds by heat

> neutralisation reactions and their practical applications in biology, industry and farming

> using electrolysis to decompose some compounds

> identifying the products of reactions by chemical tests

The early atmosphere

You will find out:
> about the early atmosphere of the Earth
> the effect of volcanoes on the atmosphere
> how we learn about the early atmosphere

Volcanoes

Some of the most spectacular geological features on Earth are volcanoes. Their violent actions have been important in shaping the surface of the Earth. They have also played an important role in the development of the atmosphere that we breathe.

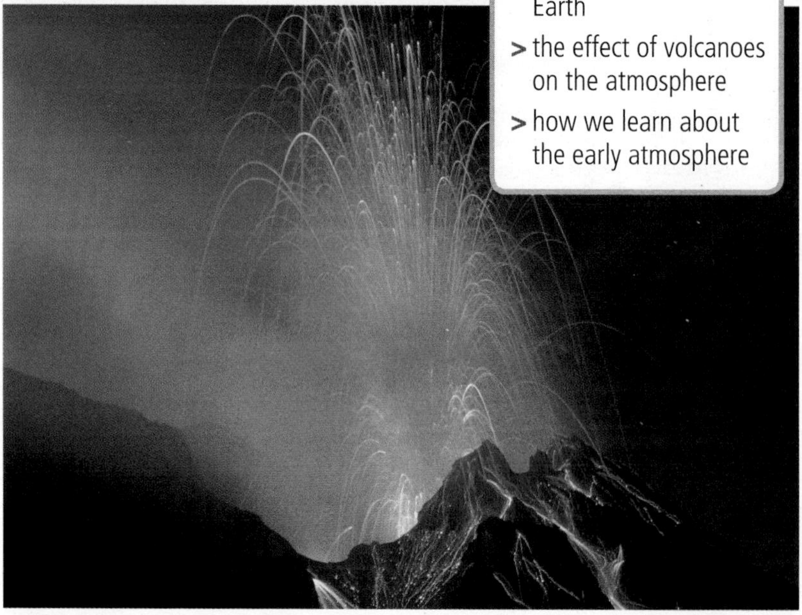

FIGURE 1: What else besides lava comes out of volcanoes?

Early Earth

Scientists believe that the Earth formed about 4.5 billion years ago.

The **atmosphere** that you and I breathe today has not always been here. The atmosphere that formed around the young Earth contained almost no oxygen. Instead it contained:

> large amounts of carbon dioxide

> large amounts of water vapour

> small amounts of various other gases.

All of the carbon dioxide and water vapour came from volcanoes.

Scientists can use geological, chemical and biological information to try to understand how the early atmosphere evolved. These sources do not allow us to be precise about the early atmosphere as assumptions have to be made about what actually occurred, but they help us to form a general idea.

The Earth began as hot molten rock. As it cooled, the interior remained hot and molten. This hot molten material (**magma**) made its way to the surface and flowed out of early volcanoes as lava, which cooled and crystallised into rock.

By studying the gases from modern volcanoes, scientists can determine which gases were in the early atmosphere.

QUESTIONS

1 State the two most common gases present in the early atmosphere of the Earth.

2 Name one source of information about the early atmosphere.

3 Give the chemical formulae for the gases named in question 1.

Evidence of the early atmosphere

Scientists have concluded that the early atmosphere contained very little oxygen and large amounts of carbon dioxide and water vapour. How do they know? Since no one was there, we must rely on evidence. One of the best sources of evidence is the rock that was formed during those early times.

Rocks formed during the different periods in the Earth's development leave a record of the environment at that time. From this, we are able to analyse and interpret the composition of these rocks which can help to give us an understanding of the early atmosphere. For example, lava, once it cools, solidifies into rock deposits. These rock deposits can be analysed to discover the composition of the magma and its gases at a particular time.

QUESTIONS

4 Describe the differences, if any, between the gases released by early volcanoes and volcanoes today.

5 Explain how scientists can tell what chemicals were present in the early atmosphere.

Did you know?

Venus' atmosphere is mainly made up of carbon dioxide. This means the Earth's early atmosphere was very similar to that found in Venus.

FIGURE 2: What does lava tell us about the atmosphere?

Oxygen as evidence

Oxygen is one of the most reactive gases in our atmosphere. Its high level of reactivity can be seen in the rusting of exposed metals and the maintenance of fire. Oxygen is so important to these two types of reactions that they are referred to as **oxidation reactions**.

If oxygen had been present in the early atmosphere, we would expect to find oxygen in the early rocks that were formed. Iron is very reactive with oxygen and so the type of iron-based rock formed in a particular period indicates how much oxygen was in the atmosphere at the time. For example, red-bed rock contains iron oxide and shows that some oxygen was present when this rock was formed.

FIGURE 3: Rust and fire: what do these two pictures have in common?

Changes through time

Figure 4 shows the variation in the concentration of gases in the Earth's atmosphere over time. Notice the dramatic changes that have occurred. The amount of carbon dioxide has dropped and the amount of oxygen has increased.

QUESTIONS

6 Describe and explain any patterns in the composition of gases in the Earth's atmosphere.

7 Research Earth's early atmosphere. Name any other gases that were present and draw a graph (similar to Figure 4), showing how the concentration of these gases varied over time.

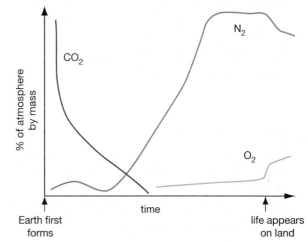

FIGURE 4: The changing atmosphere of the Earth. Do you notice any trends?

The early oceans

You will find out:

> about the condensation of water vapour

> how carbon dioxide levels change

> the effect of plants on the atmosphere

Water, water everywhere ...

Approximately 71% of the surface of the Earth is covered by water, but this was not always the case.

Where did it all come from? Volcanic activity not only formed Earth's early atmosphere, it also brought about its oceans.

FIGURE 1: Earth: where did all of the water come from?

Did you know?

There is almost 1400 billion billion kilograms of water on the Earth's surface.

The formation of oceans

The volcanoes on early Earth pumped more and more water vapour into the atmosphere. This caused the atmosphere to change.

> As the amount of water vapour increased, the temperature of the Earth and its atmosphere continued to fall, and water droplets formed in the atmosphere through a process called **condensation**.

> As the water droplets increased in size, they eventually fell to the surface of the Earth and accumulated. This was the beginning of the first oceans.

> The carbon dioxide gas in the atmosphere reacted with the accumulated water (in a process called **dissolution**) and the amount of carbon dioxide in the atmosphere decreased.

Eventually, living organisms appeared in the oceans. The organisms that evolved used the carbon dioxide available in the oceans in different ways.

> Some of the marine organisms incorporated the carbon dioxide into their shells. When those organisms died their shells accumulated on the floor of the oceans and became **carbonate** rocks.

> Other marine organisms began to use carbon dioxide in chemical reactions to produce sugars that they could store as energy reserves. This reaction released oxygen into the atmosphere. This process is called **photosynthesis**. These organisms were the first primitive plants.

FIGURE 2: Foraminifera (microscopic organisms) and the cliffs of Dover. What do these two pictures have in common?

QUESTIONS

1 Name the process that produced the first liquid water on Earth.

2 State two ways that organisms lowered the amount of carbon dioxide in the atmosphere.

Q Diatoms in sedimentary rock   Condensation

Condensation

As discussed earlier, oceans were formed by a process called condensation. Condensation occurs when molecules of a gas start to stick together and form a liquid. The intermolecular forces that hold the molecules together are strong enough to allow them to stick together but not so strong that a solid is formed.

Remember!

Chemists use symbols to indicate elements and molecules. For example, H_2O is the formula for a molecule of water. Water can be a gas (water vapour), a liquid or a solid (ice).

FIGURE 3: Boiling water. How many states of water are shown here?

QUESTIONS

3 Explain the process of condensation and how it helped to form the oceans.

4 Name the three states of matter that water can exist in.

Life on Earth

The most dramatic effect on the atmosphere of the early Earth occurred when green plants evolved. Since carbon dioxide is used by plants during photosynthesis, the total amount of carbon dioxide in the atmosphere was reduced.

As you can see in the chemical equation below, photosynthesis produces oxygen:

carbon dioxide + water → glucose + oxygen

$$6CO_2 \text{ (g)} + 6H_2O \text{ (l)} \rightarrow C_6H_{12}O_6 \text{ (aq)} + 6O_2 \text{ (g)}$$

The oxygen released by plants caused the amount of oxygen in the atmosphere to increase. That oxygen made it possible for other organisms to evolve and flourish.

Chemical states

You will notice letters in brackets after each molecule in the equation for photosynthesis. Chemists indicate the state of elements and compounds using the symbol (s) for solid, (l) for liquid or (g) for gas. Therefore, water vapour becomes H_2O (g) and liquid water would be H_2O (l).

FIGURE 4: What gas are these plants using? What gas do they produce?

Because so many things dissolve in water, there is a fourth symbol (aq) to show an aqueous solution, that is something dissolved in water.

As you have seen, carbon dioxide (CO_2) dissolved in the early oceans. When the carbon dioxide dissolved, it changed from CO_2 (g) to CO_2 (aq).

QUESTIONS

5 Explain how the appearance of life on Earth changed the atmosphere.

6 Explain why an aqueous solution has its own symbol.

Today's atmosphere

You will find out:

> how to investigate the proportion of oxygen in the atmosphere

> the current composition of the atmosphere

> the effect of volcanic and human activity on the atmosphere

Change is in the air

Every time we switch on a light or turn up the heating, we change the atmosphere. What causes these changes and how can we tell the atmosphere is changing? Chemistry gives us the tools to investigate these and other questions.

FIGURE 1: Human activities: what effect do these activities have on the atmosphere?

Investigating change

You have already seen that scientists can examine the chemical make-up of rocks to find out what kind of atmosphere they must have been formed in.

Working out the amount of oxygen – the gas vital to sustaining life on Earth – in the atmosphere today is not that difficult.

> You know how quickly iron rusts.

> Rust is formed by the oxidation of iron and occurs when iron is exposed to oxygen.

> If we measure how much iron oxide is formed when iron is exposed to air, then we can tell how much oxygen must have been in the air.

From reactions like the oxidation of iron to fractional distillation, the percentage of oxygen in the air can be determined. Scientists also use a range of instruments such as mass spectrometers and satellites to measure accurately the composition of the current atmosphere. (See Table 1.)

These kinds of measurements also allow scientists to monitor changes in the composition of the atmosphere caused by:

> volcanic eruptions

> burning **fossil fuels**

> the conversion of forest to farmland.

TABLE 1: The composition of air today.

Gas	Formula	Composition (%)
Nitrogen	N_2	78.084
Oxygen	O_2	20.9476
Argon	Ar	0.934
Carbon dioxide	CO_2	0.0314
Neon	Ne	0.001818
Helium	He	0.000524
Methane	CH_4	0.002
Krypton	Kr	0.000114
Hydrogen	H_2	0.00005
Xenon	Xe	0.0000087

FIGURE 2: Iron exposed to oxygen quickly rusts.

QUESTIONS

1 Suggest why it is necessary to paint iron.

2 Draw a pie chart showing the proportion of nitrogen, oxygen and other gases in the atmosphere.

3 Give the chemical formulae of the gases that make up the smallest and largest proportion of the atmosphere. What is the percentage difference between these two gases?

Deforestation   Balancing chemical equations

The changing atmosphere

We saw earlier how the eruption of volcanoes has changed the atmosphere. Volcanic activity continues to affect our atmosphere by adding carbon dioxide and other gases to it. Human activity can also cause changes in the composition of the atmosphere.

> In the past 300 years burning fossil fuels has brought about the biggest change in the atmosphere. Fossil fuels are mainly **hydrocarbons**, molecules composed of carbon and hydrogen. Burning these molecules produces large quantities of carbon dioxide (CO_2).

> Another significant change has been caused by the increasing amount of land used for agriculture as farmers come under pressure to produce more crops. Remember, it was the appearance of plants that dramatically changed the atmosphere of the Earth.

> When humans chop down entire forests (**deforestation**) to plant crops we change the amount of photosynthesis that occurs because large plants carry out more photosynthesis than small plants. The amount of carbon dioxide (CO_2) being removed from the atmosphere decreases and the amount of oxygen (O_2) produced decreases as well.

QUESTIONS

4 Compare the effect of volcanoes and the burning of fossil fuels on the atmosphere.

5 Explain how the increase in agricultural crops changes the atmosphere.

FIGURE 3: Coal mining. How will burning this coal affect the atmosphere?

Representing reactions using chemical equations (Higher tier only)

Chemical equations are an important way for chemists to represent chemical reactions:

$$4Fe\ (s)\ +\ 3O_2\ (g)\ \rightarrow\ 2Fe_2O_3\ (s)$$
iron + oxygen → iron oxide

The chemicals on the left-hand side of the arrow are called **reactants**. The chemicals on the right-hand side of the arrow are called **products**. The arrow is usually read as 'make' or 'produce':

$$reactants\ \xrightarrow{produce}\ products$$

If you look at the equation for the oxidation of iron, you will notice a number in front of each of the formulae. These numbers are called **coefficients**. The coefficients indicate how many of each of the molecules is required for the reaction.

Now look more closely. You will notice that the number of iron (Fe) atoms is the same on both sides of the arrow. There are 4 iron (Fe) atoms on the reactant side and 4 on the product side. Atoms are neither created nor destroyed during chemical reactions, therefore the number must be the same on each side of the equation. That is, the equation must be *balanced*.

When balancing equations it is also important to remember that you may not change the formulae of the chemicals involved. You may only change the coefficients.

QUESTIONS

6 Balance the following equations:

a $CH_4\ (g) + O_2\ (g) \rightarrow CO_2\ (g) + H_2O\ (g)$

b $Zn\ (s) + HCl\ (aq) \rightarrow ZnCl\ (aq) + H_2\ (g)$

7 Explain why the number of atoms on each side of an equation must be the same.

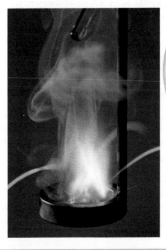

Remember!
No coefficients or subscripts are needed to show 'one'. So O_2 means $1O_2$ and Fe means $1Fe_1$.

FIGURE 4: Potassium reacting with water. What is the equation for this reaction?

Preparing for assessment: Planning an investigation

To achieve a good grade in science, you not only have to know and understand scientific ideas, but you also need to be able to apply them to other situations and investigations. This task will support you in developing these skills.

✳ Investigating the percentage of oxygen in air

The volume of oxygen in a sample of air can be determined by using a chemical reaction to remove it. If the reaction is carried out over water, the water rises to take the place of the missing oxygen.

Plan how to obtain an accurate value for the percentage of oxygen in the air.

iron wool

air

beaker

water

✳ Useful information

Iron reacts with oxygen to form iron oxide.

Iron wool is treated to stop it rusting, but propanone (acetone) (highly flammable, irritant) removes this coating.

Iron reacts slowly but small amounts of ethanoic acid speed up the reaction.

The volume of a gas increases as the temperature increases or the pressure decreases.

When there is the same pressure inside and outside the tube, the water levels inside and outside the tube are also the same.

This experiment has no independent or dependent variable. Your plan needs to show how you will remove any possible sources of error in order to obtain meaningful results.

Explain how you will be able to tell how much oxygen was in the air.

Give reasons for your choice of equipment.

✳ Planning

1. Draw a labelled diagram to explain how you will set up the equipment, what you expect to happen and why.

2. Make a list of things that could stop you getting accurate results and explain how you will deal with them.

3. Identify any hazards and explain how the risks they pose can be managed.

4. Write up the overall plan for the experiment.

Consider these points: How will you make sure all the oxygen is used up, and quickly? How will you measure the volume of air accurately? How can you prove the decrease in the volume of air is caused by the iron? How many times should you repeat the experiment?

A hazard is something that could cause harm. A risk is the likelihood of being harmed.

Remember to explain what you will measure and how your plan will test the hypothesis. Consider the wording of your plan carefully – it should be clear so that others could follow it easily and without confusion.

✳ Constructing a results table and analysing the data

When this procedure was carried out the height of the air column in the test-tube at the start was always 130 mm. Five different tests gave final heights of 103, 104, 104, 102 and 111 mm. The height of the air column is proportional to its volume.

1. Put the results into a table and use them to calculate the average change in the height of the air column.

2. Suggest a reason why one of the results is anomalous.

3. Use the results to estimate the percentage of the air that is oxygen. Show your working in full and state any assumptions you have made.

4. Compare your result with the textbook value for the percentage of oxygen in the air. How closely does the result agree?

Remember to include the units.

If any results are anomalous you should leave them out when you calculate the average.

Unexpected results are often caused by unexpected errors but they could also be a sign that the original hypothesis is wrong. You should always try to suggest why unexpected results have been obtained.

Can you ignore the volume of the steel wool?

If your result does not agree with the value other investigators have found, you need to check to see if there are weaknesses in the method. Use scientific concepts to support your ideas.

✳ Connections

How Science Works

> Collecting and analysing data.

> Planning to solve a scientific problem.

> Collecting data from secondary sources.

> Working accurately and safely when collecting first-hand data.

> Evaluating methods of data collection and verifying information sources.

> Using both qualitative and quantitative approaches.

> Presenting information using appropriate language, conventions and symbols and tools.

Maths in Science

> Understand number size and scale and the quantitative relationship between units.

> Calculate arithmetic means.

> Understand and use common measures.

> Translate information between graphical and numeric forms.

> Extract and interpret information from tables.

Types of rock

The world of rock

Some of the most dramatic and mysterious features on Earth are made of rock. We live our life surrounded by rock, walking on it and building with it.

FIGURE 1: Giant's Causeway: is this natural or man-made?

You will find out:

> about igneous rock
> about sedimentary rock
> about metamorphic rock

Different rocks

There are three major categories of rock. This classification is based on the way the rock forms, causing it to have different properties.

Igneous rock

Igneous rock is formed by the solidification of lava or **magma**:

> Igneous rock formed on the Earth's surface is characterised by small crystals. Basalt is a type of igneous rock formed from lava.

> Igneous rock that forms underground is characterised by large crystals. Granite is a type of igneous rock formed from magma.

Sedimentary rock

Sedimentary rock is formed by sediments deposited on riverbeds and ocean floors:

> **Erosion** washes material from the land into streams and rivers.

> Microscopic organisms make materials that float in the water.

> These materials settle and accumulate, building up layers that eventually harden into rock. Limestone and chalk are examples of sedimentary rock, where chalk is a soft, white type of limestone made from the skeletons of tiny marine plankton.

Metamorphic rock

Metamorphic rock, as the name implies, is rock that has changed form:

> As the layers of sedimentary rock build up, older deeper layers get pushed down.

> Under the enormous pressure and increased heat, the structure of the rock changes.

Marble is a metamorphic rock formed from limestone.

Did you know?

Marble is sometimes called metamorphosed limestone by geologists.

QUESTIONS

1 How does granite differ from basalt?

2 Describe the process that produces sedimentary rock.

3 Explain how metamorphic rock is formed and provide an example of this type of rock not given on this page.

FIGURE 2: a Chalk, **b** limestone and **c** marble. What is the difference between these three types of rock?

Cooling down

The properties of igneous rock reveal something about where it was formed. Igneous rock is formed by *molten* material from the **mantle**. The mantle is the molten layer under the crust of the Earth.

If the molten material stays underground, it is called magma:

> The magma oozes into cracks and voids in the crust, where it solidifies as **intrusive rock** like granite.

> Because the magma is insulated by the surrounding rock it cools very slowly, forming large crystals.

If the magma makes it to the surface, it is called lava:

> The lava cools very quickly when exposed to the air or sea water and solidifies to form **extrusive rock** like basalt.

> Because of the rapid cooling, lots of little crystals are formed.

Scientists can learn a lot about how rocks developed by studying crystal formation.

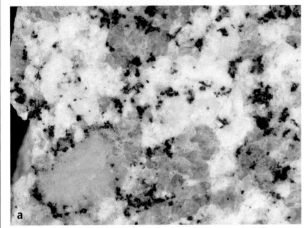

a

b

FIGURE 3: **a** Granite and **b** basalt. What is the difference between these two types of rock?

QUESTIONS

4 Explain the difference between extrusive and intrusive rock.

5 Draw up a table with two columns. In one column list all the properties for extrusive rock and intrusive rock that might be similar. In the second column list all the properties that might be different.

Crystal formation

How does the rate of cooling affect crystal size in igneous rocks? Crystals form when atoms or molecules are fitted together in a very rigid structure with regular lines and layers of particles.

All atoms and molecules have **kinetic energy**, that is they are moving. The amount of kinetic energy is related to temperature. High temperatures mean high kinetic energy. Low temperatures result in low kinetic energy.

In intrusive rock, the temperature remains high for a long time. As the molecules in the rock cool they slow down and start to bond to each other, forming a crystal. These cooler areas are widely spaced with lots of molecules around them. As those molecules slowly cool down they can be incorporated into the existing crystals, producing the large crystals found in granite.

In extrusive rock, the molecules are cooling down more quickly and therefore a lot of crystals begin to form at the same time. Because there are so many crystals forming at the same time, there are not as many molecules to be incorporated into the individual crystals. These conditions produce the many small crystals found in basalt.

QUESTIONS

6 Explain the relationship between temperature and kinetic energy in molecules.

7 Describe, with examples, how the properties of a rock result from the way that the crystals within it were formed.

Q Crystal formation   Kinetic energy

Rocks from sediments

You will find out:
> how sedimentary rock is formed
> about the properties of sedimentary rock
> how metamorphic rock is formed

The layers of rock

From dinosaurs to sea shells, cliffs are a slice through life on Earth. Each layer has been built up over time, providing scientists with information about the Earth's past.

FIGURE 1: Grand Canyon. Where did all of the layers come from?

Sedimentary and metamorphic rock

When igneous rock is eroded, it provides the raw material for two new rock types: sedimentary and metamorphic.

How sedimentary rock is formed

> All exposed rock gets broken up eventually by chemical and physical changes called weathering.

> The broken fragments are removed from the rock face by wind and rain and other agents of **erosion**.

> Rivers carry the rock fragments to the sea where they are deposited on the sea bed and covered by layer upon layer of sediments, compressing them and squeezing out the water from between the grains (**compaction**).

> Eventually, the grains get cemented together, often by concentrated solutions of silicon dioxide or calcium carbonate.

FIGURE 2: How long did it take for these layers of rock to form?

The **fossils** that we find encased by rocks are the remains of organisms that fell into the sediment millions of years ago and became compressed by the layers of material.

How metamorphic rock is formed

> Layers of chalk and limestone formed by **sedimentation** are buried by so many layers above them that they are pushed down under incredible pressure.

> They are also exposed to high temperatures either from hot magma or from the Earth's core, as they get buried so deeply.

> The high pressure and increased temperature cause them to change into metamorphic rock. Marble is an example of metamorphic rock.

FIGURE 3: Marble quarry. What factors were involved in the formation of this marble?

QUESTIONS

1 Draw a diagram to show how sedimentary rock is formed.

2 Explain the difference between sedimentary and metamorphic rock.

3 Describe how marble is formed.

Q Origin of fossils   Chalk deposits

Fossils

Fossilisation, the formation of fossils, occurs in sedimentary rock. Some fossils are direct impressions made in the layers of sediment:

> Organisms or pieces of organisms fall into the sediment when they die.

> Sometimes oxygen is absent and the organisms do not decay immediately.

> More layers of sediment then cover them.

> Under the increasing layers, the organism is compressed.

> The surrounding layers harden, leaving an impression when the organism eventually decays.

In some instances only the hardest parts of the organisms remain long enough to fossilise. These are usually bones or shells:

> If the layers are porous, water may be able to enter the space where the remains are trapped.

> The minerals in the water may start to crystallise.

> The crystals that form will take on the shape of the remains that once filled the space.

The fossilised bones of dinosaurs were formed in this way.

Fossils can also be found in chalk, which is a kind of limestone:

> Chalk is a sedimentary rock that is made of the shells of microscopic organisms that live in the sea.

> When these organisms die their empty shells settle on the bottom of the ocean.

> As the layers of the shells build up the pressure causes them to solidify into chalk.

FIGURE 4: Fossil fern leaf. Could this fern be identified from its fossil?

FIGURE 5: Fossil marine dinosaur. How did this fossil form?

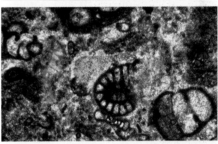

FIGURE 6: Microscopic view of limestone. Were these once living creatures?

QUESTIONS

4 Describe the different types of fossils you might find and how they were formed.

5 Describe the 'life cycle' of chalk.

Erosion

Erosion is an important process in rock formation. All exposed rock is worn by the action of wind and water, for example waves pounding against a cliff or wind blowing across a desert. The small grains that are produced are a mixture of different compounds with different physical properties. They are either blown or washed away to build up the layers that will become sedimentary rock. Some are soluble, while others are not.

Over time, the movement of the Earth's crust may expose the sedimentary rock. The sedimentary rock is then susceptible to the effects of erosion. Because of the difference in solubility, some areas of sedimentary rock erode more easily than others. This differential erosion can produce dramatic effects like those in Figure 1.

QUESTIONS

6 Describe erosion and its effect on the physical world.

7 Explain why sedimentary rock does not erode evenly and how this changes the landscape.

8 Draw a diagram to show the relationship between igneous, sedimentary and metamorphic rocks.

Quarrying limestone

You will find out:
> where calcium carbonate comes from
> about the impact of obtaining limestone
> where calcium carbonate is used

It's everywhere

How many calcium compounds have you come across today? Chances are more than you realise. If you live in a brick house they are in the mortar. They are in the cement pavements you walk on, the windows in your home and school, even the toothpaste you used this morning. Where do they all come from?

FIGURE 1: The IMAM Building. Why would concrete be a good choice of material for this structure?

Where did it come from?

Limestone is made from compressed layers of shells from microscopic organisms. Those shells are made of calcium carbonate. So **limestone**, **chalk** and **marble** are all natural forms of calcium carbonate. Calcium carbonate ($CaCO_3$) is one of the most common compounds in the Earth's crust and is an important raw material for glass, cement and concrete.

To meet the demand for large quantities of calcium carbonate, limestone must be quarried, that is, dug out of the ground. This poses some problems:

> limestone must be blasted from the ground, creating large amounts of dust

> noise pollution caused by blasting

> the destruction of habitat

> using large lorries to transport the limestone from the quarry damages the roads

> large lorries cause congestion on local roads.

With so many disadvantages there must be some important reasons why limestone is still quarried. These include:

> high demand for limestone to be used in construction

> creation of jobs in the quarries, transporting the stone and at building sites

> economic benefit to the local and national economies through wages and exports.

QUESTIONS

1 Name the main chemical component of limestone.

2 Describe how quarrying affects the environment.

3 What type of rock is limestone?

4 Suggest why quarrying is commercially important.

FIGURE 2: A limestone quarry. How would you reclaim this land?

Q Concrete architecture   Environmental impact of quarries

Processing limestone

In some cases, the limestone blocks removed from the quarry can be used to construct buildings. Some of the most beautiful buildings in the world are made from limestone. However, limestone is an important raw material in the production of glass, cement and concrete as well. To use the limestone for these materials it must be processed.

Glass

Humans have been making glass for almost 4000 years:

> To make glass the ground limestone, $CaCO_3$, is mixed with sodium carbonate (Na_2CO_3) and sand.

> This mixture is heated until it melts and then is allowed to cool to produce glass.

Cement

Heating ground calcium carbonate with clay produces cement:

> The mixture of calcium carbonate and clay is heated in a kiln to approximately 1600 °C, producing a fine powder called cement.

> Cement is an important ingredient in mortar, stucco, grout and concrete.

Concrete

The ancient Egyptians used concrete in the construction of the pyramids:

> Concrete is a mixture of sand, gravel, cement and water. These substances react together chemically to form the very hard building material we call concrete.

> Concrete is the most commonly used artificial material in construction around the world today.

Did you know?

Approximately 30 million million kilograms of concrete is produced every year.

FIGURE 3: An ancient Egyptian glass vase.

FIGURE 4: The Egyptian pyramids. Limestone and concrete were used in their construction.

QUESTIONS

5 Describe the different ways limestone can be used in buildings.

6 Explain why concrete is so useful.

Reducing the impact of quarrying

Limestone has been used in various ways in construction for thousands of years. In recent times, awareness of the social, economic and environmental impact of quarrying has increased.

There is no replacement for limestone; it must be quarried. Quarrying provides many jobs to the local and national economies. In 2004, the UK produced approximately £156 million's worth of chalk and limestone. However, the majority of that chalk and limestone was used in the production of other materials such as quicklime, steel and glass. These industries employ thousands of workers and export their products all over the world.

QUESTIONS

7 Discuss the economic and environmental impact of quarrying limestone.

Methods for alleviating the disadvantages associated with quarrying include:

> building earthen mounds around the quarry to deaden blast sound

> restricting blasting to specific times

> restoration plans to reclaim the land once the quarry closes

> use of water sprays to reduce dust

> restrictions on the size of the quarry.

FIGURE 5: A limestone quarry in Cumbria.

Atoms and reactions

You will find out:
> about atoms
> about chemical reactions
> about the conservation of matter

The smallest thing

Since the earliest recorded time humans have wondered what the smallest piece of matter is. As early as 350 BC a Greek named Democritus proposed the idea of a tiny indivisible particle. He called it an atom. We now know that not all of his ideas were correct, but the name is still used.

FIGURE 1: Artist's conception of an atom.

The fundamentals of chemistry

Everything in the Universe is made up of **matter**. The smallest particle of matter that can be studied using chemistry is the **atom**:

> Chemists classify atoms based on the way they behave.

> All atoms that behave in the same way are classified as the same **element**.

When studying chemical reactions, chemists noticed several important points:

> Atoms are the smallest particles of an element that take part in the chemical reaction.

> During chemical reactions, atoms are neither created nor destroyed.

> During chemical reactions, atoms are rearranged to make products that have different properties from those of the reactants.

> The total mass of reactant is always equal to the total mass of products. This is referred to as the **conservation of matter**.

These points are fundamental to an understanding of chemistry.

FIGURE 2: Some of the elements: clockwise from upper centre, they are chlorine (Cl), sulfur (S), mercury (Hg), copper (Cu) and silicon (Si).

QUESTIONS

1 What is the difference between an atom and an element? Use a diagram to explain your answer.

2 State what is meant by the conservation of matter.

3 Research some images produced by electron tunnelling microscopes. What do these images show?

Products and reactants

When substances react they produce products that have different properties from those of the reactants. There are two kinds of properties that must be considered. Atoms and molecules have **physical** properties, properties observed without changing the substance. Atoms and molecules also have **chemical properties**, properties that can only be observed in chemical reactions.

Physical properties

> Colour.

> Magnetism.

> Melting point.

> Boiling point.

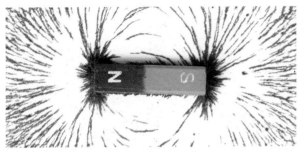

FIGURE 3: Magnetism is a physical property: the iron filings are attracted to the magnet.

Products of chemical reactions

The total mass before and after a reaction is unchanged. This can be shown by carrying out a precipitation reaction in a sealed container.

When a solution of calcium chloride reacts with a solution of sodium sulfate it forms a **precipitate**, calcium sulfate, which is not soluble in water. One of the products has different chemical properties from either of the reactants.

Notice in Figure 5 that the overall mass does not change. The reactants are in a sealed container so that no atoms can get in or out.

FIGURE 5: The conservation of matter. Notice that the mass stays the same.

Chemical properties

> Flammability.

> Reaction with acid or bases.

> Decomposition.

> Reactions started by light.

FIGURE 4: Flammability is a chemical property: sodium burning in air.

QUESTIONS

4 Explain the differences between chemical and physical properties.

5 'A candle loses mass when it burns.' Is this statement true or false? Explain your answer.

6 Write the equation for the reaction shown in Figure 5.

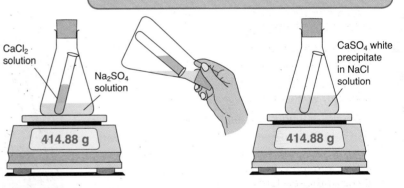

CaCl₂ solution

Na₂SO₄ solution

414.88 g

CaSO₄ white precipitate in NaCl solution

414.88 g

Conservation of matter

On pages 100–1 the method of determining the amount of oxygen in air used the following chemical reaction:

$$4Fe \text{ (s)} + 3O_2 \text{ (g)} \rightarrow 2Fe_2O_3 \text{ (s)}$$

Four iron atoms react with six oxygen atoms to produce two iron oxide molecules, each made up of two iron atoms and three oxygen atoms (see Figure 6). For this method to work, the number of atoms has to remain the same on each side of the equation, so that matter is conserved. The mass of iron on each side of the equation must be the same. Therefore, any increase in mass on the product side must be due to the oxygen. Using this method it is possible for chemists to determine how much oxygen is present in the air. This method would not work without the conservation of matter. So you can see that the conservation of matter is fundamental to understanding chemical reactions and how to balance equations.

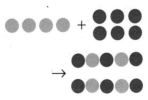

FIGURE 6: Forming iron oxide.

Remember!
The number of atoms for each chemical must remain the same for the reactant and the products.

QUESTIONS

7 Explain how the conservation of matter affects balancing equations.

8 Explain how the conservation of matter allows chemists to determine how much oxygen is in air in the equation above.

Q Photoreactivity

Thermal decomposition

You will find out:

> about thermal decomposition of calcium carbonate

> about thermal decomposition of metal carbonates

> how water reacts with calcium oxide

Hot, hot, hot!

Take a look around your kitchen. What do glass tumblers, stainless steel saucepans and a fried egg all have in common? They all need heat to make them.

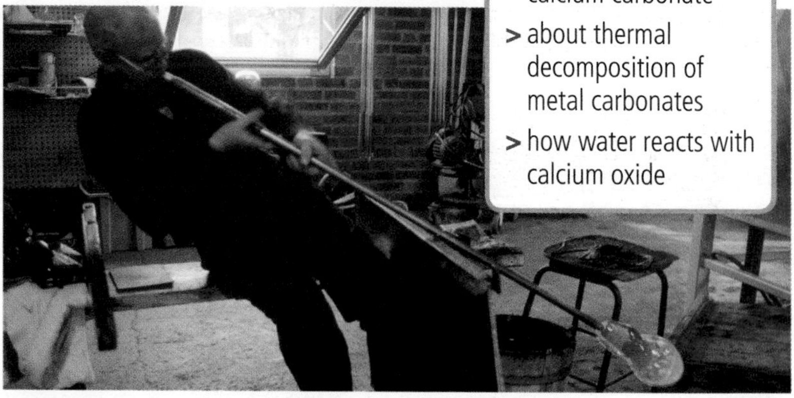

FIGURE 1: Glass-blowing.

Calcium carbonate and its uses

Limestone (calcium carbonate) is a material that is involved in lots of chemical reactions. Many of these reactions form the basis of important industries, such as glass-making and cement production.

When calcium carbonate ($CaCO_3$) is heated it undergoes a chemical reaction:

calcium carbonate → calcium oxide + carbon dioxide

This type of reaction is called **thermal decomposition**:

> The molecules of calcium carbonate are broken down, or decomposed, into calcium oxide and carbon dioxide.

> Heat is required to cause this reaction.

This very simple chemical reaction can be used with many different metal carbonates including zinc carbonate and copper carbonate.

Calcium oxide, which is one of the products of the thermal decomposition of calcium carbonate, is an important ingredient in the production of glass and cement. Another important use of calcium oxide is in the production of calcium hydroxide solution, called **limewater**, used to detect carbon dioxide.

FIGURE 2: Inside a rotary kiln. When in use, limestone and clay are heated as they travel 150 m along this tube while it slowly rotates. This produces cement.

QUESTIONS

1 Explain the term thermal decomposition.

2 Describe how limewater can be used.

Calcium oxide

Mixing calcium oxide with water causes a chemical reaction that produces calcium hydroxide:

$$CaO \ (s) \quad + \quad H_2O \ (l) \quad \rightarrow \quad Ca(OH)_2 \ (s)$$
calcium oxide + water → calcium hydroxide

This reaction gives out heat and so the calcium oxide hisses and expands when water is added to it.

Calcium hydroxide dissolves in water to form calcium hydroxide solution, known as limewater. Limewater is used in the lab to detect the presence of carbon dioxide gas. You can show that the gas you exhale is carbon dioxide by bubbling the breath you blow out through limewater (*do not suck!*). When you do, the calcium hydroxide reacts with the carbon dioxide in your breath to produce calcium carbonate and water:

$$Ca(OH)_2 \ (aq) \quad + \quad CO_2 \ (g) \quad \rightarrow \quad CaCO_3 \ (s) \quad + \quad H_2O \ (l)$$
calcium hydroxide + carbon dioxide → calcium carbonate + water

Calcium carbonate is **insoluble** in water, causing the water to turn milky white as **precipitate** forms. This reaction also demonstrates that products have different properties from the reactants. Calcium hydroxide is slightly **soluble** in water while calcium carbonate is insoluble.

FIGURE 3: Using limewater to test for the presence of carbon dioxide. Why did the solution turn white?

QUESTIONS

3 Write the method of the experiment to test for the presence of carbon dioxide. Include a risk assessment in your write-up.

4 Explain what happens when calcium hydroxide is reacted with carbon dioxide.

Remember!

Reactions that produce water are hydration reactions; those that use water are dehydration reactions.

Thermal decomposition of metal carbonates

Besides calcium carbonate, many other metal carbonates decompose when they are heated. Copper carbonate produces copper oxide using thermal decomposition:

copper carbonate → copper oxide + carbon dioxide

Copper oxide is used for many different things, from pigments in ceramic glazes to the production of semiconductors.

Zinc carbonate can be thermally decomposed to produce zinc oxide:

zinc carbonate → zinc oxide + carbon dioxide

Zinc oxide is used in many industries including rubber production and concrete manufacture. It is also used in the medical and cosmetic industries to treat skin conditions.

Thermal decomposition of metal carbonates can be done in the lab using an apparatus like that in Figure 4. In these three reactions remember that the metal carbonates are heated and decompose into the metal oxides and carbon dioxide.

TABLE 1: Thermal decomposition of three metal carbonates.

Reactant	Products	Temperature (°C)
Calcium carbonate ($CaCO_3$)	Calcium oxide (CaO) and carbon dioxide (CO_2)	825
Copper carbonate ($CuCO_3$)	Copper oxide (CuO) and carbon dioxide (CO_2)	200
Zinc carbonate ($ZnCO_3$)	Zinc oxide (ZnO) and carbon dioxide (CO_2)	300

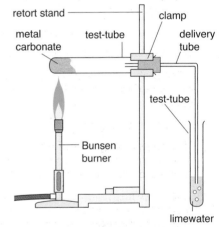

FIGURE 4: Apparatus to carry out thermal decomposition. What do you predict will happen to the limewater?

Did you know?

Other metal carbonates (e.g. sodium carbonate) do not decompose when heated.

QUESTIONS

5 Give the equations for the reactions shown in Table 1. Explain what each of these equations shows and arrange the table in order of ease of decomposition.

6 Research the uses of copper oxide and zinc oxide. Write up your findings.

Uses of zinc oxide   Rotary kiln

Calcium and neutralisation

You will find out:
> about the neutralisation of acidic soil
> how power-plant emissions can be cleaned up

Cleaning up

Calcium carbonate has an important role in industry. Apart from its uses in agriculture to neutralise acidic soil, calcium carbonate has become important in attempts to lower emissions from coal-fired power stations.

FIGURE 1: A coal-fired power station. How can we reduce the emissions?

Back to nature

Global population growth makes providing enough food for everyone an increasingly difficult task. There is only a limited amount of land suitable for agriculture available, therefore farmers are forced to turn to poor-quality land in order to grow food. For crops to grow, the soil needs to be treated.

Many plants grow best in a neutral **pH**, which is pH 7. Acidic soil with a pH less than 7 must be treated to raise the pH so that it is suitable for growing crops.

Calcium carbonate, calcium hydroxide (slaked lime) or calcium oxide (lime) can be mixed with the soil to raise the pH.

Calcium hydroxide and calcium oxide are the preferred choices because they are quick acting and smaller amounts are needed to do the job.

Coal-fired power stations produce harmful emissions and are a significant problem:

> One of those emissions is sulfur dioxide (SO_2).

> Sulfur dioxide reacts with water to produce sulfuric acid that falls in rain as **acid rain**.

QUESTIONS

1 How would you treat acidic soils?

2 Explain why sulfur dioxide (SO_2) is harmful to the environment.

FIGURE 2: Not all land is suitable for growing crops.

Lime and slaked lime

Calcium carbonate is less effective than calcium oxide and calcium hydroxide at neutralising the pH of soil. It takes three times more calcium carbonate than calcium oxide and 1.35 times more calcium carbonate than calcium hydroxide to neutralise the soil.

However, calcium oxide and calcium hydroxide are both irritants, causing severe burns to any exposed part of the body.

Many chemicals have hazards associated with them. A system of **hazard labels** to indicate the dangers associated with chemicals has been devised (Figure 3).

	Flammable			Toxic
	Corrosive			Harmful
	Explosive			Damaging to the environment

FIGURE 3: Some important hazard labels. Do you know any others?

Q pH scale   Map of acidic soil   Hazard labels

To use calcium oxide or calcium hydroxide, a farmer would need to ensure that the proper safety precautions are taken to prevent injury to anybody exposed to these chemicals. These might include:

> protective clothing

> gloves

> goggles

> breathing protection.

While calcium carbonate might be less effective than calcium oxide or calcium hydroxide, the dangers are also decreased. Farmers can use the information provided by chemists to help them decide which compound to use to neutralise the pH of their soil.

FIGURE 4: This is what acid rain can do.

QUESTIONS

3 Explain why a system of hazard symbols is necessary when dealing with chemicals.

4a Describe some of the factors that farmers must consider when deciding which compound to use to neutralise soil.

b Which compound would you use, if you were a farmer? Give reasons for your answer.

5 Research hazard labels. Draw at least two that aren't in Figure 3 and state where you might see them.

Emissions

The population of the world continues to grow, increasing the need for electricity. To keep up with the demand, every available resource must be used – including non-renewable resources such as coal. Unfortunately, coal-fired power stations produce large amounts of pollutants. Acid rain is caused when sulfur dioxide, produced when coal is burned, reacts with water in the air to form sulfuric acid.

Scientists have developed scrubber systems which are methods to remove pollutants such as sulfur dioxide from the waste gases of industrial processes. A watery mixture of calcium oxide (a slurry) is sprayed into the chimneys of the power stations.

As the gases produced by the burning coal pass through the slurry, the sulfur dioxide reacts with the calcium oxide to produce calcium sulfite:

$$CaO\ (aq) + SO_2\ (g) \rightarrow CaSO_3\ (s)$$

The calcium sulfite can then be collected and sold as a raw material for other industrial processes. These scrubber systems can be fitted to existing chimneys and reduce harmful emissions and the acid rain caused by these emissions.

QUESTIONS

6 Explain why coal must still be used to generate electricity.

7 Describe the process used to remove sulfur dioxide from the chimney gases of coal-fired power stations.

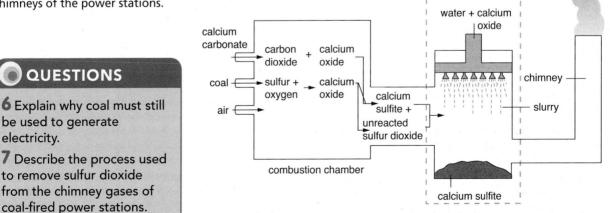

FIGURE 5: A scrubber system for removing sulfur dioxide.

Acids, neutralisation and their salts

An acidic tale

The word acid means 'sour' in Latin. You only need to suck a lemon, which contains citric acid, to see why.

You will find out:

> about hydrochloric acid
> how acids are neutralised
> how salts are produced by acids

FIGURE 1: Lemons are sour because of citric acid.

Neutralising acids

Hydrochloric acid is produced in the stomach:

> It helps with digestion.

> It helps to destroy bacteria that are accidentally consumed.

Sometimes, we make too much acid in our stomachs, causing indigestion and need to use an **antacid** to correct the problem.

Whether acidic soil or acid indigestion, the reaction of acid with alkali is an important part of chemistry. When an acid is mixed with an **alkali** they will react to produce a salt and water:

acid + alkali → salt + water

If the amounts are correct, the solution produced should have a pH of 7: neutral. This type of reaction is called a **neutralisation reaction**. Acids can be neutralised by metal oxides, metal hydroxides or metal carbonates.

Sometimes alkali and **base** are used interchangeably to identify substances that neutralise acids. They are not actually the same. Alkalis are bases that dissolve in water. Hydroxides are alkalis, while oxides and carbonates are more correctly called bases. Hence, a more general equation than the one above is:

acid + base → salt + water

However, it is important to remember that if you neutralise an acid using a carbonate, carbon dioxide is produced, coming off as bubbles:

acid + carbonate → salt + water + carbon dioxide

TABLE 1: Examples of acids, bases and the salts produced.

Acid	Base	Salt
Hydrochloric acid	Sodium hydroxide	Sodium chloride
Hydrochloric acid	Calcium carbonate	Calcium chloride
Nitric acid	Calcium oxide	Calcium nitrate
Sulfuric acid	Calcium carbonate	Calcium sulfate

FIGURE 2: An antacid tablet fizzing in a glass of water. Why might this help sufferers of indigestion?

QUESTIONS

1 Describe what happens when an acid and an alkali are mixed.

2 Write the word equations for the reactions given in Table 1. Now, try writing them using chemical formulae.

Evaluating acids

Most antacids contain an alkali to neutralise the excess stomach acid. Acids and alkalis react in a neutralisation reaction. In this reaction, the pH of an acidic solution should be raised by the alkali. With so many antacids on the market how could you determine which one is the most effective?

> If you used a specific amount of acid with a known pH, you could add an antacid tablet and allow it to react.

> Then check the pH.

> Repeat this with different tablets.

The tablet that raised the pH the most would be the most effective.

FIGURE 3: Checking pH. Is the solution acidic or alkaline?

An even more accurate way of determining the effectiveness of antacids would be to titrate them. In **titration**, a known amount of two solutions is mixed. Because neutralisation reactions produce a neutral solution containing a salt and water, the exact amount of acid and alkaline antacid needed to produce a neutral solution can be measured. Quantitative data from this technique can then be used by chemists to understand better the effectiveness of antacid products.

QUESTIONS

3 Zinc oxide is insoluble. Is it an acid, an alkali, a base or a salt?

4 Write a plan for an experiment to determine the effectiveness of antacids. How would you ensure this experiment was fair and safe?

5 Describe quantitative data and a technique that would provide this information.

Remember!
Repeatable observable changes are the key to good science.

FIGURE 4: Titration.

Acids and their salts

Did you notice the pattern in Table 1? Take a close look at the table. For example, when hydrochloric acid is mixed with sodium hydroxide the reaction produces sodium chloride and water:

$$HCl\ (aq)\quad +\quad NaOH\ (aq)\quad \rightarrow\quad NaCl\ (aq)\quad +\ H_2O\ (l)$$
hydrochloric acid + sodium hydroxide → sodium chloride + water

Notice that the salts formed always take their first name from the base that is used. The second part of the name is a modified version of the acid used. Hydrochloric acid produces chloride salts. Sulfuric acid produces sulfate salts. Nitric acid produces nitrate salts.

Making salts using the neutralisation reaction is quite simple. Recall that when an acid is reacted with an alkali it produces a salt and water. Therefore, if you mix just enough acid with an alkaline solution to achieve neutrality you will have a salt dissolved in water. Evaporate the water and what is left is the salt formed by the reaction.

QUESTIONS

6 Explain how salts formed by neutralisation reactions are named and provide three examples.

7 Write balanced equations for the reactions listed in Table 1.

Electrolysis

You will find out:
> about the use of electrolysis
> how chlorine gas is produced
> how chlorine is used

Separating compounds

Swimming pools smell of chlorine. Chlorine helps keep germs at bay, but where does it come from? The oceans are a vast source of raw materials; the problem is getting them out. By passing an electrical current through the seawater, scientists can separate out valuable substances like chlorine and sodium.

FIGURE 1: The industrial production of chlorine by electrolysis.

Using electrical energy

Chlorine

Chlorine is a very important part of modern life. Some of the uses of chlorine are:

> the manufacture of chlorine bleach by reacting chlorine with a dilute solution of sodium hydroxide

> the treatment of water to kill bacteria

> the production of plastics like poly(chloroethene) (commonly called PVC) by reacting chlorine with ethene.

Chlorine is a green toxic gas. Exposure to as little as 1500 ppm (parts per million) in air can be fatal. Because chlorine is so hazardous, large-scale industrial use of chlorine requires special precautions. These could include:

> regular medical evaluations

> constant monitoring of worker exposure

> use of protective clothing

> use of breathing protection.

Obtaining chlorine by electrolysis

One way to obtain chlorine gas is through **electrolysis**. In electrolysis, direct current (d.c.) from a power supply is passed through a solution of seawater. The seawater contains sodium chloride in solution. The sodium chloride is **decomposed** in the process. The chlorine atoms can be collected at the positive **electrode**, or **anode**.

Electrolysis of water

Electrolysis can also be used to decompose water into hydrogen and oxygen. Oxygen is produced at the anode and hydrogen at the negative electrode called the **cathode**.

Electrolysis of hydrochloric acid

The composition of hydrochloric acid can be investigated using electrolysis. If you place a dilute solution of hydrochloric acid in an apparatus like the one in Figure 2, hydrochloric acid will decompose. You will find that:

> Chlorine gas is collected in the tube above the anode.

> Hydrogen gas is collected in the tube over the cathode.

FIGURE 2: Electrolysis of hydrochloric acid. Chlorine forms in the left-hand tube and hydrogen in the right-hand tube.

QUESTIONS

1 Describe how chlorine gas can be used.

2 Describe how the elemental composition of hydrochloric acid would be investigated.

3 a Explain why so many precautions must be taken when chlorine is used industrially.

b Suggest the hazard symbols that would have to be used in the industrial production of chlorine gas.

Charged solutions

How does electrolysis work? In Figure 2 you can see that there are two electrodes inserted into the dilute hydrochloric acid solution. The electrodes are connected to a d.c. power supply, one electrode to the positive terminal and the other to the negative terminal. An alternating current (a.c.) power source cannot be used because the polarity of the electrodes would be changing constantly.

Some substances dissolve in water to produce freely moving charged atoms called **ions**. When electrical energy is passed through the solution those ions with:

> a positive charge are attracted to the negative electrode (cathode)

> a negative charge are attracted to the positive electrode (anode).

Above the electrodes are tubes filled with the solution. If gas bubbles are produced they float and become trapped in the tubes, forcing the liquid out of the tube (see Figure 2). This simple apparatus can provide chemists with information about the composition of certain substances. On a larger scale (as shown in Figure 1), this process can be used to obtain certain compounds for industrial uses.

QUESTIONS

4 Explain what effect the electrical energy has on a dilute solution of hydrochloric acid.

5 Give the electrical charge for chlorine and hydrogen in the electrolysed solution and explain how you know this.

6 Explain why a d.c. power supply is required for electrolysis.

Information in the bubble

What information can be gleaned from the bubbles that form in the tubes of the electrolysis apparatus?

If electrolysis is used to decompose hydrochloric acid, one of the tubes will contain a gas that has a slight greenish colour. Based on this information, we could make a tentative identification of the gas as chlorine. The next point to notice is that the volume of gas produced is equal in both tubes. From this we could conclude that hydrochloric acid must contain equal amounts of hydrogen and chlorine.

If water is decomposed using electrolysis, the results are dramatically different. Both of the gases produced are colourless. However, there is approximately twice as much of one gas as there is of the other. Figure 4 shows an electrolysis apparatus used to measure the volume of gas produced at the two electrodes.

Did you know?

Chlorine gas was first used as a chemical weapon in the First World War, and was still being used as recently as 2007 in Iraq.

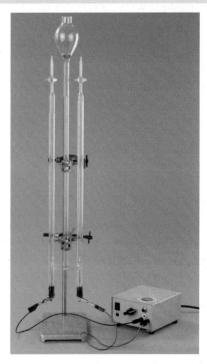

FIGURE 4: Water electrolysis apparatus.

FIGURE 3: The jar on the left contains chlorine and the jar on the right oxygen. Notice the greenish colour of the chlorine gas.

QUESTIONS

7 Compare the results of the electrolysis of hydrochloric acid and water and explain the meaning of the results.

Chemical tests

You will find out:
> about chemical tests for oxygen
> about chemical tests for hydrogen
> about chemical tests for chlorine

Identification

One of the most important jobs a chemist does is identify substances. Whether identifying unknown substances at a crime scene or substances in the blood of a sick patient, chemists all over the world are using their knowledge to identify compounds.

FIGURE 1: A police forensic scientist at work.

Into the unknown

Oxygen, hydrogen and chlorine gases can be produced using electrolysis. How can a scientist positively identify these gases?

In some instances the physical properties of the gases can be used to make an initial identification. For instance, chlorine gas has a slightly greenish colour, but this is hardly enough evidence to make a scientific decision.

Scientists require more evidence that all fits together to get a full picture before they make decisions. If we look at the other properties of chlorine there are characteristics that add further evidence to just the greenish colour. For example, chlorine gas:

> has a very distinctive strong smell

> will turn moist litmus paper or universal indicator paper red and then bleach it white

> will extinguish a burning wooden splint.

Oxygen and hydrogen are a little more difficult to identify. They are both colourless, odourless gases that have no effect on moistened litmus paper. To distinguish oxygen from hydrogen, a glowing wooden splint can be used:

> The splint will relight in the presence of oxygen.

> A glowing splint will cause a small explosion characterised by a popping sound in hydrogen.

FIGURE 2: A glowing splint relights. What gas must be in the test-tube?

QUESTIONS

1 Explain how you would identify chlorine gas.

2 Describe an experiment to distinguish oxygen and hydrogen. Note down the safety precautions you would take.

Q Identifying chemical compounds   Uses of cryogenics

The big picture

Scientists cannot make decisions based on a single piece of evidence. They must take all of the evidence available to them to decide. Table 1 summarises some of the physical and chemical properties of chlorine, oxygen and hydrogen. By using all of this information, chemists are able to make a more valid decision about the identity of an unknown gas that they have been asked to identify.

Chemists always use small quantities and wear proper personal safety equipment when carrying out tests on unknown substances.

QUESTIONS

3 From the information in Table 1 explain why a chemist would not identify an unknown gas based on a single test.

4 Describe the tests you would use to identify an unknown gas.

TABLE 1: Tests to identify chlorine, oxygen and hydrogen.

| Gas | Physical properties | | Chemical properties | |
	Colour	Odour	Litmus test	Glowing splint
Chlorine	Greenish	Pungent	Moist litmus paper turns red then white	Extinguished
Oxygen	Colourless	Odourless	No effect	Relights glowing splint
Hydrogen	Colourless	Odourless	No effect	Burns with a 'pop'

Gases and their uses

The chemical and physical properties of oxygen, hydrogen and chlorine allow chemists to identify them. The same properties make these gases suited to the uses they have in our world.

The most important use of oxygen is breathing. We use oxygen when we respire naturally; however, it can also be supplied artificially in divers' air tanks and medical oxygen tanks, to be used when we cannot access oxygen ourselves.

Oxygen is also essential to all oxidation reactions, burning being the most common example. It is this knowledge that allows a scientific approach to fire-fighting. Fire-fighters know that if they can remove the oxygen from the fire it will go out. Many fire-extinguishing systems use this principle to put out fires.

Hydrogen has many important chemical uses. The uses of hydrogen include:

> the production of ammonia (NH_3)

> liquid hydrogen in **cryogenics**

> filling balloons.

However, hydrogen is extremely flammable, which has led to at least one disaster.

It is the toxicity of chlorine that makes it so useful. Small quantities of chlorine gas are used to kill microorganisms in our drinking water and swimming pools. Chlorine is also used in chlorine bleach, one of the most effective **disinfectants** used in kitchens and toilets.

FIGURE 3: The Hindenburg disaster in 1937. Could this have been avoided?

QUESTIONS

5 Research fire extinguishers. How are they adapted for their purpose?

6 Suggest why hydrogen is no longer used in airships.

7 Research some of the uses of chlorine and explain why are they effective.

Q Disinfectant effectiveness   Making polymers

Preparing for assessment: Applying your knowledge

To achieve a good grade in science, you not only have to know and understand scientific ideas, but you also need to be able to apply them to other situations. This task will support you in developing these skills.

✳ What's that white powder?

Many compounds are white powders. The reactions they undergo can be used to identify them.

✳ Task 1

Powders A, B and C are calcium compounds. Each powder was added one spatula at a time to hydrochloric acid. They all neutralised the acid. Powder A produced a gas, but neither of the others did. When the gas was bubbled through limewater it changed from transparent to cloudy.

> Deduce the identity of powder A.

> Name two other calcium compounds that could neutralise acid.

> Write word equations to show how each calcium compound reacts with the acid.

✳ Task 2

When powder A was heated, it lost mass. It was found that 10 g of powder A produced 5.6 g of white powder and gave off a gas that turned limewater cloudy.

> Deduce why powder A lost mass and write a word equation for the reaction.

> How would the reaction differ if copper carbonate was heated instead?

> Calculate the mass of gas released when powder A was heated.

✳ Task 3

When water was dripped onto powder C, the powder doubled in size and got very hot.

> Deduce the identity of C.

> Write a word equation for the reaction that took place.

✳ Task 4

Water became alkaline when powder B was mixed with it. When carbon dioxide was bubbled through this alkali, it became cloudy. This showed that an insoluble product had formed.

> Deduce the identity of powder B.

> Write word equations for the reactions with water and carbon dioxide.

✳ Task 5

Symbol equations make it easier to see how atoms rearrange during chemical reactions.

> Convert the word equations in Tasks 1–4 into balanced symbol equations.

Higher tier only: Use state symbols in your balanced equation.

✳ Maximise your grade

These sentences show what you need to include in your work to achieve each grade. Use them to improve your work and be more successful.

E

For grade E, your answers should show that you can:
> explain that acids are neutralised by oxides, hydroxides and carbonates
> describe the thermal decomposition of calcium carbonate
> write word equations for the reactions described
> show you understand that atoms are neither created nor destroyed during chemical reactions.

C

For grades D, C, in addition show that you can:
> describe the effect of water on calcium oxide
> explain how limewater is made
> show you understand that atoms are rearranged to make new products during chemical reactions
> write simple symbol equations for the reactions described.

A

For grades B, A, in addition show that you can:
> describe the ease of thermal decomposition of different metal carbonates
> write balanced symbol equations including state symbols for the reactions described.

C1 checklist (Topics 1–3)

To achieve your forecast grade in the exam you'll need to revise

Use this checklist to see what you can do now. Refer back to pages 96–121 if you're not sure.

Look across the rows to see how you could progress – *bold italic* means Higher tier only.

Remember you'll need to be able to use these ideas in various ways, such as:
> interpreting pictures, diagrams and graphs
> applying ideas to new situations
> explaining ethical implications
> suggesting some benefits and risks to society
> drawing conclusions from evidence you've been given.

Look at pages 270–92 for more information about exams and how you'll be assessed.

To aim for a grade E	To aim for a grade C	To aim for a grade A
describe the composition of Earth's early atmosphere and how it formed	provide evidence for the composition of Earth's early atmosphere	evaluate the difficulties involved in being precise about the evolution of the atmosphere
recall that the formation of oceans, and appearance of plants and animals reduced the amount of carbon dioxide and increased the amount of oxygen in the early atmosphere	provide evidence of changes to the Earth's early atmosphere caused by plants	
recall the current composition of the atmosphere	describe how volcanoes and human activities are still causing changes in the atmosphere	interpret data sources showing the changes to the atmosphere occurring today
recall that granite is an example of igneous rock and describe how it is formed	understand that the way igneous rock forms affects its crystal size	analyse how igneous rock was formed
recall that limestone and chalk are examples of sedimentary rock and describe how they are formed	explain fossilisation in sedimentary rock	explain the composition of sedimentary rock and relate this to erosion
recall that marble is an example of a metamorphic rock	describe the formation of metamorphic rock from sedimentary and igneous rock	

To aim for a grade E

To aim for a grade C

To aim for a grade A

recall that limestone is quarried because it is important as a raw material in glass, cement and concrete, but this quarrying does have environmental, social and economic impacts	describe the use of limestone in the production of glass, cement and concrete	compare the advantages and disadvantages of quarrying limestone
recall the properties of atoms and that atoms are neither created nor destroyed during chemical reactions	describe atoms and chemical reactions in terms of products and reactants	explain the conservation of matter using examples and *use balanced chemical equations* to describe chemical reactions as the rearrangement of atoms
recall that thermal decomposition is the breakdown of substances by the use of heat	explain how to thermally decompose metal carbonates to metal oxide and carbon dioxide in the laboratory	
recall that calcium carbonate, calcium hydroxide and calcium oxide can be used to neutralise soil and chimney gases	compare calcium carbonate, calcium hydroxide and calcium oxide as agents to neutralise soil and chimney gases	explain in detail the process by which a scrubber system works evaluate whether such a system is necessary
understand that neutralisation occurs in the stomach	link chemical and biological understanding of neutralisation and evaluate antacid remedies	
recall that neutralisation reactions produce salts and water describe how indigestion remedies work, using neutralisation	describe the production of salts by reacting acids with metal oxides, metal hydroxides and metal carbonates	provide specific examples of salts formed by neutralisation reactions, giving *balanced chemical equations*
recall that electrolysis can be used to decompose compounds like sea water and hydrochloric acid	describe the decomposition of hydrochloric acid in terms of charged solutions	explain how electrolysis can be used and evaluate data from electrolysis
recall that there are tests for chlorine, hydrogen and oxygen	carry out the chemical tests for chlorine, hydrogen and oxygen safely	analyse test results to distinguish between chlorine, hydrogen and oxygen
recall that chlorine is a toxic gas	explain the use of chlorine in bleach and polymer production and explain how to minimise some of the hazards of using chlorine in these industrial processes	

1 This photograph shows a quarry on Portland where limestone for building is mined.

AO1 **a** What is the chemical name for limestone?

    A calcium
    B calcium hydroxide
    C calcium oxide
    D calcium carbonate [1]

AO1 **b** What type of rock is limestone? [1]

AO1 **c** The limestone at Portland was made millions of years ago. How was the limestone made? [2]

AO1 **d** Marble is also quarried on Portland. The quarry men know that limestone and marble are made from the same chemical. Explain how the limestone on Portland changed into marble millions of years ago. [2]

AO1 **e** Discuss the advantages and disadvantages of
AO2   quarrying limestone. [6]
                        [Total: 12]

2 Our stomachs produce hydrochloric acid to help digestion. Sometimes too much hydrochloric acid is produced and we get stomachache. An antacid tablet may cure the problem. Most antacid medicines contain an alkali to neutralise the stomach acid.

AO1 **a** Finish this general equation to show how an alkali neutralises an acid.

    acid + alkali → _____ + _____ [2]

AO1 **b** Why is this called a neutralisation reaction? [1]

AO3 **c** Emma and Sam were testing some antacid medicines to find out which was the best value for money. They added dilute hydrochloric acid to one tablet of each antacid and wrote down the volume needed to make a neutral solution.

Antacid	Volume of dilute hydrochloric acid needed to make a neutral solution (cm³)	Cost per tablet (p)
Whizzy tabs	7	10
Grumbly tabs	10	10
Settle tabs	4	10
Cure-all tabs	12	20

i Which antacid needed the largest volume of dilute hydrochloric acid to neutralise it? [1]

ii Which antacid contains most alkali per tablet? [1]

iii Which antacid is the best value for money? Give a reason for your choice. [2]
                        [Total: 7]

3 Josh is finding out how the percentage of carbon dioxide in the air changes. He knows this is linked to climate change. He has found out that the atmosphere has changed frequently in the past. These boxes give some information.

> **Early atmosphere**
>
> Oxygen – little or none
> Nitrogen – small amounts
> Carbon dioxide – large amounts
> Water vapour – large amounts
> Other gases – small amounts

> **Today's atmosphere**
>
> Oxygen – 21%
> Nitrogen – 78%
> Carbon dioxide – 0.038%
> Water vapour – small amount and variable
> Other gases – small amounts

AO1 **a** How did the carbon dioxide and water vapour in the early atmosphere get there? [1]

AO1 **b** What happened to the large amount of water vapour in the early atmosphere?

    A It evaporated
    B It condensed into oceans
    C It produced nitrogen
    D It disappeared [1]

AO2 **c** Which of the following events lowered the carbon dioxide concentration in the early atmosphere?

Event	Yes or no?
Evolution of plants	
Carbon dioxide dissolved in the oceans	
Volcanic activity	
The carbon dioxide dissolved in the oceans was used to make shells	

                        [4]

AO1 **d** Josh is concerned about the recent increase in the percentage of carbon dioxide in the air. Give one reason why the percentage of carbon dioxide is increasing today. [1]
                        [Total: 7]

Worked example

1 Jim's teacher is demonstrating an experiment. He is showing the class that bleach contains chlorine. He adds dilute acid to bleach and collects the gas given off.

a Jim added a piece of wet litmus paper to the gas.

AO1 **i** What does chlorine do to wet litmus paper? [1]

It bleaches it. ✔

AO1 **ii** Name one other test that would show that the gas is chlorine. [1]

The colour. ✗

AO3 **b** Jim tests three different bleaches in the same way. He measures the volume of chlorine gas they each produce when the dilute acid is added. The greater the volume of chlorine produced, the more powerful the bleach. His results are shown in the table.

Bleach	Volume of chlorine given off (cm^3)
Chloro	24
Cleano	47
Draino	10

i Which bleach is the most powerful? [1]

47 cm is the most powerful. ✗

ii Give a reason for your answer to **bi** [1]

There is more bleach in 47 cm than 24 or 10. ✗

iii Name a safety precaution Jim's teacher must take when doing the experiment and a reason for it. [2]

It is poisonous and can harm your breathing like in the war. ✔✗

iv The experiment must be a fair test so that the bleaches can be compared. Name two variables that must be controlled to make the test fair. [2]

He must use the same volume of bleach. ✗

He must use the same amount of acid for each test. ✔

The candidate scores 4 marks out of 8. Their answer to this question targets a grade D. Reading the questions carefully and thinking about which words to use in answers will help to improve this grade.

How to raise your grade

Take note of the comments from examiners – these will help you to improve your grade.

This is correct. Learn the tests for carbon dioxide, oxygen and hydrogen as well.

To get this mark, the colour needs naming. Chlorine gas is a green-yellow colour.

The question asks 'Which bleach …' so it needs to be named, not the volume of chlorine produced. Volume is measured in cm^3 and not cm. Always make sure the units are correct when needed.

Again, the bleaches need to be named for these marks. If an answer involves numbers, always check to see if you need to add units.

There are 2 marks for this question, so two points need to be made to get both marks. They have identified the hazard for 1 mark, but have not given the precaution needed. A good answer would include doing the experiment in a fume cupboard, so that no-one breathes in chlorine gas.

It would be better to use 'quantity' or 'amount', as this compensates for any concentration. There could be some confusion about whether mass was meant. They have listed the controlled variables separately. This is a good way to organise ideas and works well for some questions.

1 The Peak District in Derbyshire has many limestone deposits. Longcliffe manufacturers quarry limestone and heat it in large kilns to make calcium oxide.

AO1 **a** How do we use calcium oxide?

    A To produce chlorine
    B To make cement
    C To produce limestone
    C As hardcore for roads   [1]

AO1 **b** Carbon dioxide is the other product from heating limestone. Write a balanced symbol equation to show the reaction.   [2]

AO1 **c** Explain why the manufacturers describe this reaction as thermal decomposition.   [2]

AO2 **d** The manufacturers have calculated that they can obtain a maximum of 56 tonnes of calcium oxide when 100 tonnes of limestone are heated. How many tonnes of carbon dioxide will they produce?   [2]

AO2 **e** Sam and Jo carried out a small-scale version of this process in their chemistry lesson.

    i What test could they carry out to check that one of the products was carbon dioxide?   [2]

    ii Name a safety precaution they must take when doing this experiment and give a reason for it.   [2]
    [Total: 11]

2 As we use up supplies of oil, many scientists and politicians think hydrogen may be the fuel of the future. We have an abundant supply of water on Earth and water is H_2O.

    a This apparatus can be used to obtain hydrogen from water.

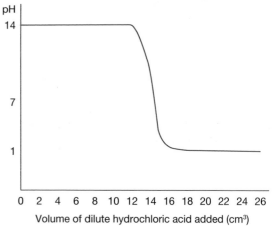

AO1 **i** What is this process called?   [1]

AO1 **ii** What do we call the two electrodes in the apparatus?   [2]

AO1 **iii** Explain why there is twice as much gas above one electrode as the other.   [2]

AO2 **b** A scientist carried out tests on each gas to identify it. Describe two tests they used and give the result for each.   [4]
    [Total: 9]

3 The main ingredient of sea salt is sodium chloride, NaCl. The oceans contain abundant supplies of sea salt, but we can make sodium chloride in the lab from dilute hydrochloric acid (HCl) and sodium hydroxide solution (NaOH).

AO2 **a** Write a balanced symbol equation for the reaction to make sodium chloride.   [1]

AO3 **b** Harry and Sophie make a sample of sodium chloride in the lab. They start with 25 cm^3 sodium hydroxide solution in a beaker and add dilute hydrochloric acid until the mixture is neutral. They use a pH meter to track the experiment. The graph shows how the pH changed when sodium hydroxide was added.

pH
14

7

1

0 2 4 6 8 10 12 14 16 18 20 22 24 26

Volume of dilute hydrochloric acid added (cm^3)

    i What was the pH of the sodium hydroxide solution?   [1]

    ii What volume of dilute hydrochloric acid was needed to exactly neutralise the sodium hydroxide solution?   [1]

    iii Which substances were present in the beaker when 10 cm^3 dilute hydrochloric acid had been added?   [3]

    iv Which substances were present in the beaker when 22 cm^3 dilute hydrochloric acid had been added?   [3]
    [Total: 9]

Summary of Assessment Objectives

AO1   recall the science   AO2   apply your knowledge   AO3   evaluate and analyse the evidence

✴ Worked example

1 The biggest diamonds in the world form deep underground. They are made when pockets of molten carbon cool and solidify. They are usually found with igneous rock and near volcanoes.

AO1 **a** How do igneous rocks form? [2]

They are made from molten rock. ✔ ✘

AO2 **b** Why are igneous rocks found near volcanoes? [1]

Because volcanoes have extremely high temperatures. ✘

AO2 **c** Crystals like diamond consist of a regular pattern of particles. Explain why slow cooling is essential for large diamonds to form. [2]

The particles move around when it is a liquid. When it cools, they sort themselves into a regular pattern. This takes time. The more time they have, the bigger the pattern and the bigger the diamond. If it cools quickly, the particles do not make a good regular pattern and the diamonds will be small. ✔ ✔

AO2 **d** **i** What happens to the size of the diamond if the molten carbon cools faster? [1]

The diamonds will be smaller. ✔

> A correct answer.

AO2 **e** Rocks around volcanoes are usually metamorphic or igneous. Mining companies searching for diamonds near volcanoes do not expect to find fossils. Explain why not. [2]

The heat from the volcano destroys them. ✔ ✘

> The candidate scores 5 marks out of 8. Their answer to this question targets just below a grade B. Practising exam questions and anticipating the mark scheme will help improve this grade.

How to raise your grade

Take note of the comments from examiners – these will help you to improve your grade.

> This is correct, but there are 2 marks for this question and only one piece of information is given, what they are made from. To gain the second mark, it needs to say that they form when molten rock or magma (1) cools and solidifies (1). Try to use scientific terminology all the time.

> To gain this mark, the answer should state that magma reaches the surface of the Earth on a volcano and forms igneous rock. The high temperature is relevant, but not the whole answer. Always read the question very carefully.

> The candidate has all the points of a correct answer here and has applied science to this situation. You will come across topics (like diamonds) in exams that have not been covered in science lessons. The examiner wants to know if you can apply your science to other situations. The last sentence is not needed (but marks are not lost for this).

> The terms metamorphic and igneous are used in the question. The answer needs to be on the same lines. A better answer would be 'Fossils form in sedimentary rocks. Any sedimentary rocks around a volcano are changed to metamorphic or igneous rocks. This destroys the fossils.'

What you should know

Metals

Metals have different levels of reactivity.

Metals react with oxygen and water, leading to corrosion.

All metals share certain properties like malleability and conductivity.

 Name one very reactive metal and one very unreactive metal.

Fuels

Fossil fuels formed from dead plant and animal matter include coal, oil and natural gas.

Fossil fuels can be burned to produce energy but they may also produce pollutants.

Fossil fuels are non-renewable fuels.

Name two gases produced when burning oil or coal.

Alternative fuels

Alternative fuel sources include biofuels and hydrogen.

Suggest the advantages of using alternative fuels.

Organic compounds

Crude oil is a substance used to produce petrol.

Describe how crude oil was formed.

You will find out about

> extracting metals from their ores using different techniques depending on the metal's reactivity

> specific examples of how properties of metals dictate their uses

> moving oxygen from one substance to another in oxidation and reduction reactions

> creating alloys to alter the properties of metals making them, for example, more flexible or hard wearing

> the position in the reactivity series affecting the likely corrosion of metals

> recycling metals to reduce the cost and the environmental damage caused by their production

> fossil fuels, which are mainly hydrocarbons, being burned in combustion reactions

> carbon monoxide, produced by incomplete combustion

> how using hydrocarbons for fuel releases carbon dioxide, a greenhouse gas

> impurities contained in hydrocarbons being responsible for pollutants that lead to acid rain

> how human activity, including burning fossil fuels, may influence the climate

> the factors that make a good fuel

> the advantages and problems of biofuels as a possible renewable energy source

> hydrogen as a possible energy source offering some unique possibilities as well as serious drawbacks

> fuel cell technology using hydrogen and oxygen to produce electricity

> how hydrocarbons can be separated into useful fractions with different properties using fractional distillation

> organising organic compounds into homologous series including saturated hydrocarbons (alkanes) and unsaturated hydrocarbons (alkenes)

> producing useful hydrocarbons by cracking less useful hydrocarbons including alkenes used in the production of polymers

> the special consideration that must be given to the disposal of polymers

Sources of metals

You will find out:
> about the source of metals
> how metals are extracted
> about the reactivity series

It's elemental

If you look at all the elements in the world most of them are metals. They include some of the most precious substances on Earth and some of the most common. Let's see where they come from and how we get them.

FIGURE 1: This mine in Levant, Cornwall, mined copper and tin for over 200 years, much of it from under the sea.

Rocks and minerals

The rocks in the Earth's crust are rarely pure substances.

Rocks are usually mixtures of compounds called **minerals**.

If the minerals contain metals, they are referred to as **ores**.

Ores are mined from the crust of the Earth and the metals are extracted from them.

A few metals are largely unreactive and can be found in their pure states as uncombined elements. Gold is an excellent example of an unreactive metal.

FIGURE 3: A gold nugget: one of the few metals found in its pure form.

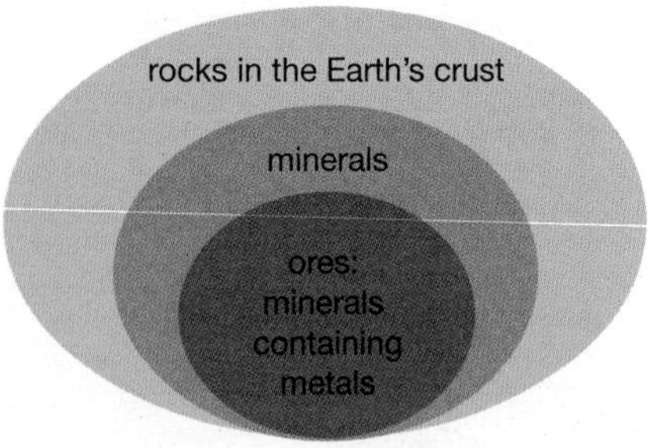

rocks in the Earth's crust

minerals

ores: minerals containing metals

FIGURE 2: The composition of the Earth's crust.

QUESTIONS

1 Describe the relationship between ores and minerals.

2 Explain why you might find a nugget of gold in a rock.

Ores

Ores are rocks or minerals containing metal. Often, the minerals are metals that have reacted to produce various compounds.

The cost of producing metals depends on three factors:

> the availability of the ore

> the method of extraction

> how much metal is in the ore.

If the ores are very rare, the cost will be high. Gold is very rare and therefore very expensive. Iron, on the other hand, is cheap because its ore is plentiful.

Once the ore has been mined, the metals have to be extracted. There are two main methods for extracting ores: chemical reduction and electrolysis. The method chosen is determined by the chemical properties of the metal to be extracted.

In chemical reduction, the crushed metal ore is heated in the presence of carbon. The carbon reacts with the oxygen, removing it from the ore. This is the method of choice for extracting iron.

In **electrolysis**, the crushed ore is melted and then an electrical current is passed through the ore to extract the metal. This is the method of choice for metals like aluminium.

Metals that can be extracted by heating with carbon are generally cheaper than metals that must be extracted by electrolysis. This is because carbon can be produced cheaply while electricity is expensive.

FIGURE 4: **a** Haematite, the ore of iron, and **b** bauxite, the ore of aluminium.

TABLE 1: Common metals and their ores.

Metal	Ore	Formula	Name
Iron	Iron oxide	Fe_2O_3	Haematite
Aluminium	Aluminium oxide	Al_2O_3	Bauxite

QUESTIONS

3 Explain how iron is extracted from its ore.

4 Describe the process for extracting aluminium and explain why aluminium extraction is often carried out near hydroelectric power stations.

5 Research the method for extracting copper from its ore.

Did you know?

Many of medieval Britain's forests were cut down to make charcoal for iron smelting.

Choosing a method

Extracting metals from their ore involves separating the metal from the other substances that they are mixed or chemically combined with.

The method used to extract metals from their ore is based on their chemical properties. Chemists have devised a tool called the **reactivity series** that guides the choice of method used. Figure 5 show a version of the reactivity series.

The reactivity series shows the important metals arranged with carbon in their order of reactivity. Those metals above carbon are more reactive than carbon. Those metals below carbon are less reactive.

Those metals that are below carbon on the reactivity series can be heated with carbon to extract the metal from the ore. Since carbon is more reactive than those metals, when the ore and the carbon are heated the oxygen in

the ore will react with the carbon, leaving a pure metal.

Those metals above carbon are more reactive than carbon and the smelting process cannot be used. For those metals, one potential method of extraction is electrolysis.

Did you know?

The reactivity series can be based on the reaction of metals with water, oxygen and acid.

FIGURE 5: The reactivity series. Which metals are found in their pure form?

Most reactive

Potassium
Sodium
Calcium
Magnesium
Aluminium
Carbon
Zinc
Iron
Tin
Lead
Hydrogen
Copper
Silver
Gold
Platinum

Least reactive

QUESTIONS

6 Discuss how a commercial manufacturer would determine the best method to extract a metal from its ore.

7 Describe the method you would use to extract magnesium from its ore.

Oxidation and reduction

You will find out:
> about oxidation and reduction
> about metal extraction
> about the causes of corrosion

From ore to rust

The chemistry of metal extraction and the chemistry of corrosion are closely related. The role of oxygen is crucial in both processes. Because of its reactivity, oxygen is at the heart of some of the most important reactions in the world.

FIGURE 1: The Angel of the North. What gives it that distinctive colour?

Oxidation and reduction

Metals exposed to oxygen undergo an **oxidation reaction**:

> An oxidation reaction adds oxygen to a substance.

> The iron oxide in the Earth's crust was formed by the oxidation of iron.

Items made of metal will corrode when exposed to oxygen. Corrosion is an oxidation reaction.

To extract iron from iron oxide, the oxygen must be removed:

> Removing oxygen from a substance is a **reduction reaction**.

> The iron oxide is reduced to form iron.

The metals that we use go through a continuous cycle of oxidation and reduction:

> The iron in the Earth's crust was oxidised to form iron oxide (rust).

> The iron oxide is reduced during extraction to form iron.

> The iron is used to make things like cars and bridges that will eventually oxidise.

> The corroded metal items can be recycled by reducing them again to form iron.

QUESTIONS

1 Define oxidation and reduction reactions.

2 Describe the corrosion of zinc.

3 Using a photograph or your own drawings, illustrate the cycle of oxidation and reduction.

Remember!
For one substance to be reduced, another has to be oxidised.

Extracting iron

Iron ore is iron oxide. In order to obtain iron from iron oxide there must be a reduction reaction:

$$2Fe_2O_3 \text{ (s)} + 3C \text{ (s)} \rightarrow 4Fe \text{ (s)} + 3CO_2 \text{ (g)}$$
iron oxide + carbon → iron + carbon dioxide

Did you know?

Early blast furnaces were powered by charcoal. It is estimated that one 17th-century furnace required 1700 ha of woodland to fuel it.

🔍 Blast furnace   Smelting

Smelting takes place when iron oxide is heated in the presence of a form of carbon, usually coke. It is carried out in a blast furnace.

> Coke burns in the hot air.

> The oxygen moves from the iron to the carbon because carbon is more reactive.

> The iron is reduced and carbon is oxidised. These two reactions are always paired. For one substance to be reduced, another has to be oxidised.

> Heat decomposes the limestone.

> Calcium oxide reacts with the impurities in the ore to form liquid **slag**.

> Molten iron sinks below the slag and is run off.

Unless it is protected, as soon as it is extracted, the iron starts to oxidise. We call this oxidation process corrosion. The iron reacts with oxygen in the atmosphere to form iron oxide:

$$4Fe\ (s)\ +\ 3O_2\ (g)\ \rightarrow\ 2Fe_2O_3\ (s)$$
$$iron\ +\ oxygen\ \rightarrow\ iron\ oxide$$

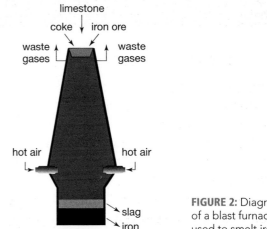

FIGURE 2: Diagram of a blast furnace used to smelt iron.

QUESTIONS

4 Name three metals that could be extracted by a reaction with carbon and three that cannot. Explain your answer.

5 The furnace is used to remove oxygen from the ore. So, why do we add air?

Reactivity and corrosion

Corrosion occurs when metal, oxygen and sometimes water are exposed to each other and react together.

Scientists can use the reactivity series (see pages 132–3) to help reduce corrosion. Note that the higher an element is on the reactivity series, the more reactive it is. In addition, the more reactive a metal is, the more likely it is to corrode.

Painting iron objects removes oxygen and water and so prevents corrosion.

Galvanising is another means of preventing corrosion. Metal objects are coated with a layer of zinc. The zinc coating quickly oxidises and creates a thin layer that is resistant to further corrosion. If the zinc layer is damaged, the zinc corrodes instead of the object because it is more reactive. This process is called **sacrificial protection**.

Sacrificial protection can be used on large metal structures like ships and bridges. Small blocks of a sacrificial metal, usually zinc or magnesium, are attached to the structures. The sacrificial blocks are corroded instead of the structure.

FIGURE 3: A galvanised metal staircase. Why is zinc a good material for this structure?

FIGURE 4: Sacrificial block on a ship's keel.

QUESTIONS

6 Explain why it is necessary to oil metal objects such as machinery or guns.

7 Describe how corrosion can be prevented on metal bridges other than by painting.

Uses of metals

You will find out:

> about the link between properties and uses of metals

> about the uses of aluminium, copper, gold and steel

> about alloys

Choosing metals

Imagine a copper bridge or electrical wires made of iron. The properties of metals make them better suited for some uses than for others. An understanding of those properties allows the best choice of metal for a specific job.

FIGURE 1: The world's first cast-iron bridge was built at Coalbrookdale in 1779.

Properties dictate uses

Metals all share some common properties:

> most have high **melting points**

> good conduction of heat and electrical current

> **malleability**

> **ductility**.

Individual metals have properties that make them particularly suited to specific uses.

FIGURE 2: This parabolic reflector made from aluminium is part of a solar oven which gets its energy directly from the Sun. Can you suggest why aluminium is a suitable material for this?

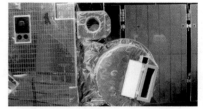

FIGURE 3: Gold foil is used as a heat shield on this satellite.

TABLE 1: The properties and uses of aluminium, copper and gold.

Metal	Properties	Uses
Aluminium	Strong and light Excellent conductor of heat Good reflector of heat and light	Aircraft components Containers for food and drink Reflective surfaces for telescope mirrors
Copper	Best electrical conductor of all cheap metals Very ductile Very malleable	Electrical wiring Plumbing pipes
Gold	Excellent electrical conductor Corrosion resistant Very reflective Rare (expensive)	Electrical connectors Satellite shields Jewellery Dentistry

QUESTIONS

1 Using Table 1 explain why not all electrical components are made of gold.

2 Using Table 1 explain why gold would be used to make solar shields for satellites.

3 Draw a similar table for the following metals: silver, iron, titanium. You can use the internet or other books to help you.

Alloys of iron

The iron extracted using the smelting technique is called cast iron. It is approximately 96% iron with 4% carbon impurities. Although strong, cast iron is very brittle and not suitable for anything needing flexibility.

To change the properties of iron, chemists remove some of the carbon and add different substances to produce alloys called steels. Steels are stronger and more resistant to corrosion that iron.

In pure metals, the atoms are able to align in a very regular pattern. This allows the atoms to slide along each other very easily, making the metal very soft and easily bent.

By introducing atoms of a different type into the mix, the atoms of the metal cannot align as regularly as in the pure metal. These different atoms prevent the metal atoms from sliding as freely as in the pure

Q Metallic properties   Steel alloys   Gold alloys

metal, making the metal harder to bend and less brittle (see the model in Figure 4). The new metal is known as an alloy. In the case of iron, the alloy is called steel.

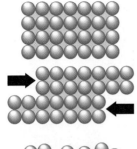

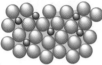

FIGURE 4: In pure metals the atoms are aligned in a very regular pattern (top) but in alloys the atoms of different substances disrupt the alignment of the metal atoms (bottom).

TABLE 2: The properties and uses of steels.

Name	Composition	Properties	Uses
Low carbon steel or mild steel	>0.25% carbon	Cheap Strong Easily shaped	Construction Car body parts Appliance cases
High carbon steel	<0.5% carbon	Hard Stronger than mild steel but more brittle	Tools
Stainless steel	80% iron 15% chromium 4% nickel 0.5–1% carbon	Strong Hard Very corrosion resistant	Cookware Cutlery Industrial chemistry
Titanium steel	0.5–2% titanium Varying amounts of chromium, nickel and vanadium	Very strong Reduced weight Resistant to corrosion	Aircraft components

QUESTIONS

4 Describe the effect of carbon content in iron and its alloys.

5 Explain why low carbon steel is well suited to making car body parts.

6 Draw a model to show how brittle iron is transformed into strong stainless steel.

Special alloys (Higher tier only)

People have been modifying gold for thousands of years. In its pure form, gold is too soft for most uses. By mixing gold with other metals, it can be strengthened, making it more versatile. Typically, the gold is alloyed with copper, silver or some other **base metal**.

The colour of gold can be changed by alloying it with other metals. Figure 5 shows the proportions of gold used to produce various colours.

The purity of gold is measured using carats:

> pure gold is 99.99% pure and is referred to as 24-carat gold

> 75% gold is 18-carat gold

> 50% gold is 12-carat gold.

The purity of gold is also measured using the **fineness system**. Fineness refers to parts per thousand (ppt). For example, 24-carat gold is 999 ppt; 18-carat gold is 750 ppt gold.

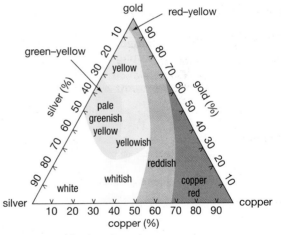

FIGURE 5: Gold colour formulae.

Nitinol is one of the most recent alloys created by scientists. Nitinol is an equal mixture of nickel and titanium. Nitinol is also known as shape memory metal. Once a piece of nitinol has been shaped, it will change its shape in response to a change in temperature. It will return to its original shape as the temperature changes back. Nitinol has many applications including medical instruments, spectacle frames and stents for repairing damaged blood vessels, and is just one example of how scientists create new materials to fit new applications.

QUESTIONS

7 Compare the carat system and the fineness system for stating the purity of gold.

8 Explain why shape memory metals would be useful in medical applications. You may wish to research examples to support your explanation.

Recycling

You will find out:

> about the environmental advantages of recycling metals

> about the economic advantages of recycling metals

What goes around ...

More than 1.9 million tonnes of steel was produced in the world in 2009. On average, each household in the UK uses approximately 600 steel cans a year. This kind of consumption cannot continue forever without putting a strain on our resources and impacting our world.

FIGURE 1: Scrap metal. Will it be recycled?

Old becomes new

The metals we use all come from ores. Ores are a **non-renewable** resource. There is a finite amount of ore on planet Earth. The more ore that is mined, the further the deposits of ore are reduced and the harder to find it becomes. This means it must be mined from more environmentally sensitive areas.

There are both environmental and economic advantages to recycling metals. Recycling is an important way to lower the cost of and environmental damage caused by metal production. It also allows us to save existing supplies of these valuable raw materials.

FIGURE 2: Refrigerator cases. This is the kind of metal that can easily be recycled.

Environmental advantages

> Less fuel burned to mine and transport ore.

> Fewer mines causing less environmental damage.

> Less land used to dispose of waste metal.

Economic advantages

> Reduced fuel costs.

> Reduced land reclamation costs after mining and reduced use of land-fill.

QUESTIONS

1 Describe what is meant by non-renewable resources.

2 Explain why recycling reduces the cost of producing metals.

Aluminium recycling

The production of metal requires mining the ore and extracting the metal from that ore. The ore is typically in the form of an oxide. Recall from pages 134–5 the process for iron extraction:

$$2Fe_2O_3 \text{ (s)} + 3C \text{ (s)} \rightarrow 4Fe \text{ (s)} + 3CO_2 \text{ (g)}$$

Also, remember that iron starts to corrode almost immediately:

$$4Fe \text{ (s)} + 3O_2 \text{ (g)} \rightarrow 2Fe_2O_3 \text{ (s)}$$

These two reactions clearly illustrate that old, corroded iron can be recycled by reprocessing it.

The situation with iron applies to the other important metals as well.

It is estimated that recycling aluminium requires approximately 5% of the energy required to process aluminium ore. It doesn't need to be mined, so there is no cost or energy expended in the mining; there is also a saving in the transportation costs. Scrap aluminium is almost pure aluminium. The ore, however, contains unusable compounds that are removed during processing. Although the scrap must be processed, the costs are significantly less than for processing ores. In addition, kilogram for kilogram, scrap is more economical to transport.

There are two kinds of scrap metal. The easiest kind of scrap metal to recycle is the scrap produced during the production of metal objects. This metal is usually

FIGURE 3: Aluminium cans. Enough energy is saved by recycling one can to power a television for 3 hours.

untreated and can be placed directly back into the extraction process. The other is already used scrap metal: cans, cars, old fridges and so on.

There is one drawback to recycling used scrap metal. It must be sorted and cleaned of any non-metal substances. In relation to the processing involved in making ore usable, the savings are still significant.

Remember!

Chemical states are only assessed at Higher tier.

QUESTIONS

3 Explain how recycling aluminium can save as much as 95% of the energy required for extracting aluminium from its ore.

4 Comment on the disadvantages of recycling used scrap metal.

5 Discuss whether recycling metals should be compulsory.

Climate change

The 95% reduction in energy needed for processing recycled aluminium compared to its ore means that there is a corresponding reduction in carbon dioxide (CO_2) emissions.

Carbon dioxide is an important **greenhouse gas**. It is estimated that carbon dioxide accounts for approximately 75% of the greenhouse gases in our atmosphere. Carbon dioxide is produced when fossil fuels are burned:

$$CH_4 \text{ (g)} + 2O_2 \text{ (g)} \rightarrow CO_2 \text{ (g)} + 2H_2O \text{ (g)}$$
methane + oxygen → carbon dioxide + water

Greenhouse gases are thought to be responsible for **climate change**. Sunlight penetrates the atmosphere and warms the Earth. Some of that solar energy is radiated into space. As the CO_2 level in the atmosphere increases, the amount of energy that can be radiated back into space is reduced, trapping energy in the Earth's atmosphere. This causes the temperature to rise, similar to the way glass works in a greenhouse.

Recycling metals reduces the amount of energy required to produce metals from their ore. It also reduces the amount of CO_2 released into the atmosphere and therefore reduces the effects of greenhouse gases.

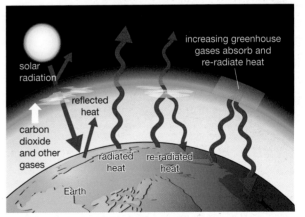

FIGURE 4: The greenhouse effect.

QUESTIONS

6 Explain why carbon dioxide is considered a greenhouse gas.

7 Describe the relationship between carbon dioxide levels and solar energy reflection.

8 Evaluate the impact of recycling metals on the environment, economy and society.

Preparing for assessment: Applying your knowledge

To achieve a good grade in science, you not only have to know and understand scientific ideas, but you also need to be able to apply them to other situations. This task will support you in developing these skills.

✹ Vorsprung durch Technik – 'Progress through Technology'

Most car bodies are made of steel because it is cheap, strong and easy to shape, but some luxury cars like the Audi R8 have expensive aluminium bodies.

Swapping steel for aluminium reduces a car's mass, so it uses less fuel and releases less carbon dioxide. Pure aluminium isn't stiff enough to be used in this way so it is alloyed with other metals.

Another advantage of aluminium is that it doesn't corrode like steel, so the car lasts longer. Aluminium does oxidise but a surface layer of oxide protects the rest of the metal. When the iron in steel corrodes it forms rust. This weak crumbly material allows oxygen through to the metal below.

✹ Task 1

Decide whether steel, aluminium, or both, could satisfy these design features:

> Car bodies should not corrode as this weakens them and spoils their appearance.

> Car bodies need to be lightweight so they don't use too much fuel.

> Car bodies need to be cheap as the car market is very competitive.

✹ Task 2

Steelmakers need to overcome the weaknesses of steel so they can keep their share of the market. Aluminium is gradually replacing the steel used in cars.

> Name the main metal and non-metal in steel.

> What makes the steel in cars corrode?

> Why is it odd that corrosion is less of a problem in cars made from aluminium?

✸ Task 3

Advances in technology have produced new types of steel with improved properties.

> Explain what an alloy is.

> Use diagrams to explain why converting pure metals to alloys often increases their strength.

> What properties would make steel more useful in cars?

> Designers are replacing the steel in some car parts with Nitinol (an alloy of nickel and titanium). What is special about this alloy?

✸ Maximise your grade

These sentences show what you need to include in your work to achieve each grade. Use them to improve your work and be more successful.

E
For grade E, your answers should show that you can:
> relate the properties of aluminium to its use in car bodies
> explain what makes metals corrode.

For grades D, C, in addition show that you can:
> explain what an alloy is
> relate the properties of steel to its use in car bodies
> use models to explain why alloys are usually stronger than pure metals
> show you understand that alloys of steel are stronger and more corrosion resistant.

C

For grades B, A, in addition show that you can:
> show you understand how a metal's reactivity determines its resistance to corrosion
> describe the properties of Nitinol and explain how it could be used in cars.

A

Hydrocarbons

You will find out:
> about crude oil
> some of the properties of hydrocarbons
> about some useful hydrocarbons

The importance of crude oil

How did you get to school today? If you used some form of motorised transport, the chances are a hydrocarbon fuel was used to make the journey. Most of the fuels we use to power vehicles nowadays come from crude oil.

FIGURE 1: Public transport. What kind of fuel does this speeding bus use?

What are hydrocarbons?

Hydrocarbons:

> are **compounds** made of carbon and hydrogen only

> the main difference between **hydrocarbons** is the number of carbons that are bonded together in a chain.

Crude oil is the largest source of hydrocarbons.

Crude oil

Crude oil is found in large underground deposits and:

> is a complex mixture of hydrocarbons

> was formed from the remains of small plants and animals that died long ago and were covered by layers of sand and mud.

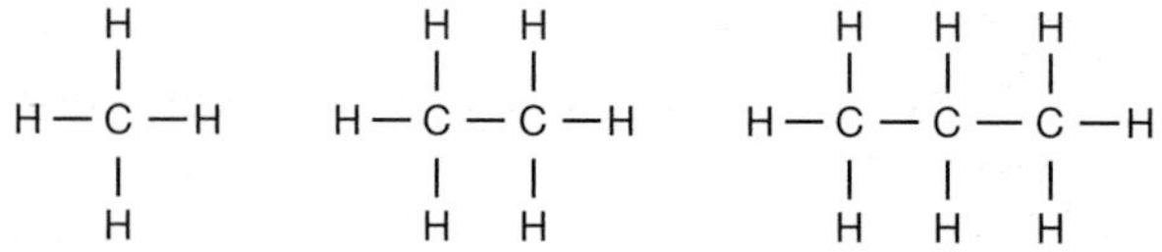

FIGURE 2: Hydrocarbons. What is the difference between these hydrocarbons?

The different length chains in hydrocarbons (as shown in Figure 2) produce different **physical properties**:

> These are characteristics of a compound that can be observed without changing the compound.

> One important physical property is boiling point.

> Chemists can use these different physical properties to separate the mixture of hydrocarbons found in crude oil.

Did you know?

Russia produces more crude oil than any other country.

QUESTIONS

1 State what is meant by hydrocarbons.

2 Describe crude oil.

Fractional distillation

Hydrocarbons that have short chains of carbon atoms have low boiling points. The longer the chain, the higher the boiling point. The process of fractional distillation uses the differences in boiling points to separate crude oil into different fractions of simpler mixtures. The crude oil is heated and those hydrocarbons that have similar length chains of carbon atoms have similar boiling points and can be collected.

TABLE 1: Some of the products of fractional distillation.

Product	Use	Chain length	Boiling Point	Ease of ignition	Viscosity
Gases	Heating and cooking	Shortest	Lowest	Easiest	Lowest
Petrol	Fuel for cars				
Kerosene	Fuel for aircraft				
Diesel oil	Fuel for some cars and trains				
Fuel oil	Fuel for ships and some power stations				
Bitumen	Tarmac and roofing	Longest	Highest	Hardest	Highest

The products of fractional distillation

The products of fractional distillation are all useful. The different physical properties associated with these different products help to determine their uses:

> The gases that are used for heating and cooking need to burn easily and therefore they need to ignite easily.

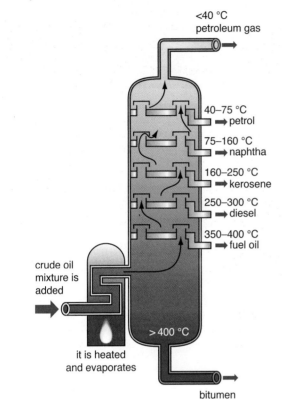

crude oil mixture is added

it is heated and evaporates

bitumen

FIGURE 3: Fractionating column. Where are the longest chain hydrocarbons?

> Bitumen is well suited to its use in tarmac and roofing materials. These items need to be tough and waterproof.

> Ease of ignition decreases as chain length increases.

FIGURE 4: Fractional distillation column at an oil refinery.

QUESTIONS

3 State two characteristics that make gases suitable for cooking and heating.

4 Describe the trends of hydrocarbon products indicated in Table 1.

5 Explain what is meant by physical properties, using examples.

Homologous series

A **homologous series** is a group of compounds that change in an incremental way. For instance, the hydrocarbons in crude oil differ in the number of carbon atoms in the chain. These simple-chain hydrocarbons are called **alkanes** and have a general formula of $C_nH_{(2n+2)}$. The simplest hydrocarbon is methane, CH_4. Next is C_2H_6 and so on.

Each alkane has different physical properties. This is because of the different structure of the molecules and the different forces between the interacting molecules (intermolecular forces). As the chain length gets longer, the intermolecular forces get stronger, causing the molecules to stick together more.

The trend in viscosity (Table 1) is a result of these increased intermolecular forces. Viscosity is a measure of a fluid's resistance to flow. Think about the difference between water and treacle: water has a very low viscosity and treacle has a very high viscosity.

Another result of these strong intermolecular forces is increasing boiling points. Heating molecules increases the kinetic energy in the molecules and allows them to move around more. If molecules have enough kinetic energy they overcome the intermolecular forces and separate from each other. In other words, they vaporise and become a gas.

QUESTIONS

6 Draw the structure of alkanes with three, four and five carbons.

7 Explain the effect of heating on the viscosity of a substance.

Combustion

You will find out:

> about the complete combustion of hydrocarbons

> about a chemical test for carbon dioxide

A burning question

Hydrocarbon-based fuels heat our homes, cook our meals, and power our cars and the aeroplanes that take us on holiday. What is actually happening when we burn hydrocarbons?

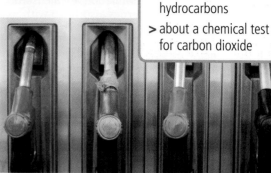

FIGURE 1: Where do our fuels come from?

Energy from fuel

To release the energy in fuels they first must be burned. The hydrocarbon fuels that are distilled from crude oil are all composed of carbon and hydrogen. When hydrocarbons react with oxygen, it is called a **combustion reaction**. For example:

methane + oxygen → carbon dioxide + water (and energy)

This reaction always produces three things:

> carbon dioxide

> water

> large amounts of heat energy.

This reaction is an example of an **oxidation reaction**. The hydrocarbon is oxidised to carbon dioxide and water. If the carbon in the hydrocarbon is completely reacted to produce carbon dioxide, then **complete combustion** has occurred. Recall that in oxidation reactions oxygen is added to a compound.

FIGURE 2: The combustion of hydrocarbons. What gases are being produced here?

QUESTIONS

1 State the products of the complete combustion of a hydrocarbon.

Limewater test

It is possible to look for the presence of carbon dioxide using a simple test. Calcium hydroxide reacts with carbon dioxide to produce calcium carbonate and water.

$$Ca(OH)_2 \text{ (aq)} + CO_2 \text{ (g)} \rightarrow CaCO_3 \text{ (s)} + H_2O \text{ (l)}$$
calcium hydroxide + carbon dioxide → calcium carbonate + water

This test is called the **limewater test**. Calcium hydroxide is slightly soluble in water, while calcium carbonate is insoluble. The calcium hydroxide solution is clear and turns white when the insoluble calcium carbonate is formed.

Chemists can use the limewater test to check for the presence of carbon dioxide from many sources. Certain metal carbonates will undergo **thermal decomposition** when heated. The case of calcium carbonate has already been discussed (pages 112–13). Other similar metal carbonates undergo the same reaction. For example:

$$MgCO_3 \text{ (s)} \rightarrow MgO \text{ (s)} + CO_2 \text{ (g)}$$
magnesium carbonate → magnesium oxide + carbon dioxide

Remember!
The limewater test can be used to demonstrate that the air we breathe out contains carbon dioxide.

Did you know?

Beryllium forms a carbonate of similar formula to magnesium carbonate.

If the gas produced by this reaction is bubbled through limewater, a white **precipitate** (calcium carbonate) will form.

Recall from pages 114–15 that another important application of the reaction we see in the limewater test is the removal of carbon dioxide from power-plant smokestacks that burn hydrocarbons or coal.

QUESTIONS

2 Explain how the limewater test works.

3 Write a chemical equation for the thermal decomposition of beryllium carbonate.

4 Recall all the facts you have learned about thermal decomposition.

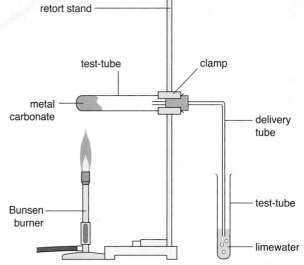

FIGURE 3: Apparatus for testing for the presence of carbonates using thermal decomposition and limewater.

Balancing input and output

All chemical equations must be balanced. The number of atoms for each element on each side of the arrow must be equal. In the complete combustion of methane, for instance:

$$CH_4 \text{ (g)} + 2O_2 \text{ (g)} \rightarrow CO_2 \text{ (g)} + 2H_2O \text{ (g)}$$
methane + oxygen → carbon dioxide + water

Another important oxidation reaction occurs inside the cells of living organisms. Most living organisms use carbon-based molecules for their main energy source. These carbon-based compounds are called **carbohydrates**.

Carbohydrates, as their name suggests, are composed of carbon and water. They have the generalised formula of $C_nH_{2n}O_n$. The most common of these carbohydrates are sugars. Cells oxidise these molecules to release the energy stored in the chemical bonds:

$$C_6H_{12}O_6 \text{ (aq)} + 6O_2 \text{ (g)} \rightarrow 6CO_2 \text{ (g)} + 6H_2O \text{ (l)}$$
glucose + oxygen → carbon dioxide + water

This equation explains why you require oxygen to live and where the carbon dioxide you exhale comes from. The oxygen is used to oxidise the carbohydrate, and carbon dioxide, water and energy are the products.

FIGURE 4: Carbohydrates. What is this carbohydrate called?

Remember!
Atoms are neither created nor destroyed in chemical reactions.

Did you know?

Your daily intake of carbohydrates should be around 200 g. There are approximately 144 grams of carbohydrates in a typical chocolate bar.

QUESTIONS

5 a Explain why the use of sugars by your cells is considered an oxidation reaction.

b In biology what is this reaction more commonly known as?

6 Discuss how plants and animals are linked in the carbon cycle.

Q Carbohydrates   Aerobic respiration

Incomplete combustion

You will find out:

> about the incomplete combustion of hydrocarbons

> why carbon monoxide is dangerous

> the problems associated with incomplete combustion

The silent killer

Carbon monoxide is an odourless toxic gas. About 20 people die from carbon monoxide poisoning every year in the UK. What is the source of this deadly gas, and what can be done to prevent these unnecessary deaths?

FIGURE 1: Every home should have one: a carbon monoxide detector.

Carbon monoxide and its dangers

The **incomplete combustion** of hydrocarbons produces carbon and **carbon monoxide**:

> Carbon monoxide does not have an odour or a colour.

> Carbon monoxide is poisonous and can be lethal.

The most common cause of carbon monoxide poisoning is the faulty operation of gas heaters or cookers. Effective prevention is the annual inspection and servicing of gas appliances.

Did you know?

The National Union of Students says house or flat renters must check that landlords have a gas safety certificate for student lets.

Besides annual servicing, hydrocarbon-fuelled heaters or equipment should be used in well-ventilated areas. This is to make sure that there is the proper amount of oxygen for complete combustion, but also to allow any carbon monoxide to be vented before reaching toxic levels.

QUESTIONS

1 Describe the properties of carbon monoxide.

2 Draw a leaflet aimed at students showing how to prevent carbon monoxide poisoning.

Incomplete combustion and its effects

The combustion of hydrocarbons requires oxygen, a lot of oxygen. Methane, for example, requires two oxygen molecules for every methane molecule:

$$CH_4\ (g)\ +\ 2O_2\ (g)\ \rightarrow\ CO_2\ (g)\ +\ 2H_2O\ (g)$$
methane + oxygen → carbon dioxide + water

If there is not enough oxygen present for all the carbon to turn into carbon dioxide (and undergo complete combustion), then the combustion reaction will be incomplete and only one carbon molecule (CO) will be formed. The products of incomplete combustion are carbon monoxide, carbon particles and water.

Since carbon monoxide is colourless and odourless, the carbon particles are the most obvious sign of incomplete combustion. These will appear as a sooty residue. Any soot or discoloration around a gas appliance indicates incomplete combustion, and means the appliance needs to be switched off immediately.

Another sign of incomplete combustion of methane is the colour of the flame.

> With complete combustion, the colour of the flame is blue.

> With incomplete combustion, the flame will appear yellow.

Did you know?

The Health and Safety Executive suggests that household heating systems should be inspected annually.

Q Incomplete combustion   Carbon monoxide detectors

TABLE 1: Characteristics of combustion.

Characteristics	Complete combustion	Incomplete combustion
Products	Carbon dioxide and water	Carbon monoxide, carbon and water
Colour of flame	Blue	Yellow

QUESTIONS

3 Explain why you should not use the old camping gas stove you found in the shed to heat your tent.

4 Write an equation to show incomplete combustion.

5 Research carbon monoxide detectors. Write a report describing how they work.

FIGURE 2: What does this photograph tell us about the combustion of this substance?

Consequences of incomplete combustion

Carbon monoxide poisoning

Why is carbon monoxide so toxic? **Red blood cells** are responsible for carrying oxygen throughout the body and they contain molecules called **haemoglobin**. These molecules have an attraction to oxygen molecules, which allows them to pick up oxygen molecules as the blood circulates through the lungs. However, if these haemoglobin molecules are exposed to carbon monoxide, the carbon monoxide attaches to the haemoglobin instead of oxygen. This attachment is irreversible. Therefore, if you are exposed to carbon monoxide your haemoglobin molecules start to carry carbon monoxide instead of oxygen. As more and more haemoglobin molecules are occupied with carbon monoxide, they cannot carry oxygen. A concentration of more than 2% carbon monoxide in the air can be fatal in under 2 hours. Lower levels of carbon monoxide over long periods can cause brain damage.

Soot

In the home, the soot produced by the incomplete combustion of hydrocarbons can cause breathing problems, especially for people who suffer from asthma.

On an industrial scale, the soot from incomplete combustion poses a serious pollution problem. The particles of soot absorb some of the light from the Sun and are responsible for global dimming. They also speed up the condensation of water in the atmosphere, causing clouds to form.

QUESTIONS

6 Explain why even small amounts of carbon monoxide in the air can be toxic.

7 A patient brought to A&E was found unconscious in a small shed warmed by a portable kerosene heater. Why might the doctor diagnose the patient as suffering from carbon monoxide poisoning?

8 Suggest how carbon monoxide poisoning might be treated. You may use your own research to help you.

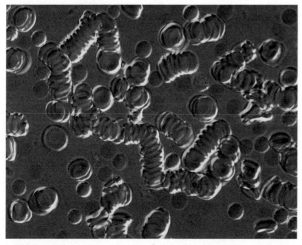

FIGURE 3: Red blood cells. The haemoglobin in these cells should be carrying oxygen, not carbon monoxide.

Q Haemoglobin   Carbon monoxide poisoning

Acid rain

You will find out:
> about sulfur impurities in hydrocarbons
> about the effects of sulfur impurities on the environment
> possible solutions to acid rain

No April shower

Imagine a world where trees are stripped bare, buildings crumble, and dead fish float on the surface of rivers and lakes. That is what happens when acid rain falls.

FIGURE 1: The effects of acid rain. What do you think this statue used to look like?

Destruction from the sky

Hydrocarbon fuels contain impurities. One of the most important of those impurities is sulfur. When sulfur impurities are burned with the hydrocarbon, the sulfur is oxidised to sulfur dioxide:

sulfur + oxygen → sulfur dioxide

The sulfur dioxide reacts with oxygen in the atmosphere to form sulfur trioxide. The sulfur trioxide then reacts with water in the atmosphere to form sulfuric acid:

sulfur trioxide + water → sulfuric acid

The sulfuric acid then dissolves in the rain, lowering the pH, and falls as **acid rain**, causing damage:

> increased weathering of buildings and statues

> damage to tree leaves leading to death of the trees

> lowered pH of soil reducing productivity of crops

> lowered pH of streams and ponds killing some organisms.

The damaging effects can be hundreds or thousands of kilometres from the source. The sulfur dioxide leading to the formation of sulfuric acid is carried by the atmosphere and seldom falls near the starting point of the pollution.

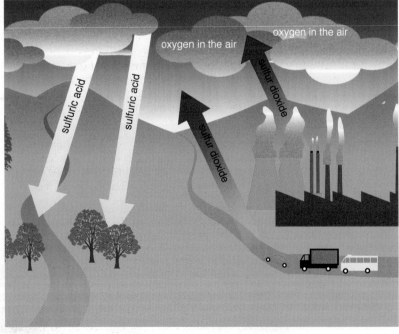

FIGURE 2: The formation of acid rain.

QUESTIONS

1 State the source of the sulfuric acid associated with acid rain.

2 State two ways that plants can be damaged by acid rain.

3 a Give the chemical formulae for sulfur, sulfur dioxide and sulfur trioxide. What pattern do you notice?

b Use your answer to part **a** to give the chemical equation for the oxidation of sulfur.

Flue gas desulfurisation   Effects of acid rain

The effects of acid rain

Rain is naturally acidic because of the carbon dioxide present in the atmosphere. However, the addition of the acid by-products of hydrocarbon combustion lowers the pH dramatically:

$$S\ (s) + O_2\ (g) \rightarrow SO_2\ (g)$$

$$2SO_2\ (g) + O_2\ (g) \rightarrow 2SO_3\ (g)$$

$$SO_3\ (g) + H_2O\ (l) \rightarrow H_2SO_4\ (aq)$$

The effects of acid rain can be seen on plants, animals and buildings. The leaves of trees are damaged by the acidic rain. This prevents them from being able to photosynthesise efficiently and eventually leads to their death.

As the acid rain falls on fields, it lowers the pH of the soil. Since most plants grow best in neutral soil, the plants fail to grow as well as they should, leading to a reduced yield.

Acid rain also lowers the pH of streams and ponds. Some organisms cannot tolerate the low pH and die. This can lead to the complete collapse of the **ecosystem**.

The limestone used to construct buildings and statues reacts with the acid rain to form calcium sulfate:

$$CaCO_3\ (s) + H_2SO_4\ (aq) \rightarrow CaSO_4\ (aq) + CO_2\ (g) + H_2O\ (l)$$

| calcium carbonate | + sulfuric acid → | calcium sulfate | + carbon dioxide | + water |

Calcium carbonate is not soluble in water; however, calcium sulfate is slightly soluble. It dissolves and is washed away.

FIGURE 3: Acid rain can lead to the entire destruction of forests.

FIGURE 4: Measuring the pH of soil. What is the pH of this soil?

QUESTIONS

4 Explain why acid rain causes the increased weathering of buildings and statues made of limestone or marble.

5 Explain how acid rain affects the food chain.

Solutions to acid rain

To reduce acid rain, the sulfur dioxide levels must be minimised. The use of low-sulfur coal is one way to reduce sulfur dioxide emissions. The sulfur content of coal can range from less than 0.5% to over 10%. Most of the coal burned in the UK is around 1–3%.

Another way to reduce emissions is to switch to natural gas, which is mainly methane. Natural gas contains only trace amounts of sulfur and produces even lower emissions than low-sulfur coal.

When switching fuels is impractical, the exhaust gases can be cleaned using scrubbers.

Education also plays a part in reducing emissions. If the public is educated in the need to reduce the amount of electricity used, then the amount of coal burned can be decreased, further minimising emissions.

By implementing these different methods, the UK is attempted to lower sulfur dioxide emissions from 4898 kilotonnes in 1980 to 980 kilotonnes in 2010.

QUESTIONS

6 Discuss the various methods of reducing sulfur dioxide emissions and their practical application.

Q Catalysts   Catalytic converters

Climate change

You will find out:
> how certain gases in the atmosphere help keep the Earth warm
> about human activities that may affect the Earth's temperature
> that carbon dioxide levels vary in the Earth's atmosphere

A transparent blanket

The Earth is surrounded by a layer of gas approximately 60 km thick. This relatively thin layer protects us from the dangerous radiation of the Sun and stabilises the temperature of the Earth.

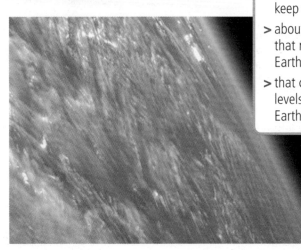

FIGURE 1: The Earth's atmosphere as seen from space.

Keeping warm

The atmosphere of the Earth provides a warm and stable environment for life by trapping heat from the Sun. The gases responsible for trapping this heat are called **greenhouse gases,** and they include:

> carbon dioxide

> methane

> water vapour.

The temperature of the Earth is affected by many variables, including solar activity, and so some variation in the Earth's temperature is normal.

Human activity can also have an effect on the temperature. Two activities that may affect the temperature of Earth are:

> burning fossil fuels for energy

> burning forests to clear land for farming.

These activities change the proportion of carbon dioxide in the atmosphere as they produce large quantities of the gas. Efforts are being made to try to reduce the amount of greenhouse gases in the atmosphere. Two methods that are currently being investigated include:

> iron seeding of oceans

> converting carbon dioxide into hydrocarbons.

These methods are still experimental but show promise for the future.

QUESTIONS

1 State the three gases responsible for the greenhouse effect.

2 Describe how human activities could affect the temperature of Earth.

3 Research iron seeding or the conversion of carbon dioxide to hydrocarbons. Write a short paragraph on your chosen topic to explain the concept to a classmate.

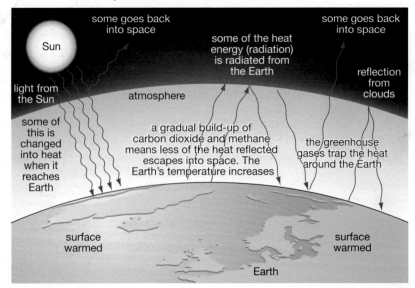

FIGURE 2: The greenhouse effect. Heat energy is trapped by the atmosphere.

Q Greenhouse effect   Greenhouse gases

The greenhouse effect

Carbon dioxide, methane and water vapour are able to absorb **infrared radiation**. Because these molecules absorb the infrared radiation, the heat energy is kept in the atmosphere. This retained heat energy is responsible for the increased temperature of the Earth and its atmosphere, known as the **greenhouse effect**.

Some scientists believe there is a correlation between the amount of carbon dioxide in the atmosphere and the temperature of the Earth. However, other scientists point out that a correlation does not prove a cause-and-effect relationship.

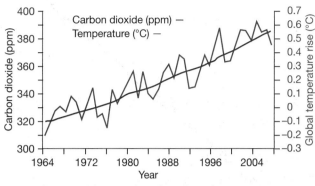

FIGURE 3: Atmospheric carbon dioxide and temperature.

QUESTIONS

4 Evaluate the relationship between carbon dioxide and 'global warming'.

5 Explain infrared radiation. (You can use your textbook to help you.)

Removing carbon dioxide from the atmosphere

Scientists are currently investigating methods that can be used to control the amount of carbon dioxide in the atmosphere. These methods are still in the experimental stages and require further study to determine their effectiveness.

Iron seeding

Algae are dependent on dissolved minerals for growth. Because of the low solubility of iron, it is usually the limiting factor in algal growth. Introducing iron into the upper levels of the ocean encourages the growth of algae there. The algae use the carbon dioxide for **photosynthesis** and this produces carbohydrates:

$$6CO_2 \text{ (g)} + 6H_2O \text{ (l)} \rightarrow C_6H_{12}O_6 \text{ (aq)} + 6O_2 \text{ (g)}$$
carbon dioxide + water $\rightarrow$ glucose + oxygen

There are also algae that make carbonate-based shells, which will increase the usage of carbon dioxide as their numbers increase.

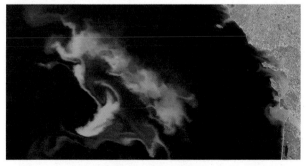

FIGURE 4: Algal bloom in the Bay of Biscay as seen from space.

From carbon dioxide to hydrocarbon

A more industrial approach to the problem involves converting carbon dioxide into hydrocarbons in a chemical process using **nanotechnology**. While this method is in the early stages, promising results have been achieved.

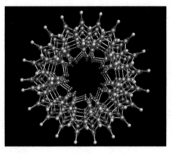

FIGURE 5: A nanotube. Nanotechnology can provide a suitable environment for the conversion of carbon dioxide to hydrocarbons.

Until these or other methods, such as reforestation, of lowering carbon dioxide levels are fully developed, the most effective way to reduce carbon dioxide levels is to reduce the amount of energy being used.

QUESTIONS

6 Describe how the addition of iron to the oceans could lead to a reduction in the amount of carbon dioxide in the atmosphere.

7 Describe ways in which you can lower the amount of carbon dioxide released into the atmosphere and discuss their advantages and disadvantages.

Biofuels

You will find out:
> why biofuels are an alternative to fossil fuels
> about ethanol as an example of a biofuel
> the advantages and disadvantages of biofuels
> the characteristics of a good fuel

It runs on chip fat

Almost every day there is news of another alternative fuel. Whether it is cars that run on chip fat or electricity, the search for alternative fuels has scientists all over the world working overtime.

FIGURE 1: A bus in Brighton. What makes used cooking oil a good alternative fuel?

Fuels from plants

As the supply of fossil fuels gets smaller and the cost of extracting them gets higher, alternative fuel sources become more important. **Biofuels** are one alternative to fossil fuels:

> Biofuels are fuels made from living or recently living material.

> Ethanol is a good example of a biofuel.

> Ethanol can be produced by processing sugar beets or sugar cane.

> The ethanol can then be used as an additive to reduce the amount of petrol used by internal combustion engines.

A big advantage of biofuels is that they are a **renewable resource**. That is, the sugar cane or sugar beets can be grown and converted to ethanol. The fields can be planted again to produce more ethanol.

As biofuels become more important, the disadvantages must also be considered:

> Farmland will be used to grow crops for biofuels rather than food. This could have a bad impact on food supplies, making food more expensive.

> Biofuels produce carbon dioxide too: when they are burned and also very likely when they are transported from place to place. This production of carbon dioxide needs to be evaluated and balanced against the carbon dioxide removed from the atmosphere by the growing biofuels.

QUESTIONS

1 State why biofuels have become more important.

2 Describe the advantages and disadvantages of biofuels.

3 Research other alternative fuels. Write a short paragraph (including images if possible) describing your findings.

FIGURE 2: Sugar cane (left) and sugar beets (right) are good raw materials for ethanol production.

Selecting a good fuel

The selection of good alternative fuels requires attention to many different factors. Each of these factors must be balanced with the others to find suitable alternatives to fossil fuels:

> For a substance to make a suitable fuel it must burn easily. It should ignite easily and burn in a controlled manner.

> Good fuels should burn cleanly. The fuel should not produce a lot of ash or smoke. Smoke and ash both contribute to air pollution. They need to be reduced as much as possible.

> It should contain almost no sulfur, so sulfur dioxide emissions are extremely low.

> The cost of making or modifying an engine.

> The amount of heat energy produced by alternative fuels needs to be similar to the fuel it is replacing. Vehicles should be able to travel at least an equal distance per unit volume of the alternative fuel as with petrol. The heat produced in our homes should be the same to prevent an increase in fuel costs.

> The storage and transport of fuels must also be considered. The alternative fuel should be easily stored and transported. The fuel should be safe to transport over public roads. It should also be close by so that long-distance transport can be avoided.

Did you know?

The proposed building of agrofuel power stations in the UK is the subject of much debate because of the possible harmful emissions and effects on global food production.

Remember!

Ethanol is extremely flammable. When used in the lab, special care must be taken.

QUESTIONS

4 How would you measure heat energy?

5 Explain why the amount of smoke and ash must be considered when selecting a fuel.

6 Describe the advantage ethanol has over fossil fuels when considering storage and transport.

7 Suggest which criteria ethanol might fulfil to make it a 'good alternative fuel'.

8 State whether you think any one criterion listed is more important than the others. Give a reason for your answer.

Ethanol production

Ethanol is produced by the **fermentation** of plant carbohydrates. Fermentation is a biochemical process; many organisms, like yeast, use carbohydrates as an energy source and produce ethanol as a by-product:

$$C_6H_{12}O_6 \text{ (aq)} \rightarrow 2C_2H_5OH \text{ (aq)} + 2CO_2 \text{ (g)}$$
$$\text{a sugar} \rightarrow \text{ethanol} + \text{carbon dioxide}$$

The yeast contains enzymes that are responsible for the conversion of sugar into ethanol and carbon dioxide. **Enzymes** are biological **catalysts**. Catalysts are compounds that allow chemical reactions to happen at a lower temperature. Enzymes are biological catalysts because they are complex molecules produced by living organisms.

QUESTIONS

9 Write the balanced chemical equation for the production of ethanol.

10 Explain why yeast is required to produce ethanol by fermentation.

11 Discuss the properties that a material would need to make a good source of biofuel.

FIGURE 3: An ethanol production plant.

Fuel cells

You will find out:
> about using fuel cells to combine hydrogen and oxygen to release energy
> about the advantages and disadvantages of using hydrogen to fuel cars
> about non-renewable fuels
> how fuels can be compared

Hydrogen power

For a long time scientists have understood that hydrogen is extremely flammable and can be used as a fuel. The Space Shuttle uses hydrogen in its main engines. Unfortunately, its flammability is also a big drawback.

FIGURE 1: The main engines of the Space Shuttle use hydrogen as a fuel source.

Cells and electricity

Internal combustion engines and most power stations use non-renewable resources.

> Internal combustion engines use fuels refined from crude oil: petrol, diesel oil and kerosene.

> Electrical power stations are fuelled by **fossil fuels**: coal, methane from natural gas and oil. Fossil fuels are **non-renewable** resources and replacements need to be found.

Hydrogen potentially could be used in place of petrol. Some advantages are:

> It is abundant in a stable compound (water).

> It does not produce pollutants.

Some of the disadvantages are:

> It is extremely flammable.

> The technology to produce, store and transport hydrogen is still being developed.

In an **electrochemical cell**, chemical energy is converted to electrical energy through **oxidation–reduction reactions**. The batteries used in a torch are an example of an electrochemical cell. The electrical energy will stop when the chemical reaction ends. A reaction stops when the reactants are used up.

One solution to this problem is to construct a cell where the reactants can be continuously replenished. This kind of cell is called a **fuel cell**.

FIGURE 2: Electrochemical cells. Why wouldn't you want to power your car with these?

One kind of fuel cell works by using hydrogen and oxygen. The hydrogen and oxygen react in the cell to release electrical energy and produce water as a by-product.

Fuel cells like this could:

> generate electrical energy as long as the supply of hydrogen and oxygen lasts

> replace internal combustion engines

> replace power plants that burn fossil fuels like coal or methane.

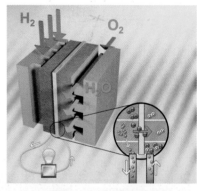

FIGURE 3: Drawing of a fuel cell showing the continuous supply of hydrogen and oxygen.

QUESTIONS

1 State whether the fuel used in an internal combustion engine is renewable or non-renewable.

2 State one advantage fuel cells have over electrochemical cells.

3 Give one advantage and one disadvantage of using hydrogen as a fuel.

4 Write a word equation to show the reaction that happens is a fuel cell.

Comparing fuels

Scientists can use a **calorimeter** to measure the amount of heat released by different fuels. A measured amount of water is placed in the calorimeter, which is then heated using a burner containing a known amount of fuel. The temperature increase in the water is measured and recorded. The amount of fuel used is also recorded.

The amount of energy released by the fuel is calculated by:

$$\text{mass of water} \times \text{the specific heat capacity of water} \times \text{the change in temperature}$$

Specific heat capacity is the amount of energy in **joules** (J) needed to raise the temperature of 1 kg of a substance 1 °C. The specific heat capacity of water is 4200 J/kg/°C.

If the temperature of 100 g of water is raised by 61 °C by 1.26 g of fuel then:

$$0.10 \text{ kg} \times 4200 \text{ J/kg/°C} \times 61 \text{ °C} = 25\,620 \text{ J}$$

This is the energy released by the fuel. To determine the amount of energy per gram of fuel, divide the energy produced by the mass of fuel used:

$$\text{energy per gram of fuel} = \frac{25\,620 \text{ J}}{1.26 \text{ g}} = 20\,333 \text{ J/g}$$

This is equivalent to 20.3 J/kg.

> ### QUESTIONS
>
> **5** Plan an experiment to investigate the difference in temperature rise when water is heated by a Bunsen burner and a candle.
>
> **6** Explain why it is necessary to compare fuels.
>
> **7** In an experiment 1.1 grams of fuel was required to raise the temperature of 100 g of water by 80 °C. Calculate the amount of heat energy released per gram of this fuel. Which is the better fuel: this or the one in the example?

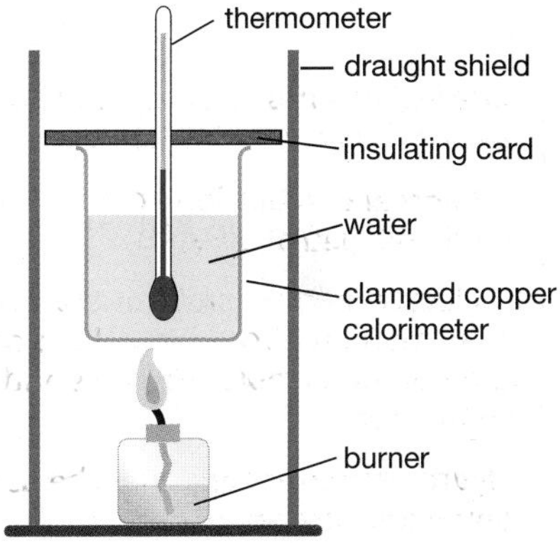

FIGURE 4: Diagram of a basic calorimeter.

[Diagram labels: thermometer, draught shield, insulating card, water, clamped copper calorimeter, burner]

Where does the hydrogen come from?

At present, there is no system in place to provide hydrogen in road-side service stations, as there is for petrol. Another problem is the flammability of hydrogen, which would require special containers to transport it in cars or buses.

One possible solution to these problems is to produce the hydrogen on demand. Research has shown that petrol heated in the presence of steam produces large quantities of hydrogen. This hydrogen could be used to power a fuel cell. While this system still uses petrol, the petrol is not used in an internal combustion engine and therefore is pollution free. The efficiency is almost double that of the most efficient internal combustion engines, achieving 80 mpg.

This one solution eliminates both problems. There is no need for an extensive production and supply system. In addition, there is never a large quantity of hydrogen being stored in vehicles since it is being made on demand.

FIGURE 5: Hydrogen fuel cell bus being tested in England.

> ### QUESTIONS
>
> **8** Evaluate the advantages of producing hydrogen on demand to be used in a fuel cell.

Alkanes

You will find out:

> what is in natural gas
> about alkanes
> how to draw the structure of alkanes

It's a gas

Hydrocarbon gas heats our homes, cooks our food and fuels some of our power stations. Where does it come from?

FIGURE 1: An oil and gas rig. Alkanes are present in crude oil.

Natural gas

Natural gas is found in underground deposits usually associated with crude oil. The main gases found in natural gas are:

> methane

> ethane

> propane.

These three gases all share certain characteristics:

> They all are **hydrocarbons** and present in crude oil.

> Their formulae all follow a pattern of $C_nH_{(2n+2)}$.

> Their names all end in -ane.

Chemists refer to a group of compounds like this as a **homologous series**. A homologous series changes in some consistent way. In this case, a CH_2 group is added in going from one alkane to the next. This homologous series is called the **alkanes**. The name of all alkanes ends with -ane.

The structure and formulae of these compounds are shown in Table 1. Notice that:

> Each carbon is bonded to four other atoms by single bonds.

> The single bonds are shown by a single straight line.

Carbon can form four bonds. Because each of these four bonds is linked to a different atom these alkane molecules are called **saturated hydrocarbons**.

QUESTIONS

1 Describe the characteristics that all alkanes have in common.

2 Define saturated hydrocarbons.

3 Give the formula for the alkane that has 12 hydrogen atoms and five carbon atoms.

TABLE 1: The structure and formulae of methane, ethane and propane.

Hydrocarbon	Formula and structure		No. of carbon atoms	State
Methane	CH_4 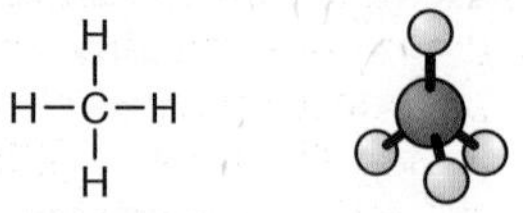	H–C–H with H above and below	1	Gas
Ethane	C_2H_6 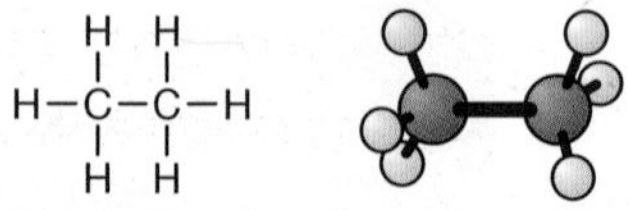	H–C–C–H structure	2	Gas
Propane	C_3H_8 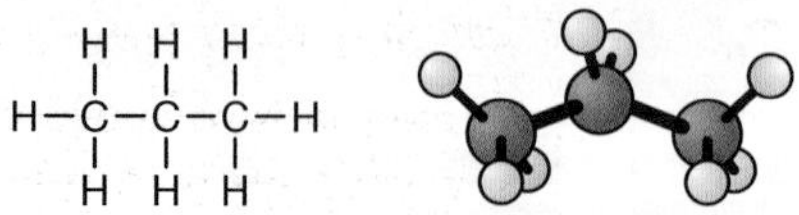	H–C–C–C–H structure	3	Gas

Uses of alkanes

Natural gas is a mixture of hydrocarbons that have one, two or three carbon atoms in each molecule. Methane makes up the largest percentage (70–90%) of natural gas. Ethane and propane are the next largest portions.

TABLE 2: Typical composition of natural gas.

Substance	Formula	Volume (%)
Methane	CH_4	70–90
Ethane	C_2H_6	0–20
Propane	C_3H_8	
Butane	C_4H_{10}	
Carbon dioxide	CO_2	0–8
Oxygen	O_2	0–0.2
Nitrogen	N_2	0–5
Hydrogen sulfide	H_2S	0–5
Rare gases	Ar, He, Ne, Xe	Trace

Methane

Methane is separated and piped into our homes to fuel our heaters and cookers. It is also used in power stations. Characteristics that make methane a good fuel are:

> It produces less carbon dioxide than other fuels.

> It produces the most heat for its mass.

Ethane

The ethane separated from natural gas is used mainly for industrial processes. These include the production of very large molecules called **polymers**.

Propane

Propane has the advantage that it can be converted to a liquid under pressure. This liquid form of propane is called liquid petroleum gas (LPG). LPG can be used to power vehicles. Easily transported, it can be used in rural areas where piped natural gas may not be available.

QUESTIONS

4 Draw the structure of butane.

5 Draw a graph or chart to represent the composition of natural gas.

6 Explain why methane is the preferred gas for heating our homes and power stations.

7 Write chemical equations for the complete combustion (see pages 144–5) of methane and propane.

Covalent bonding

Alkanes are fairly unreactive molecules. They can be burned but don't do much else. This is because the atoms are covalently bonded.

Covalent bonding is the sharing of electrons. Atoms share electrons to increase their stability. An atom is composed of a central core, the **nucleus**, surrounded by **electrons**. Electrons are arranged in **shells** like the layers of an onion. The innermost shell can hold two electrons. The next shell can hold eight electrons. Atoms are most stable when their outer shell is full or contains eight electrons.

Carbon has an **atomic number** of 6. The atomic number is the number of **protons** in

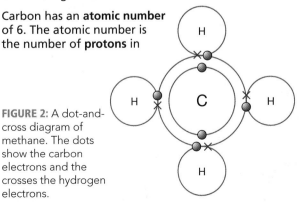

FIGURE 2: A dot-and-cross diagram of methane. The dots show the carbon electrons and the crosses the hydrogen electrons.

the nucleus. It is also usually the number of electrons. Carbon has six protons in its nucleus. Therefore, carbon has six electrons; two in the innermost shell and four in the next shell. Carbon needs four more electrons to achieve stability.

Hydrogen has an atomic number of 1. Hydrogen has one proton in its nucleus and one electron surrounding the nucleus. Hydrogen needs one more electron to achieve a stable electron configuration.

When hydrogen and carbon encounter each other, they attempt to take an outer shell electron to help them reach stability. This leads to a situation where two electrons are held between the nuclei of the two atoms. The atoms are bonded together by this attraction to electrons.

QUESTIONS

8 Draw dot-and-cross diagrams to show the bonding in methane and ethane.

9 Use the term 'covalent bonding' to explain how propane is formed.

Alkenes

Fruit and veg don't always get ripened by the Sun

Alkenes have many uses but perhaps the most unexpected is their use to ripen fruit and vegetables. It has been found that plants use an alkene naturally as a plant hormone and growers can increase ripening by storing produce in a room with a high level of this alkene.

FIGURE 1: Fruit hanging in a market stall ripens naturally.

You will find out:

> about unsaturated hydrocarbons called alkenes

> how to draw the structure of alkenes

> about a laboratory test to distinguish between alkanes and alkenes

Unsaturated hydrocarbons

Unsaturated hydrocarbons:

> all have one double bond between a pair of adjacent carbon atoms

> have the general formula C_nH_{2n}

> have names that end in -ene

> belong to the **homologous series** called alkenes.

The presence of the double bond makes alkenes much more reactive than alkanes.

Ethene

Ethene is an **unsaturated hydrocarbon** with a formula of C_2H_4. Compare ethene with ethane in Figure 2:

> The two carbons are double-bonded to each other in ethene.

> The ending of the name is different from the alkanes that were discussed on pages 156–7.

The second bond between the carbons prevents each carbon being bonded to another hydrogen atom. The molecule is therefore described as unsaturated. Ethene is often used commercially to cause fruit and vegetables to ripen artificially.

Propene

The next alkene in the series is propene:

> Like propane, it has three carbons.

> Like ethene, it has a carbon to carbon double bond.

Propene is a raw material in many different industrial processes.

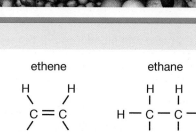

FIGURE 2: The structure of ethene and ethane.

Bromine water test

One method chemists can use to tell the difference between alkanes and alkenes is by their reaction with bromine water:

> Bromine water has a brownish tint.

> When added to alkenes the bromine reacts and becomes colourless.

> With alkanes there is no reaction so the bromine water remains brownish.

The brownish colour of bromine disappears because it reacts with the double covalent bond of the alkene. This is called an addition reaction, because the bromine is added in place of the double bond (see Figure 3).

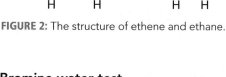

FIGURE 3: How bromine water is decoloured by ethene.

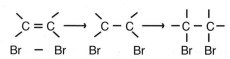

Forced ripening   Important alkenes

FIGURE 4: Bromine water is decolourised by alkenes.

More than fuel from crude oil

Hydrocarbons belong to a large group of compounds called **organic compounds**. Organic compounds all contain carbon and hydrogen. The name comes from the fact that people used to think that these compounds all came from living or once-living organisms.

As our knowledge of organic compounds has increased, we have developed the ability to synthesise some organic compounds in the laboratory. Crude oil is an important raw material in this synthesis because it consists of a wide range of long-chain hydrocarbons that can be modified to produce other organic compounds.

One of the most important groups of organic compounds synthesised in the lab is the penicillin-like **antibiotics**. These compounds allow us to treat a wide range of infections.

Did you know?

More ethene is produced industrially than any other organic compound. This is because of its usefulness in many different chemical-manufacturing processes.

Naming organic compounds

When naming organic compounds there are strict rules that must be followed. These rules are established by the International Union of Pure and Applied Chemistry (IUPAC). This ensures that all chemists around the world are talking about the same compound.

The first consideration when naming organic compounds is the length of the longest carbon chain. The number of carbons is indicated by a prefix for that number (see Table 1).

TABLE 1: Prefixes used in naming organic compounds.

Number of carbon atoms	Prefix
1	Meth-
2	Eth-
3	Prop-
4	But-
5	Pent-

The next thing to consider is the type of bonding present in the chain. As we have already seen, saturated hydrocarbon chains are called alkanes and

the suffix -ane is used. If there is only a single carbon in the chain and it is saturated; this gives us methane.

If the number of carbons is increased to two, the prefix used will be eth-. The next question needing an answer is the type of bonding. As both of the carbons are saturated then the name must be ethane. However, if the carbons are double-bonded the name would have to be ethene.

Cracking

You will find out:
> about the cracking of long-chain hydrocarbons
> why cracking is necessary

Big becomes small

It is the dream of every business person: take a product that no one wants and change it into something everyone wants. That is exactly what the cracking of hydrocarbons does.

FIGURE 1: Catalytic cracking facility at a petroleum refinery.

Breaking the chain

Not all crude oil is the same. The composition can vary considerably from location to location. The most desirable crude oil contains a high percentage of short-chain hydrocarbons. This type of crude oil is referred to as light sweet crude and can contain as much as 97% short-chain hydrocarbons. The heavier crude oils can contain less than 50% short-chain hydrocarbons.

Cracking is a technique that:

> splits long-chain saturated hydrocarbons (alkanes) into short-chain hydrocarbons of various lengths

> produces alkanes, alkenes and sometimes hydrogen.

Some hydrocarbons can be cracked in more than one way. The following shows two ways that butane can be cracked:

butane   →   ethane   +   ethene

butane   →   methane   +   propene

Did you know?

Short- and medium-chain hydrocarbons are especially important in making petrol.

Figure 2 shows a set-up to allow the cracking of **paraffin** in the laboratory. This arrangement uses aluminium oxide as a **catalyst**. The test-tube containing the paraffin is heated. This heats the aluminium oxide and causes the paraffin to vaporise. As the paraffin vapour passes over the catalyst, the **thermal decomposition** of the paraffin occurs, producing hydrocarbon gases that are collected in the other test-tube.

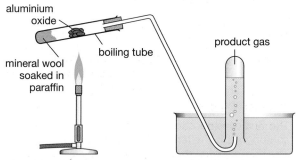

FIGURE 2: Laboratory apparatus to crack hydrocarbons.

QUESTIONS

1 Explain why light sweet crude oil is the most desirable.

2 Explain what heating accomplishes in the laboratory cracking of paraffin.

3 State the two products of cracking long-chain hydrocarbons.

4 Which process produces paraffin?

Catalysts

Catalysts are an important part of chemistry. Chemists, and especially chemical engineers, spend a good deal of time trying to make reactions happen more quickly. The speed at which a reaction happens is called the **rate of reaction**. Catalysts increase the rate of reaction without being used up in the reaction.

Several factors affect the rate of reaction. Heating will increase the rate of reaction. However, this may not be practical as the amount of energy required could make the process too expensive.

Catalysts allow reactions to happen at a rate achieved by higher temperatures without actually raising the reaction to that temperature. For example, the cracking of hydrocarbons without a catalyst usually requires temperatures above 850 °C, while the addition of a catalyst allows the same reaction to occur at 750 °C.

While 100 °C may not sound that significant, when applied to an industrial scale like the cracking plant in Figure 1 the savings can be very important. Aluminium oxide can be used as a catalyst in the cracking of long-chain hydrocarbons.

QUESTIONS

5 Describe a catalyst.

6 Explain why chemical engineers would be interested in speeding up reactions.

7 Butane can be cracked in two ways. Represent these two ways as an equation and a structure diagram.

8 Hydrogen peroxide (H_2O_2) can be decomposed to form water and oxygen. Write a word equation and balanced symbol equation for this reaction.

Why is cracking necessary? (Higher tier only)

For many years oil companies selectively pumped up light sweet crude from underground deposits because it contained the highest percentage of short-chain hydrocarbons. As supplies of light sweet crude are used up the reliance on the heavier crude increases. The cracking of long-chain hydrocarbons has become more important as a way to meet the demand for short-chain hydrocarbons.

TABLE 1: Comparison of the supply and demand of the different fractions obtained from a typical crude oil.

Fraction	Approximate composition of supply (%)	Approximate demand (%)
Petroleum gases	2	4
Petrol and naphtha	16	27
Kerosene	13	8
Diesel	19	23
Fuel oil and bitumen	50	38

Decane has a very limited usefulness. By cracking decane, it is possible to produce two useful products, an alkane and an alkene:

$$C_{10}H_{22} \text{ (l)} \rightarrow C_8H_{18} \text{ (l)} + C_2H_4 \text{ (g)}$$

$$\text{decane} \rightarrow \text{octane} + \text{ethene}$$

Octane is used as petrol and ethene is an important chemical in polymer production.

FIGURE 3: Crude oil being pumped from underground reserves.

QUESTIONS

9 Explain why cracking is necessary.

10 State which fractions are most in demand and why.

11 Discuss possible solutions to the reduced supply of light sweet crude oil. Use data from Table 1 in your answer.

Remember!

Kerosene is more commonly called paraffin in the UK.

Making polymers

You will find out:

> that ethene can be used to make polymers

> about the properties of polymers and their uses

> how other alkenes are used to make polymers

Fantastic plastic

Look around the room. What would it look like if all of the plastic items were to disappear? Would you find yourself sitting on a bare concrete floor? What about your book bag and the clothes you are wearing?

FIGURE 1: Just a few of the uses of polymers.

Making the chain

Ethene is produced by the cracking of long-chain hydrocarbons and is produced in larger quantities than any other organic compound. Ethene is an important ingredient in the production of **polymers**. Polymers are:

> very large molecules

> made by connecting many smaller molecules together

> made from alkenes.

The smaller molecules are called **monomers**.

Large numbers of ethene molecules are linked together to form long chains of repeating molecules in a **polymerisation reaction**. The compound formed is called poly(ethene) or more commonly polythene. 'Poly' indicates that it is a polymer; ethene is the name of the monomer.

These polymers are usually referred to as plastics. However, in science the term **plastic** means that a substance can be shaped or moulded.

Table 1 shows other important polymers made from alkene monomers. Each of these polymers has specific properties that make it best suited for specific uses. These properties are determined by the monomers that are used to create them.

QUESTIONS

1 State another name for plastics.

2 Using Table 1, explain why ethene is produced in such large quantities.

3 Explain what makes
   a poly(chloroethene) and
   b poly(tetrafluoroethene)
   suitable for their purposes.

TABLE 1: Some important polymers.

Name	Properties	Uses
Poly(ethene)	Waterproof, strong, cheap, easily moulded	Shrink wrap, carrier bags, kitchen utensils
Poly(propene)	Strong, hard, can be moulded	Packing crates, rope, furniture
Poly(chloroethene) (PVC)	Flexible, good insulator, cheap	Raincoats, Wellington boots, insulator on wire
Poly(tetrafluoroethene) (PTFE)	Inert, shiny, very slick	Non-stick pans, waterproof fabrics

The chemistry of polymerisation

Under the right conditions, molecules of ethene can be linked together. Those conditions include:

> high temperatures

> high pressure

> presence of a catalyst.

Under these circumstances one of the bonds between the carbons breaks. This enables the ethene molecule to form a bond with another ethene molecule. Ethene molecules can be added to the growing chain indefinitely. This is referred to as **addition polymerisation**.

Bakelite   Vulcanisation

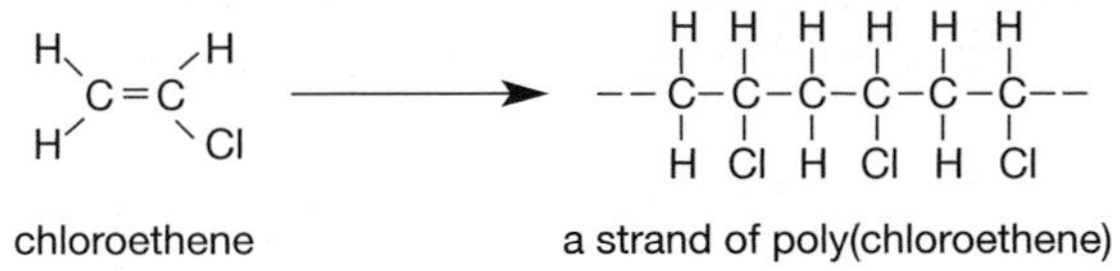

chloroethene

a strand of poly(chloroethene)

FIGURE 2: An equation showing polymerisation from ethene.

These long chains act as threads that interweave. These interwoven 'molecular threads' can then be formed into long fibres or flat sheets of various thicknesses.

The long fibres can then be used just like natural fibres to make fabrics or woven to produce string or rope. The flat sheets can be moulded into almost any imaginable shape, making polymers one of the most versatile materials in the world today.

QUESTIONS

4 Describe the process of addition polymerisation of poly(ethene).

5 Discuss how the molecular structure of polymers makes them so versatile.

Modifying properties of polymers (Higher tier only)

The properties of polymers can be modified by using different monomers. Think of the differences between cling film, a 'plastic' spoon and a foam cup. These three represent three different polymers made using different monomers.

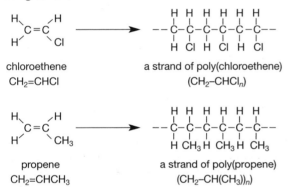

chloroethene
$CH_2=CHCl$

a strand of poly(chloroethene)
(CH_2-CHCl_n)

propene
$CH_2=CHCH_3$

a strand of poly(propene)
$(CH_2-CH(CH_3))_n)$

FIGURE 3: Two equations showing polymerisation from two different monomers.

Another way to modify the properties of polymers is to cause chemical bonds to form between the individual chains of polymers. The **cross-linking** between the individual chains strengthens the polymers and makes them more rigid. The more cross-links that are formed, the more rigid the polymer.

QUESTIONS

6 Explain why aircraft windows are made of thermosetting polymers.

7 The structure of tetrafluoroethene is:

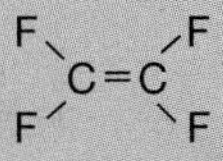

Draw the structure of the polymer, called PTFE, which could be obtained from this molecule.

Polymers that do not contain cross-links can be heated and reshaped and are referred to as **thermosoftening** polymers (see Figure 4). Poly(ethene) is an example of a thermosoftening polymer.

Polymers that form large numbers of cross-links when cooled are called **thermosetting** polymers (see Figure 5). The polymer used to make aircraft windows is an example of a thermosetting polymer.

Thermosetting polymers cannot be melted again and reshaped as they decompose when reheated.

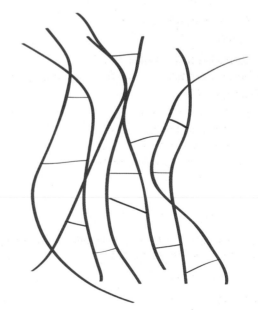

FIGURE 4: Drawing showing how individual polymer fibres interact.

FIGURE 5: Drawing showing the cross-links between polymer chains in thermosetting polymers.

Disposing of polymers

You will find out:
> about the problems associated with the disposal of polymers
> how polymers can be recycled
> how biodegradable polymers are developed

They won't go away

If you had asked chemists 100 years ago to make a substance that would last for thousands of years, they would have said it was impossible. Today, however, chemists are being asked to suggest methods for the disposal of polymers that seem almost indestructible.

ALEC GUINNESS
JOAN GREENWOOD
CECIL PARKER

THE MAN IN THE WHITE SUIT

FIGURE 1: *The Man in the White Suit.* In this 1951 comedy film, a chemist invents a fabric that never gets dirty and never wears out. What problems might this cause?

Recycling polymers

One of the properties of polymers that makes them such an important material also causes one of the biggest problems. They seem to last forever. Most polymers:

> are not **biodegradable** (they do not decompose), unlike paper

> produce toxic compounds when burned, such as hydrochloric acid which contributes to acid rain.

Because of these problems, **recycling** is the best possible solution to disposing of polymers. Recycling means converting the unwanted polymers into a usable product.

FIGURE 2: Shredded polymers at a recycling plant.

Over 5 million tonnes of polymers is used in the UK every year. It is estimated that only 19% of those polymers are currently being recycled. Recycling offers several benefits:

> reduction of polymers in landfills

> less oil being used in the production of polymers

> less energy used in production.

Another possible solution to the problem of unwanted polymers is the development of biodegradable polymers. Two types of biodegradable polymers are currently being produced. One is being used to make takeaway food containers. The other is being used for packaging and carrier bags.

QUESTIONS

1 Define biodegradable.

2 Explain the advantages of recycling polymers.

3 Design a poster encouraging homeowners to recycle their polymers.

Complications

With all of the benefits of recycling, why is it not more widespread? The first problem is that most people throw polymers away without even thinking about it. This situation is being addressed by education programmes that inform the public about recycling.

Another problem with recycling polymers stems from their chemical properties. Because of the extremely long length of the carbon chains, polymers made from different monomers do not mix easily when heated to melting. The liquid separates into layers, like oil and water do.

To solve this problem, items have to be sorted before reprocessing. The sorting is made easier by the use of a code that indicates the type of polymer. This identification code is international and is used to sort polymers in the recycling process. Each polymer is indicated by a specific code (see Table 1). The code consists of a number and an abbreviation.

These recycling codes allow for the efficient sorting and recycling of polymers around the world.

TABLE 1: Recycling codes for common polymers.

Symbol	Common name	Examples	Recyclable?	Symbol	Common name	Examples	Recyclable?
1 PET or PETE	Polyethylene terephthalate (PET)	Bottles for fizzy drinks, mineral water, squashes and cooking oils	Recycling points are located throughout the UK	3 PVC or V	Polyvinyl chloride (PVC)	Usually in bottle form; however, not that common these days	Some recycling points in the UK
2 HDPE	High-density polyethylene (HDPE)	Milk bottles Juice bottles Washing-up liquid Bath and shower bottles	Recycling points are located throughout the UK	4 LDPE	Low-density polyethylene (LDPE)	Many types of packing are made from these materials; for example, plastic formed around meats and vegetables	Due to the mixture of compounds these plastic types are hard to recycle and are not generally recycled in the UK
				5 PP	Polypropylene (PP)		
				6 PS	Polystyrene (PS)		
				7 OTHER	Other. All other resins and multimaterials		

QUESTIONS

4 Describe the steps being taken to increase polymer recycling.

5 Explain why polymers must be sorted for recycling.

6 Why are plastic bottles more difficult to recycle than metal drinks cans?

7 Research recycling programmes and write a report on one that is particularly innovative or successful, in the UK or worldwide.

Future polymers

When considering the future of polymers two different ideas need to be considered. The first idea is the production of biodegradable polymers. This involves polymers that will decompose either in compost heaps or in landfills. The other idea is the production of polymers from renewable resources like plant material.

Biodegradable polymers are polymers that can be decomposed by microorganisms in the environment. This would reduce the environmental impact of the polymers.

One way to produce biodegradable polymers is to include additives in oil-based polymers that make them easier for microorganisms to break them down. Another possible solution is to make them out of compounds that are made by living organisms rather than from crude oil.

Plants already produce large polymers in the form of **starch** and **cellulose**. If these polymers could be used to produce materials with the necessary properties to replace oil-based polymers it would solve both problems at once. Polymers made from renewable resources reduce the demand for crude oil and are biodegradable.

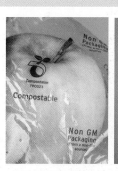

FIGURE 3: How could you dispose of all of the things in these pictures?

QUESTIONS

8 Explain two problems associated with the high use of polymers.

9 Discuss how polymers made from renewable resources could have a double benefit.

10 Dehydrating ethanol gives ethene.

a Write the equation that proves this.

b How is this process beneficial?

Preparing for assessment: Analysis and conclusions

To achieve a good grade in science, you not only have to know and understand scientific ideas, but you also need to be able to apply them to other situations and investigations. This task will support you in developing these skills.

✳ Task

> Test the hypothesis that the more carbon atoms there are in a fuel molecule the more energy it releases per gram.

✳ Context

When hydrocarbons burn they react with oxygen to make carbon dioxide and water vapour. In the process, the bonds between the atoms in the fuel molecule break and new bonds form with oxygen. The energy that fuels release can be compared by using them to raise the temperature of a fixed mass of water.

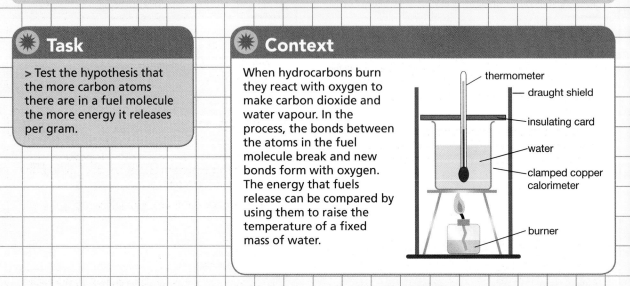

thermometer
draught shield
insulating card
water
clamped copper calorimeter
burner

✳ Method and results

Each hydrocarbon was used to make 100 cm³ of water 10 °C hotter. The experiment was set up as shown in the diagram above. The results are shown in the table below.

Fuel	Number of carbon atoms	Mass of burner at start (g)	Mass of burner at end (g)	Mass of fuel used (g)	Average mass used (g)	Temperature rise (°C/g)
Methanol	1	158.32	157.24	1.08	1.10	10/1.1 = 9.1
		155.31	154.19	1.12		
Ethanol	2	168.43	167.67	0.76	0.80	10/0.8 = 12.5
		203.86	203.02	0.84		
Propanol	3	173.45	172.77			
		198.23	197.51			
Butanol	4	142.52	141.90			
		123.23	122.65			
Pentanol	5	173.91	173.24			
		134.74	134.21			

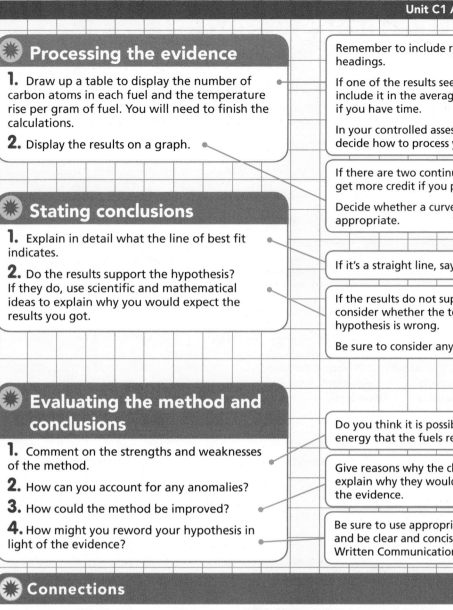

Processing the evidence

1. Draw up a table to display the number of carbon atoms in each fuel and the temperature rise per gram of fuel. You will need to finish the calculations.

2. Display the results on a graph.

Remember to include relevant units in the table headings.

If one of the results seems anomalous, don't include it in the average. Repeat the experiment if you have time.

In your controlled assessment you will be need to decide how to process your data by yourself.

If there are two continuous variables you always get more credit if you plot a line graph.

Decide whether a curve or line of best fit is more appropriate.

Stating conclusions

1. Explain in detail what the line of best fit indicates.

2. Do the results support the hypothesis? If they do, use scientific and mathematical ideas to explain why you would expect the results you got.

If it's a straight line, say so.

If the results do not support the hypothesis, consider whether the test method is faulty or the hypothesis is wrong.

Be sure to consider any anomalies.

Evaluating the method and conclusions

1. Comment on the strengths and weaknesses of the method.

2. How can you account for any anomalies?

3. How could the method be improved?

4. How might you reword your hypothesis in light of the evidence?

Do you think it is possible to collect all the heat energy that the fuels release?

Give reasons why the changes are needed and explain why they would improve the quality of the evidence.

Be sure to use appropriate scientific language, and be clear and concise to obtain Quality of Written Communication marks.

Connections

How Science Works

> Collecting and analysing data.

> Interpreting data to provide evidence for testing ideas and developing theories.

> Collecting data from secondary sources.

> Working accurately and safely when collecting first-hand data.

> Evaluating methods of data collection and verifying information sources.

> Using both qualitative and quantitative approaches.

> Presenting information using appropriate language, conventions and symbols and tools.

Maths in Science

> Understand number size and scale and the quantitative relationship between units.

> Understand and use direct proportion and simple ratios.

> Calculate arithmetic means.

> Understand and use common measures and simple compound measures such as speed.

> Plot and draw graphs selecting appropriate scales for the axes.

> Translate information between graphical and numeric forms.

> Extract and interpret information from charts, graphs and tables.

C1 checklist (Topics 4 and 5)

To achieve your forecast grade in the exam you'll need to revise

Use this checklist to see what you can do now. Refer back to pages 132–65 if you're not sure.

Look across the rows to see how you could progress – *bold italic* means Higher tier only.

Remember you'll need to be able to use these ideas in various ways, such as:
> interpreting pictures, diagrams and graphs
> applying ideas to new situations
> explaining ethical implications
> suggesting some benefits and risks to society
> drawing conclusions from evidence you've been given.

Look at pages 270–92 for more information about exams and how you'll be assessed.

To aim for a grade E	To aim for a grade C	To aim for a grade A
recall that most metals are extracted from ores found in the Earth's crust	explain why some ores are extracted by heating with carbon and some are extracted by electrolysis	use the reactivity series to decide on an extraction technique
define oxidation as the gaining of oxygen and reduction as the loss of oxygen	describe oxidation and reduction using examples	compare oxidation and reduction and relate them to the corrosion and extraction of metals
recall the properties of metals	describe the uses of metals based on their properties	apply understanding of how the properties of a metal affect how it is used
recall that alloys are two or more metals combined to change their properties	describe iron alloys and their properties use models to explain why alloys have different properties	*describe special alloys, such as gold alloys and shape memory alloys* *explain the practical application of these alloys*
describe the importance of recycling metals		discuss the advantages of recycling metals, using the reduction in greenhouse gases as an example
describe hydrocarbons as molecules composed of hydrogen and carbon	explain how crude oil is separated into useful mixtures through the process of fractional distillation explain the properties that make certain fractions of crude oil useful	
describe the products of complete and incomplete combustion, including the toxic gas carbon monoxide	explain why incomplete combustion produces soot and carbon monoxide	explain why carbon monoxide and soot are problematic products of incomplete combustion suggest how to prevent carbon monoxide poisoning

To aim for a grade E   To aim for a grade C   To aim for a grade A

To aim for a grade E	To aim for a grade C	To aim for a grade A
recall that acid rain is caused by impurities in hydrocarbon fuels	describe the effects of acid rain	discuss solutions to the problem of acid rain
recall that carbon dioxide, methane and water vapour trap heat in the atmosphere recall that human activities can change the amount of carbon dioxide in the atmosphere	evaluate the relationship between global temperature and the amount of carbon dioxide in the atmosphere	discuss how carbon dioxide can be removed from the atmosphere using iron seeding and nanotechnology
recall that fossil fuels are non-renewable resources and describe ethanol as a possible alternative to fossil fuels describe how ethanol is formed from sugar cane or sugar beet		discuss the advantages and disadvantages of replacing fossil fuels with biofuels
understand the factors that make a good fuel	plan and carry out an investigation to compare fuels	use data to evaluate the factors that make a good fuel
recall that fuel cells combine hydrogen and oxygen to release energy	evaluate the advantages and disadvantages of replacing petrol with hydrogen	
recall that alkanes are saturated hydrocarbons and alkenes are unsaturated hydrocarbons	describe the uses of alkanes	write the formulae and draw the structures of some alkanes and alkenes
recall that bromine water can be used to distinguish between alkanes and alkenes	explain how to use bromine water safely to distinguish between alkanes and alkenes	
describe cracking as the breaking down of large hydrocarbons into smaller ones describe how to carry out cracking in the laboratory	describe the use of cracking to convert long-chain hydrocarbons into useful shorter hydrocarbons and some alkenes	*explain the importance of cracking in meeting the demand for short-chain hydrocarbons and the production of alkenes*
define polymers as large molecules made from smaller molecules, and relate the properties of polymers to their uses	describe the production of various polymers using different alkenes	*explain how the properties of polymers can be altered by the use of different alkenes*
recall that most polymers are not biodegradable	describe some of the problems caused by non-biodegradable polymers	discuss how the problems associated with non-biodegradable polymers can be overcome

1 St Paul's Cathedral is made from limestone. Since it was built, 1.5 cm of limestone has been lost from its surface. The culprit is acid rain. Battersea power station, closed in 1983, was blamed for the acid rain.

AO1 **a** Put these events in order to explain how acid rain forms:

    1 sulfur dioxide reacts with oxygen and water to make sulfuric acid

    2 the pH of rain water falls

    3 fuels like coal have sulfur impurities

    4 sulfur burns in the air (oxygen) to make sulfur dioxide [2]

AO1 **b** Limestone is calcium carbonate. Finish the word equation to show how acid rain weathered St Paul's.

calcium carbonate + sulfuric acid → _____ + _____ + _____ [3]

AO3 **c** Look at these two pieces of information:

    A Between 1980 and 1990 St Paul's Cathedral lost 0.5 mm from its surface. Between 1990 and 2000, it lost 0.25 mm.

    B Battersea power station is south-west of St Paul's Cathedral. Up to 1983, the south-west corner of St Paul's weathered at ten times the rate of the rest of the cathedral. Now it weathers at the same rate.

    i Suggest a reason for A [1]

    ii Suggest a reason for B [1]

[Total: 7]

2 The fruit in supermarkets is always just about right to eat. Suppliers use ethene gas to control how quickly the fruit ripens.

Ethene is

AO2 **a** **i** Complete the molecular formula for ethene: C_H_ [2]

AO1 **ii** What part of the displayed formula shows a double bond? [1]

AO2 **b** The suppliers can check to see if ethene is present by bubbling the atmosphere through orange bromine water. What will they see if ethene is present? [1]

AO2 **c** Supermarkets also rely on ethene to make its plastic bags. Ethene is used to make the plastic poly(ethene). What is this process called?

    A poly(chloroethene)

    B polymerisation

    C cracking

    D fractional distillation [1]

AO2 **d** Supermarkets sell reuseable shopping bags because disposing of plastics like poly(ethene) in landfill sites is a problem.

    i Why is poly(ethene) a problem in landfill sites? [1]

AO3 **ii** One solution is to recycle plastics. Discuss the benefits and drawbacks of recycling plastics. [6]

[Total: 12]

3 Gold makes impressive jewellery that stays shiny. Objects made from pure iron quickly corrode.

AO1 **a** Why doesn't gold corrode? [1]

AO1 **b** When iron corrodes, it reacts with oxygen (and water) in the air. Is this:

    A oxidation

    B reduction

    C extraction

    D decomposition? [1]

AO1 **c** Iron ore is iron oxide. Describe a link between iron ore and iron corroding. [1]

AO2 **d** Iron ore is heated with carbon to extract iron, but gold occurs as the element in the Earth. Describe where you would expect to find iron and gold in the reactivity series and give a reason. [4]

AO2 **e** Most of the iron we produce is converted to steel. Steel is an alloy. Explain why we have more uses for steel than pure iron. [2]

[Total: 9]

Worked example

1 Laura is finding out where the substances used to make her lipstick came from. She thinks the waxes and colours in her lipstick started off in a barrel of crude oil.

AO1 **a** The mixture of chemicals in crude oil is separated in an oil refinery. What do we call the separated groups of chemicals?

    A fractional distillation
    B polymerisation
    C polymers
    D fractions   [1]

Fractional distillation. ✗

b Chemicals in crude oil are separated by their boiling points.

AO1 **i** What happens to the temperature inside the fractionating column as you go up?   [1]

It is heated at the bottom so it stays hot. ✗

AO2 **ii** Which letter on the diagram shows where chemicals with the lowest boiling point are collected?   [1]

A ✔

AO2 **iii** The waxes in Laura's lipstick have long carbon chains in their molecules. Suggest where these might be collected on the diagram.   [1]

F ✔

AO2 **iv** Apart from boiling point and the length of the carbon chain, give another difference between chemicals collected at the top of the fractionating column and at the bottom.   [2]

The chemicals from the bottom of the column are dark in colour. ✔ ✗

AO2 **c** Laura finds out that methane is collected in one of the groups of chemicals from the fractionating column.

The displayed formula for methane is:

$$\begin{array}{c} \text{H} \\ | \\ \text{H} - \text{C} - \text{H} \\ | \\ \text{H} \end{array}$$

What is the molecular formula for methane?   [1]

H₄C ✔

Diagram labels (fractionating column): A, B, C, D, E, F; crude oil mixture is added; it is heated and evaporates; bitumen

This candidate scores 4 marks out of 7. Their answer to this question targets a grade C. The candidate has revised, but lost marks for not reading the questions carefully and not answering them fully.

How to raise your grade

Take note of the comments from examiners – these will help you to improve your grade.

Fractional distillation is the process of separating the substances in crude oil. They are separated into fractions. The candidate could have probably avoided this error by reading the question carefully.

The fractionating column cools as you go up. The answer to the next question shows that they know this. There are lots of ideas to fit together here and careful revision is key.

Correct.

Correct. The mark scheme would allow E or F. The question is testing whether they know how the length of carbon chains collected changes down the column and this is shown in the answer.

If you are describing a difference, you need to give both sides. Here, they need to describe the colour of the chemicals from the top of the column to get the second mark. This gives you the difference.

The formula for methane is usually written as CH_4. It's convention. Most of the organic chemicals you met at GCSE put carbon first in the formula. The candidate does not lose the mark for getting the order wrong.

1 A camping stove uses propane gas as its fuel.

AO1 **a** **i** What homologous series of chemicals does propane belong to? [1]

AO1 **ii** Propane is C_3H_8. Draw its displayed structural formula. [1]

b When the camping stove is used, the propane fuel is oxidised.

AO1 **i** What does oxidised mean? [1]

AO1 **ii** What are the products when propane is oxidised? [2]

c Many homes have a gas boiler in the kitchen and a carbon monoxide detector on the wall.

AO1 **i** Describe how carbon monoxide could be formed when the gas boiler is in use. [3]

AO1 **ii** Carbon monoxide is toxic. Describe how it affects the body. [3]

[Total: 11]

2 Many of the motor fuels sold in petrol stations now contain up to 5% bioethanol. Traditional petrol contains a mixture of hydrocarbons produced from crude oil.

AO1 **a** Name the process used in oil refineries to separate the mixture of hydrocarbons in crude oil. [1]

b Some of the longer hydrocarbon molecules from crude oil are broken into shorter molecules that can be used in petrol.

AO1 **i** What is this process called? [1]

AO1 **ii** Why is it necessary? [2]

AO1 **iii** Complete the equation to show the process:

$$C_{10}H_{22} \rightarrow \underline{\hspace{2cm}} + C_2H_4$$ [1]

c When petrol is burnt in a combustion engine, carbon dioxide and water vapour are the major products. The table shows how the percentage of carbon dioxide in the atmosphere has changed since 1960.

Year	Percentage of carbon dioxide in the atmosphere
1960	0.0300
1970	0.0325
1980	0.0340
1990	0.0355
2000	0.0370
2010	0.0390

AO2 **i** Name another human activity (apart from using petrol) that may have contributed to the change in the table. [1]

AO3 **ii** Scientists think the increase in carbon dioxide in the atmosphere contributes to global warming and climate change. Discuss whether using bioethanol as motor fuel will help to reduce carbon dioxide emissions from motor vehicles. [6]

[Total: 12]

3 When electrolysis was first used to extract aluminium from its ore in 1827, aluminium was more expensive than gold.

a Use this section of the reactivity series to help you answer the questions:

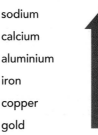

sodium

calcium

aluminium   reactivity increases

iron

copper

gold

AO1 **i** Explain why iron is extracted from iron ore by heating with carbon, but electrolysis is needed to extract aluminium. [3]

AO2 **ii** Aluminium is the commonest metal in the Earth's crust. Why was the first aluminium extracted very expensive? [2]

AO1 **b** **i** Pure aluminium is very soft. Use the diagram to explain why:

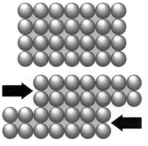

[2]

AO2 **ii** An aluminium and scandium alloy is now used to make state-of-the-art baseball bats. Explain how and why alloying aluminium with scandium changes the properties of aluminium. [4]

[Total: 11]

Summary of Assessment Objectives

AO1 recall the science   AO2 apply your knowledge   AO3 evaluate and analyse the evidence

✳ Worked example

1 Prices of petrol on the forecourts are rising as oil resources are being used up. Car manufacturers are evaluating alternative fuels. Hydrogen and bioethanol can be used as motor fuels.

AO1 **a** What do we mean by a '*fuel*'? [1]

A fuel is something we burn to get energy ✔

b The table shows how much heat energy (kJ) can be obtained when 1 g of fuel burns.

Fuel	Heat energy (kJ) per 1 g fuel
Petrol	48
Bioethanol	30
Hydrogen	143

AO1 **i** The amount of heat energy a motor fuel can produce is important. Name two other properties of a good motor fuel. [2]

It must be cheap and easy to use. ✘ ✘

AO3 **ii** Evaluate the benefits and disadvantages of using hydrogen fuel and bioethanol fuel in cars. [6]

Hydrogen is a gas and difficult to store and transport.

It is explosive, but it gives out more energy than bioethanol when it is burnt. ✔

Hydrogen makes water when it burns, but bioethanol makes carbon dioxide, which is a greenhouse gas. ✔

We can grow sugar or corn to make bioethanol and keep growing it year after year. We have to use electricity to get hydrogen from water and electricity is expensive. Fossil fuels are used to make electricity. ✔

The candidate scored 4 marks out of 9. Their answer to this question targets a grade C. The candidate could have improved their grade by organising their ideas clearly in **bii**.

How to raise your grade

Take note of the comments from examiners – these will help you to improve your grade.

This is a good answer and gets a mark.

No motor fuels are cheap, so the answer is not really relevant. The answer is too vague. The candidate could refer to how easily the fuel is transported, how easily it is stored or its hazards.

Because this question asks for several sentences, they are assessing use of English, using suitable terminology and organising ideas clearly.

A comparison with bioethanol is needed. Bioethanol is a liquid at room temperature. Liquids are easier to store and transport.

The information in the table has been used to gain this mark. A more accurate answer would include 'more energy per gram of fuel burnt'. Look carefully at information given in questions. 1 g of hydrogen gas has a very large volume compared to 1 g of ethanol liquid. Volume is important when comparing fuels because they have to be stored in the vehicle.

Remember that water and carbon dioxide are products when bioethanol burns. Both are greenhouse gases.

Using the word 'renewable' to describe growing crops to produce bioethanol would improve the quality of written communication mark.

P1 Universal physics (Topics 1–3)

What you should know

Solar System and space

The Earth spins on its axis and orbits the Sun.

Our Solar System consists of the Sun, its planets, asteroids and the natural satellites of the planets.

The planets and satellites are seen by reflected light and the Sun, as a star, emits light.

Artificial satellites provide information about the Solar System and the Universe.

- Name the planets in our Solar System.

Light and sound

We see objects using light and the lenses in our eyes.

Light can be split using a prism to make a spectrum.

Light can be reflected at a mirrored surface and refracted as it passes through a glass block.

Sound travels in waves. It will travel at different speeds through solids, liquids and gases.

- Is the speed of light faster or slower than the speed of sound?

Gravity

Gravitational pull exists between all bodies. It depends on the mass of the bodies and their separation.

Gravity makes the planets and satellites go round the Earth.

- Why is the gravitational force stronger on Earth than on the Moon?

You will find out about

> the geocentric and heliocentric models of the Solar System

> how scientists observe the Solar System and the Universe using the naked eye, photography, and telescopes and space probes

> how telescopes work using different waves, where they are located and their impact on our understanding of the Universe

> converging lenses

> how all waves can be reflected and refracted

> how waves are described and about the wave equation $v = f \times \lambda$

> different types of wave

> the electromagnetic spectrum and electromagnetic waves

> the uses and dangers of electromagnetic waves

> ionising radiations from radioactive sources

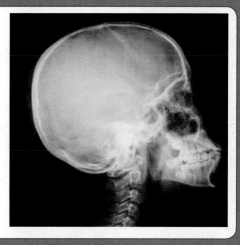

> the objects in the Universe and the Milky Way, and their relative sizes

> the role of gravity in the formation of the Sun and how the Sun will evolve

> how massive stars evolve

> the Steady State and Big Bang theories of the Universe

> the evidence that led to the acceptance of the Big Bang model of the Universe

Modelling the Solar System

You will find out:
> about the geocentric model of the Solar System
> about the heliocentric model of the Solar System
> about the contributions of Galileo

The sky at night

Look up into the night sky and you will see stars. Ancient astronomers recognised five 'wandering stars' which they called planets. The planet Mercury races across the sky taking 88 days to return to the same spot. Saturn takes 30 years to do the same. What were these planets orbiting? According to Ptolemy (90–170 AD), the planets moved round the Earth.

FIGURE 1: Ptolemy believed in the Earth-centred Solar System.

Geocentric model

The **geocentric model** of the **Solar System** was proposed by Ptolemy nearly 2000 years ago. It consisted of the Earth, five planets (Mercury, Venus, Mars, Jupiter and Saturn), the Moon, the Sun and the stars. Ptolemy believed that all heavenly objects moved round the Earth. The Earth (*geo* in Greek) was at the centre of the Solar System.

In the geocentric model:

> The Earth was stationary.

> The Moon, Sun, planets and the stars moved round the Earth in *circular* orbits.

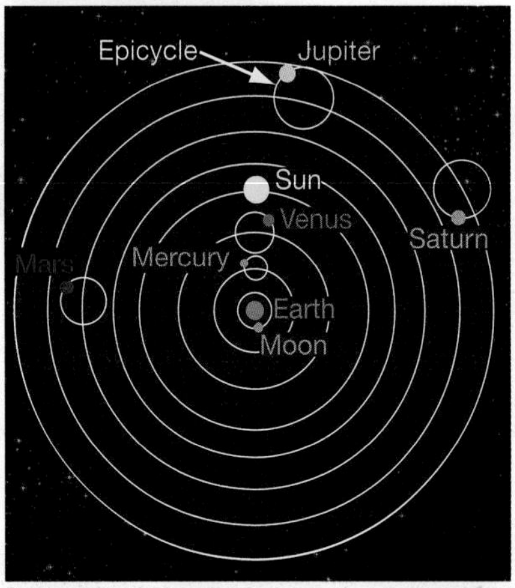

FIGURE 2: The geocentric model.

Mars has a strange motion in the night sky. Most of the time it moves in a certain direction but every so often, it appears to stop and then changes direction. This backward motion of a planet is known as **retrograde motion**.

Ptolemy tried to explain this backward motion by using a model to make the planet move in a circle (known as an epicycle) on top of its circular orbit.

The model started to look quite complex and sadly, it failed to predict the exact positions of the planets.

QUESTIONS

1 Name all the objects in the geocentric model of the Solar System.

2 According to the geocentric model, name the object orbited by the Sun and the Moon.

3 State one of the problems with the geocentric model.

Heliocentric model

Nikolaus Copernicus (1473–1543) proposed the **heliocentric model** of the Solar System. The Sun (*helio* in Greek) was at the centre.

> The planets, including the Earth, went round the Sun in circular orbits.

> The planets furthest from the Sun moved more slowly.

> The Moon went round the Earth.

> The stars formed a dome beyond the planet Saturn.

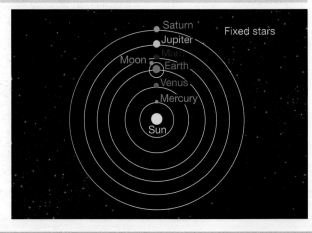

FIGURE 3: The heliocentric model.

At this time the Roman Catholic Church believed the Earth's rightful place was at the centre of the Solar System. Copernicus was a devout Catholic and did not want to upset the Church. He only published his ideas close to his death.

The heliocentric model was successful at explaining the retrograde motion of Mars. Mars moves backwards against the stars when the fast-moving Earth overtakes it.

Copernicus' model was much simpler than Ptolemy's model. Sadly, it was equally bad at predicting the position of the planets because Copernicus still used circular orbits. The heliocentric model was perfected later by Johann Kepler (1571–1630), who realised that the planets had *elliptical* (oval-shaped) orbits.

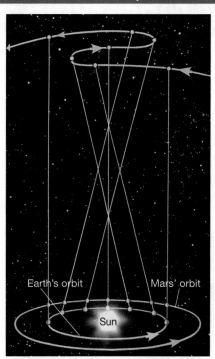

FIGURE 4: The retrograde motion of Mars.

QUESTIONS

4 Describe the heliocentric model of the Solar System.

5 Explain how the retrograde motion of Mars was explained by the heliocentric model.

6 State one thing that was the same in the models proposed by Ptolemy and Copernicus.

Galileo Galilei

Galileo (1564–1642) was the first person to use a telescope to explore the night sky. He saw craters and mountains on the Moon.

Galileo also discovered four moons orbiting Jupiter. This might not seem extraordinary now, but at Galileo's time, this was simply not allowed by the geocentric model. All heavenly bodies had to orbit the Earth in line with the geocentric model of the Solar System. Galileo's observations supported the new heliocentric model of the Solar System

Through his telescope, Galileo also saw the **phases of** Venus. These were similar to the crescent or half shapes shown by our Moon. The phases of Venus could only be explained if:

> the Earth and Venus orbited the Sun

> the orbit of Venus was between the Earth and the Sun.

Galileo's observations led him to support the heliocentric model of the Solar System. Sadly, his views went against the Church and he was held under house arrest for the rest of his life.

QUESTIONS

7 Suggest why we cannot see the phases of Venus with the naked eye.

8 Name two observations that led Galileo to believe in the heliocentric model of the Solar System.

9 State whether or not Jupiter would show phases. Explain your answer.

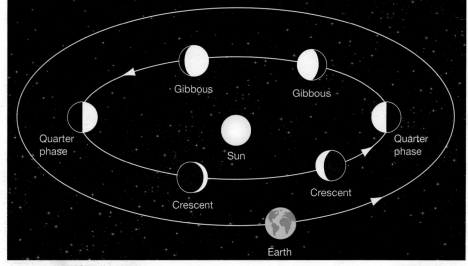

FIGURE 5: Can you see why Venus shows phases?

Observing the Universe

You will find out:
> about the Solar System
> the methods used to observe the Universe

A very odd-looking telescope

This image shows an arrangement used by astronomers in the 16th century to accurately measure the position of stars and planets. It was made of wood and had no lenses. It could be used to measure stars separated by 1/60°.

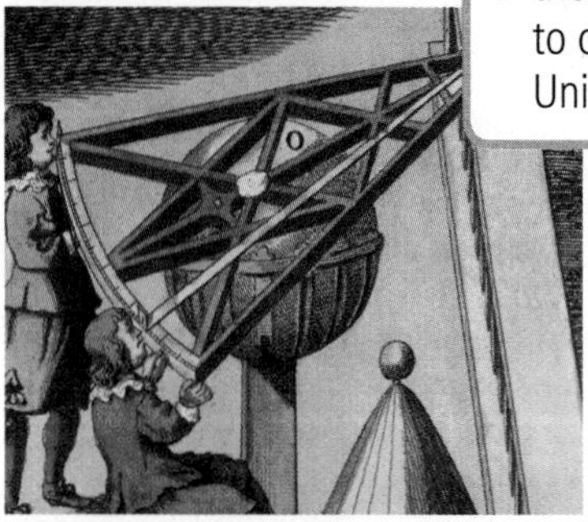

FIGURE 1: A simple arrangement to observe the heavens using the naked eye.

Using light

We see the stars in the night sky because they emit visible light. We can see the planets in our Solar System because they reflect the light from the Sun. Early astronomers used their naked eyes to pinpoint the positions of stars, planets and comets. Astronomers could not see much detail until the invention of the **telescope** in the 17th century.

> A telescope gathers more light. This made the images brighter and larger (magnified). In 1610, Galileo used a metre-long telescope to discover the moons of Jupiter and sunspots on the surface of the Sun.

> As telescopes became bigger, astronomers were able to see fainter objects. In 1781, William Herschel used a large telescope to discover Uranus.

> With the arrival of **photography** in the 1850s, astronomers were able to keep a permanent record of their observations. Photographic techniques were used to discover Pluto in 1930.

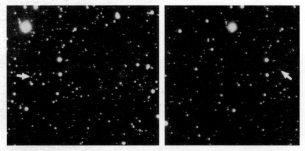

FIGURE 2: The discovery of Pluto. Two photographs were taken six days apart. Pluto is identified by the arrow.

> Astronomers use huge telescopes to get stunning images of the Solar System. Figure 3 shows a composite image of the transit of Venus across the Sun.

> We now send telescopes onboard unmanned spaceships to distant planets. The photographs they take show incredible detail.

Modern astronomers are also able to use waves other than visible light to look further into the Universe.

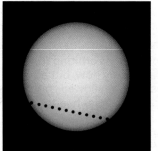

FIGURE 3: The transit of Venus photographed on 8 June 2004.

FIGURE 4: Jupiter's moon Io. Jupiter is in the background, Io is the round object on the left. Io is about half the diameter of the Earth.

QUESTIONS

1 State two advantages of using a telescope over naked-eye observations.

2 Explain why photographic techniques led to many discoveries in astronomy.

Solar System

Astronomers observe the Solar System using the naked eye, telescopes and photographs.

Figure 5 shows the objects in our Solar System:

> The Sun, a star, surrounded by the planets Mercury, Venus, Earth, Mars, Jupiter, Saturn, Uranus and Neptune.

> An asteroid belt, consisting of lumps of rock, lies between Mars and Jupiter. The largest asteroid, Ceres, is 974 km wide.

> Pluto was demoted to a dwarf planet in 2006 because of its small size.

> The Kuiper belt consists of frozen objects (mainly methane, ammonia and water) that lie mostly beyond Neptune. The Kuiper belt is thought to be the source of comets.

> The outermost region of the Solar System is known as the Oort cloud. It lies at a distance of 1.5 light years from the Sun. It consists of billions of small lumps of rock and ice. The objects of the Oort cloud are too faint to be seen using visible light.

Did you know?

It would take you 3000 years to get to the Kuiper belt on a high-speed train.

QUESTIONS

3 Name the objects in the Solar System.

4 Suggest why the icy objects in the Kuiper belt or the Oort cloud cannot be seen.

5 The diameter of the Earth is 12 800 km. Calculate how many times smaller the asteroid Ceres is compared to Earth.

FIGURE 5: Our Solar System. Can you spot the Earth?

Using different waves

Astronomers use waves other than light for their observations of the Solar System, the Milky Way and the Universe. Here are some examples.

The Hubble space telescope orbiting the Earth can also take images using **infrared waves** and **ultraviolet waves**.

The Chandra X-ray observatory, a space probe launched in 1999, takes images in **X-rays**. Chandra has successfully taken images of distant galaxies and our own Milky Way. X-rays are emitted when electrons are slowed down or when electrons hit atoms at high speeds.

The Herschel space observatory, launched in 2009, uses infrared waves to take images. Cooler objects emit a greater amount of infrared waves than visible light. Among other things, infrared astronomy may help to gather information about the Kuiper belt.

QUESTIONS

6 Discuss three types of wave used to observe the Universe.

7 The Universe may be observed using naked eye, photography and telescopes. Compare and contrast these three methods.

FIGURE 6: Image taken by Chandra of the centre of our Milky Way. The blue dots are hot, young stars, emitting X-rays.

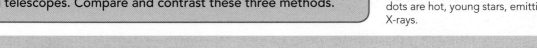
Q William Herschel   Kuiper belt   Oort cloud   Planets in our Solar System

Reflection and refraction

You will find out:
> about reflection of waves
> about refraction of waves
> about the cause of refraction

Looking in the mirror

We take mirrors for granted. They help us to see our own reflections when we stumble into the bathroom every morning. They are often made of glass and are quite cheap. The oldest known mirrors date back to 6000 BC in what is now modern-day Turkey. About 3000 years later, Egyptians made mirrors from polished copper and bronze as well as precious metals.

FIGURE 1: Is this real or not?

Reflection

Light waves will bounce off, or reflect at, a shiny surface. Figure 2 shows the **reflection** of a laser beam from the surface of a glass mirror and Figure 3 is a ray diagram of this event.

There are two *laws of reflection*:

> The angle of incidence i is equal to the angle of reflection r. (Note that the angles are measured relative to the normal.)

> The incident ray, reflected ray and normal lie in the same plane.

All waves can be reflected.

> Sound waves can be reflected off walls or buildings. We call these reflected sounds *echoes*.

> Dolphins and bats use reflected ultrasound (echolocation) to monitor their surroundings.

> Radio waves can be reflected off the ionosphere surrounding the Earth. The ionosphere contains charged particles; it acts like a mirror to the radio waves.

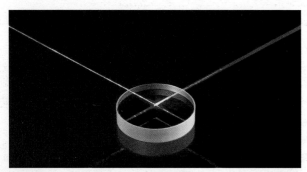

FIGURE 2: The reflection of red laser light.

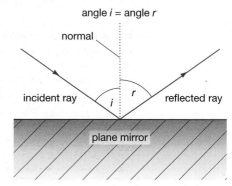

angle i = angle r

normal

incident ray i r reflected ray

plane mirror

FIGURE 3: A ray diagram showing reflection.

FIGURE 4: Dolphins use echolocation when hunting fish and to stop them bumping into each other.

QUESTIONS

1. Copy out all the words that mean reflection:

   light   echo   bounce   sound   microwaves

2. A ray of light has an angle of incidence of 30° at a flat mirror. Determine the angle:

   a of reflection and

   b between the mirror and the reflected ray.

Refraction

As a ray of light travels through a glass block, it changes direction twice: once when it enters the glass block and again when it leaves. This change in direction at the boundary between air and glass is known as **refraction**.

All waves can be refracted. A wave will only refract at the boundary between two different materials. A drinking straw partially immersed in water looks broken (see Figure 6). This illusion is due to refraction.

Figure 7 is a ray diagram to show the refraction of light as it travels from air into glass. In this case, the angle of refraction r is smaller than the angle of incidence i.

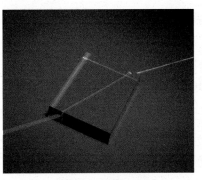

FIGURE 5: Light is refracted twice by the glass block.

FIGURE 6: Is this drinking straw really broken?

QUESTIONS

3 Explain what is meant by refraction.

4 Is the statement: 'Only some waves can be refracted', true or false? Explain your answer.

5 The angle of incidence for a ray of light in air at the boundary of water is 60°. State whether the angle of refraction in water is greater than, equal to or less than 60°.

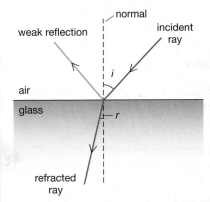

FIGURE 7: A ray of light is refracted towards the normal when it travels from air into glass.

Cause of refraction (Higher tier only)

Refraction is caused by the change in the **speed** of light at the boundary between two materials. The speed of light depends on the **density** of the material. In air, light travels at a speed of about 3.0×10^8 m/s. It travels much more slowly in water and much more slowly still in glass or diamond.

When light travels from a less dense material (such as air) into a more dense material (such as glass), it gets *slower*. This makes the light bend *towards* the normal (see Figure 7).

When light travels from a more dense material (such as glass) into a less dense material (such as air), it gets *faster*. This makes the light bend *away from* the normal (see Figure 8).

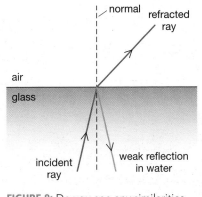

FIGURE 8: Do you see any similarities with Figure 7?

QUESTIONS

6 State the reason for the refraction of light at a boundary between two materials.

7 The speed of light in a transparent plastic object is the same as that in water. Explain whether or not you can see this object when it is submerged in water.

8 The speed of light in glass is 2.0×10^8 m/s and in water it is 2.3×10^8 m/s. State and explain what will happen to a ray of light travelling from water into glass.

Lenses

You will find out:

- > about converging lenses
- > about the focal length of a converging lens
- > about the magnification of a converging lens

It was the Romans

Glass was made by the Romans in the 1st century AD. They discovered that glass, thicker in the middle and thin at its edges, when held over an object made it look bigger. They had invented a magnifying glass.

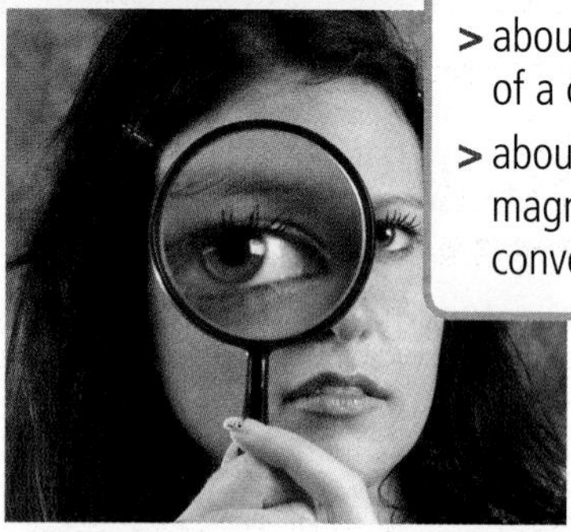

FIGURE 1: Make things bigger.

Understanding lenses

Lenses *refract* light and form images. There are two types of lens (see Figure 2):

> **Converging** (convex) **lens** – this is thickest in the middle.

> **Diverging** (concave) **lens** – this is thinnest in the middle.

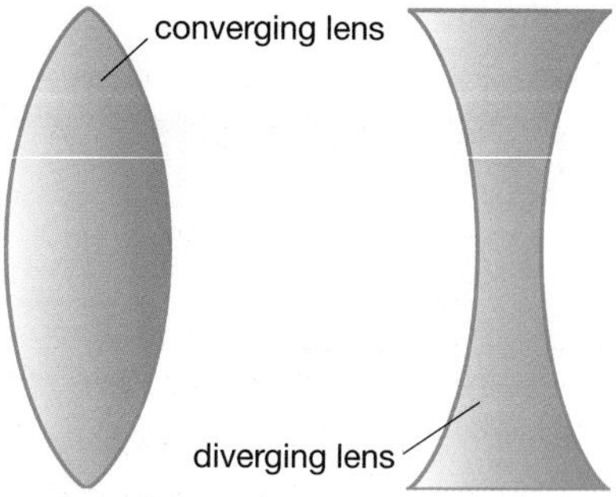

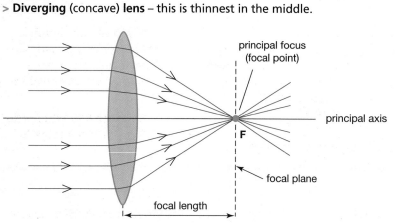

FIGURE 2: Lenses

FIGURE 3: Some important things about a converging lens. **F** is the principal focus.

You only need to know about the converging lens for your exam. This type of lens is found in cameras, telescopes, binoculars and even our eyes.

When light rays *parallel* to the principal axis pass through a converging lens, they all bend inwards. Each ray of light is refracted twice by the lens. The rays converge (meet) at a point on the principal axis known as the **principal focus** (or simply, *focus* or *focal point*) of the lens (see Figure 3).

The distance between the centre of the lens and the principal focus is known as the **focal length** *f* of the lens.

A thin lens has a longer focal length compared with a fat lens (see Figure 4).

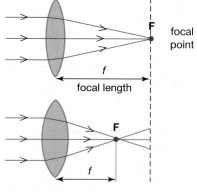

FIGURE 4: Thin and fat lenses have different focal lengths.

QUESTIONS

1 Explain the difference between focus (focal point) and focal length.

2 Two converging lenses **X** and **Y** have focal length 20 cm and 30 cm, respectively. State which lens is thinner in the middle.

Image formed by lenses   Magnifying glass

Determining the focal length

This is what you do to find the focal length of a converging lens:

> Hold the lens in front of a screen.

> Point the lens towards a distant object (building, cloud, tree, etc.).

> Adjust the position of the lens until a sharp image is formed on the screen.

> The rays from the distant object are parallel; hence the image is formed at the focal point of the lens.

> The distance between the lens and screen is the focal length of the lens.

The image of the distant object is **real**, which means that it can be formed on a screen. The image is also *inverted* ('upside down').

Finding the image

You can locate the position and work out the size of the image by drawing a *ray diagram* (see Figure 5).

> Rays 1 and 2 start from the top of the object.

> Ray 1 starts off parallel to the principal axis of the lens. After refraction at the lens, it passes through the focal point **F**.

> Ray 2 passes through the centre of the lens and travels in a straight line.

> The top of the image is where these two rays cross.

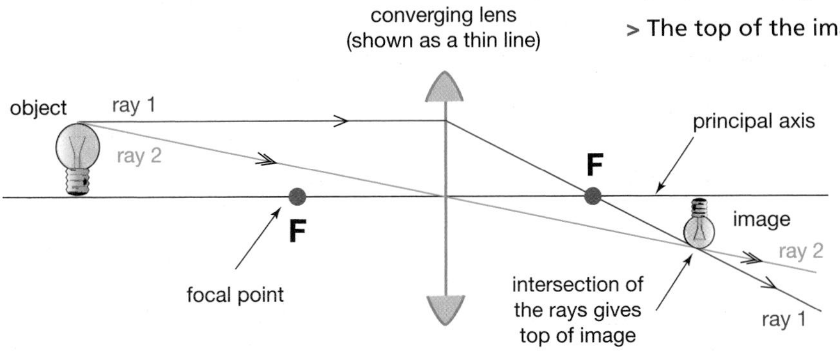

object ray 1
ray 2
converging lens
(shown as a thin line)
principal axis
F
image
ray 2
F
focal point
intersection of
the rays gives
top of image
ray 1

FIGURE 5: A ray diagram showing how to find the properties of an image.

QUESTIONS

3 A lens of focal length 8.0 cm forms an image of a distant tree on a screen. Explain where the image is formed.

4 State the main properties of the image in Figure 5.

Magnification

The magnification of an image can be found using the following equation:

$$\text{magnification} = \frac{\text{image height}}{\text{object height}}$$

For a lens of focal length f, the image magnification depends on the position of the object (there are other factors that also affect magnification, such as lens thickness as it changes the focal length). The image is:

> larger than the object (**magnified**) when placed between f and $2f$ from the lens

> smaller than the object (**diminished**) when placed beyond $2f$ from the lens.

Magnifying glass

For an object placed between the lens and the focal point **F**, the image is **virtual** (not real, hence cannot be formed on a screen), *upright* and *magnified*.

A virtual image can only be seen by the eye when you look at the object through the lens (see Figure 6).

QUESTIONS

5 Calculate the image magnification for the camera lens and the projector lens.
Camera: image height = 1.6 cm, object height = 120 cm.
Projector: image height = 2.5 m, object height = 1.6 cm.

6 An object of height 0.8 cm is placed 5.0 cm from a lens of focal length 10 cm. With the help of a ray diagram, determine the height and magnification of the image.

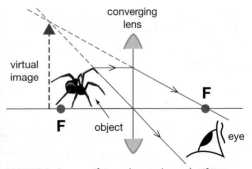

virtual image
converging lens
F
F
object
eye

FIGURE 6: A magnifying glass only works if you have your eye in the right place.

Telescopes

You will find out:
> about the refracting telescope
> about the reflecting telescope
> about the purpose of an eyepiece

Telescopes are much bigger now

The first telescope was about the length of an arm. Modern telescopes are much bigger and capable of detecting very faint objects in our Universe. Figure 1 shows Albert Einstein at the Yerkes Observatory in Chicago, USA, in 1921. Can you spot him?

FIGURE 1: Can you spot Albert Einstein?

Telescopes

One of the earliest telescopes made by Galileo consisted of a tube with a *converging* lens at the front and a *diverging* lens at the other end. The tube was pointed towards the object in the night sky and Galileo would peer through the lens with his eye.

The lens at the front of the telescope is called the **objective lens** and the lens the astronomers look through is called the **eyepiece**.

As you already know from earlier, this simple telescope led to some exciting discoveries in astronomy. However, Galileo's telescope suffered from one major problem. The glass converging lens did not refract all the colours of light towards the same focal point (see Figure 2). This made the final image a bit blurred.

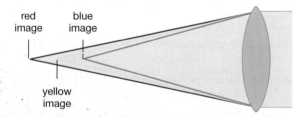

FIGURE 2: The lens has different focal lengths for different colours.

In order to make the image clearer, early astronomers such as Isaac Newton used a concave (parabolic) mirror in place of the objective lens. A concave mirror reflects parallel rays of different coloured light to the same point (see Figure 3).

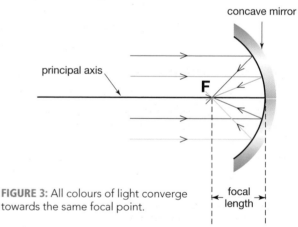

FIGURE 3: All colours of light converge towards the same focal point.

Figure 4 shows the telescope built and used by Newton. The telescope mirror had a focal length of just 15 cm.

FIGURE 4: The tiny telescope built by Isaac Newton around 1670.

QUESTIONS

1 State the type of lens used in the front of a telescope.

2 Name the lens that you look through in a telescope.

3 State the main problem with the glass objective lens in a telescope. Explain how this was sorted out by Newton with his reflecting telescope.

Q Largest telescopes in the world   Design of telescopes

Two types of telescope

Refracting telescope

A simple **refracting telescope** is shown in Figure 5. It has two lenses.

> The objective lens and the eyepiece are both converging lenses.

> The objective lens forms an image of a distant object (for example, a galaxy) at its focal point.

> The eyepiece *magnifies* this image of the object.

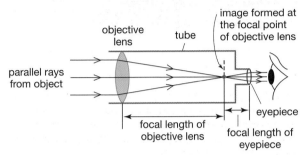

FIGURE 5: A refracting telescope.

> ## QUESTIONS

4 Compare refracting and reflecting telescopes.

5 A refracting telescope has two lenses of focal lengths 1.5 cm and 220 cm. Use Figure 5 to estimate the length of the telescope.

Reflecting telescope

The largest telescopes are not made from bulky glass lenses; they use lightweight mirrors instead. Telescopes made from mirrors are easier to steer. A simple **reflecting telescope** (known as a Newtonian telescope) is made from a concave mirror, a flat mirror and an eyepiece (see Figure 6).

The concave mirror forms an image of a distant object at its focal point. A small flat mirror is used to reflect the rays of light towards the eyepiece. The eyepiece *magnifies* the image of the object formed by the concave mirror.

The eyepiece is found on the side of the telescope tube. When using the telescope, you are often looking down towards the ground when the object is high in the night sky!

For large image magnification, the objective lens (or the concave mirror) has a long focal length and the eyepiece has a short focal length.

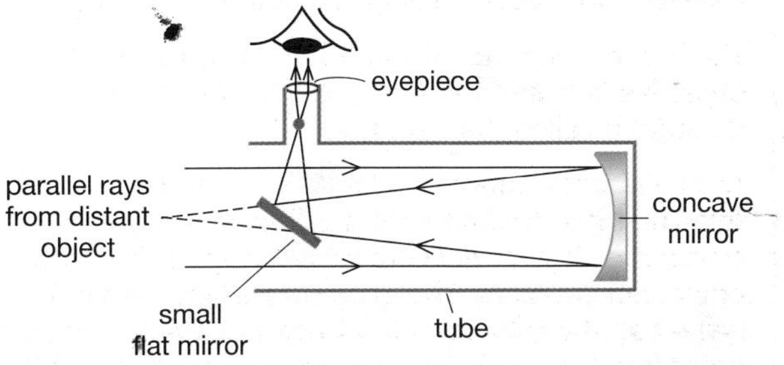

FIGURE 6: A reflecting telescope.

Telescopes in space

Modern telescopes are huge. They are housed in observatories on the tops of mountains where the skies are clearer, the air is cooler and there are no city lights to spoil the view of the night sky. The image quality is better because of less air turbulence at cooler temperatures.

Astronomers also have lightweight reflecting telescopes in space. The most well-known example of this is the Hubble space telescope. It can provide images with a magnification of about 5000. Fainter objects can be seen by taking longer exposures. It can detect objects that are 10 million million times less bright than the full Moon.

The Hubble space telescope can also take images using infrared waves and ultraviolet waves.

FIGURE 7: The Hubble space telescope orbits about 600 km above the Earth.

> ## QUESTIONS

6 Warm air refracts light more than cooler air. Explain why the image quality is better with telescopes on the top of mountains.

7 The amount of light from a full Moon is about 3×10^{-3} W/m^2. Estimate the amount of light from the faintest object detectable by the Hubble space telescope.

Understanding waves

You will find out:
> how waves transfer energy
> the terms used to describe waves
> about the wave equation

Energy from the Sun

How did the grass gets its energy? All the energy needed by plants and animals comes from the Sun. This energy is carried through space by waves. These waves travel at 300 million metres per second, cover a distance of 150 billion metres and take just over 8 minutes to reach the Earth.

FIGURE 1: A grazing cow.

Making waves

All waves:

> transfer energy and information from one place to another

> create vibrations

> *do not* transfer matter in the direction they are travelling.

You can see waves on the surface of water when you throw a stone into a pond. The splash creates ripples or waves that travel outwards at a constant speed.

The waves make the water vibrate or oscillate. A tiny insect on the water simply bobs up and down. The water itself does not travel with the wave.

Important definitions and terms

Figure 3 shows a sensible way to show a wave. It is a 'snapshot' of the wave shown as a **displacement** (distance from the undisturbed position) against distance graph.

> The uppermost point on the wave is known as the **peak** (or crest) and the lowest point is known as the **trough**.

> The **wavelength** is the distance between adjacent peaks or troughs. It is measured in metres (m).

> The **amplitude** is the maximum displacement of the wave. It is measured in metres (m).

(Take care: amplitude is not measured from the peak to the trough.)

> The **frequency** is the number of complete waves passing any point per second. It is measured in hertz (Hz), named after the German physicist Heinrich Hertz (1857–1894).

(Note: a frequency of 3 Hz also means '3 complete vibrations per second'.)

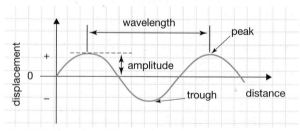

FIGURE 2: Ripples on water. Does the water move with the wave?

FIGURE 3: Important things you need to know about a wave.

QUESTIONS

1 State one similarity between amplitude and wavelength.

2 A guitar string vibrates at a frequency of 150 Hz. Calculate the number of complete vibrations in a time of 1 minute.

Important equations

Speed of a wave

Waves travel at different speeds. For example, in air, sound travels a million times more slowly than light. This is why during a distant thunderstorm you see the lightning flash well before you hear the sound of thunder.

The wave **speed** v can be determined from the distance x it travels in a time t using the equation:

$$\text{wave speed (metres/second, m/s)} = \frac{\text{distance (metres, m)}}{\text{time (seconds, s)}}$$

or

$$v = \frac{x}{t}.$$

You can also calculate the distance x and the time t using the equations:

$$x = vt \quad \text{and} \quad t = \frac{x}{v}.$$

Wave equation

For a wave, its frequency f, wavelength λ (Greek letter lambda) and wave speed v are related to each other by the following **wave equation**:

$$\text{wave speed (metres/second, m/s)} = \text{frequency (hertz, Hz)} \times \text{wavelength (metres, m)}$$

or

$$v = f \times \lambda$$

The wave equation can be applied to all waves.

> **Did you know?**
>
> It only takes one second for light to travel from the Earth to the Moon.

QUESTIONS

3 Calculate the speed of a wave that travels 1200 m in 20 s.

4 Determine the amplitude and wavelength of the water wave shown in Figure 4.

5 A saxophone emits sound of wavelength 1.3 m at a frequency of 260 Hz. Calculate the speed of sound.

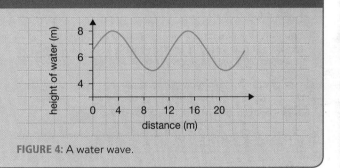

FIGURE 4: A water wave.

Finding the wavelength

A stretched string vibrates at a frequency of 120 Hz. The waves on the string travel at a speed of 48 m/s. Calculate the wavelength in metres of the waves on the string.

> *Step 1*: Write down what is given in the question and what you need to find:

speed = 48 m/s, frequency = 120 Hz, wavelength = ?

> *Step 2*: Write down the equation and substitute the values. Rearrange the equation to find the wavelength of sound:

$$\text{speed (m/s)} = \text{frequency (Hz)} \times \text{wavelength (m)}$$

$$48 = 120 \times \lambda$$

$$\lambda = \frac{48}{120} = 0.40 \text{ m}$$

The wavelength of the waves is 0.40 m.

QUESTIONS

6 Calculate the frequency of sound waves of wavelength 0.35 m. The speed of sound is 340 m/s.

7 Calculate the wavelength of radio waves of frequency 2.0×10^5 Hz. Radio waves travel at 3.0×10^8 m/s.

8 Red light has a longer wavelength than blue light. They both travel at the same speed. Explain which colour of light has the greater frequency.

Two types of waves

You will find out:
> about transverse waves
> about longitudinal waves
> about seismic waves

Earthquakes

The Earth is not a solid object – it has several layers. Its outer layer (the *crust*) is in constant motion, causing the continents to drift slowly at a speed of a few centimetres per year. At times, the motion of the crust triggers devastating earthquakes which in turn produce shock waves called seismic waves. Understanding these waves is important for predicting earthquakes.

FIGURE 1: Seismic waves carry enormous energy and cause lots of devastation.

Transverse and longitudinal waves

You can use a Slinky to create two different types of waves.

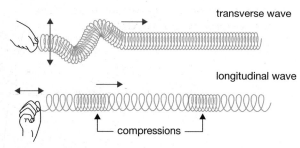

FIGURE 2: Using a Slinky to create waves.

Stretch a Slinky across the floor. Shake one of its ends at right angles to its length. You will see the coils of the Slinky vibrating at right angles to its length. The wave produced is called a **transverse wave**.

> For a transverse wave, the vibrations are at *right angles* to the direction in which the wave travels.

If you shake one end of the stretched Slinky along its length, then you will see a **longitudinal wave**. The coils of the Slinky are squashed in places. These squashed or **compression** regions travel at a constant speed along the length of the Slinky.

> For a longitudinal wave, the vibrations are along the direction in which the wave travels.

All waves can be divided into two groups –

transverse and longitudinal. The table below shows some other examples of transverse and longitudinal waves.

Transverse wave	Longitudinal waves
Electromagnetic waves (light)	Sound in air or water
Surface water waves	**P wave** (seismic)
Waves on stretched strings	
S wave (seismic)	

QUESTIONS

1 Copy the following and fill in the missing words.

   a For a transverse wave, the v____ are at r____ ____ to the direction of the wave velocity.

   b For a longitudinal wave, the v____ are p____ to the direction of the wave velocity.

2 Sound needs a material to travel through. Explain why there cannot be sound in outer space.

Sound and seismic waves

Figure 3 shows a vibrating ruler creating sound.

The ruler makes the surrounding air vibrate. Sometimes it pushes the air molecules closer together and creates regions of slightly higher pressure. (Just as for the Slinky, these regions are called

compressions.) At other times, the ruler moves the air molecules apart and creates slightly lower pressure regions. These regions are called **rarefactions**. In air, the compression or rarefaction regions travel at a speed of 340 m/s.

Q Detecting earthquakes   Simulations of transverse and longitudinal waves

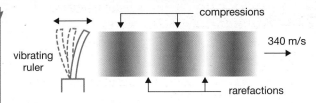

compressions

340 m/s

vibrating ruler

rarefactions

FIGURE 3 : A vibrating ruler in air.

Seismic waves

Seismic waves are produced by earthquakes. They can also be produced by explosions, for example, chemical explosions such as dynamite or nuclear explosions. There are two types of seismic waves:

> A primary wave (or simply P wave) is a longitudinal wave.

> A secondary wave (or simply S wave) is a transverse wave.

> S waves travel more slowly than P waves.

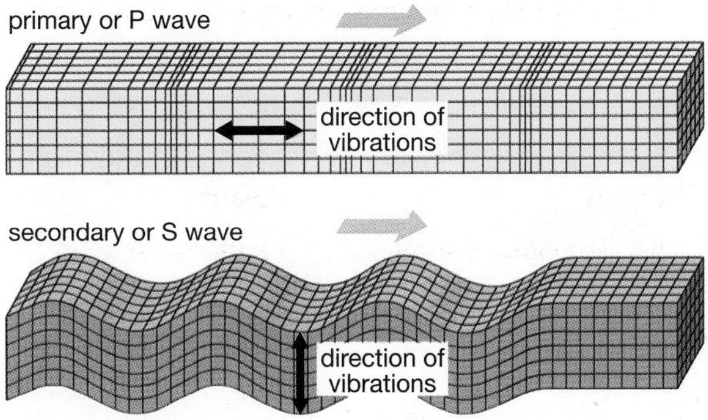

primary or P wave

direction of vibrations

secondary or S wave

direction of vibrations

FIGURE 4: Two types of seismic waves.

People have been trying to predict earthquakes for centuries. Figure 5 shows a Chinese earthquake detector from 200 AD. Small balls were balanced in the dragons' mouths. Tiny Earth tremors would release the balls into the frogs' mouths below.

FIGURE 5: An ancient earthquake detector.

QUESTIONS

3 Calculate the time it would take sound to travel a distance of 1.0 km in air.

4 Figure 6 shows a trace (seismogram) from an earthquake monitoring station. Identify the S waves. Explain your answer.

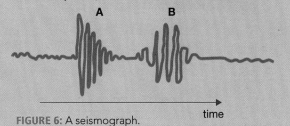

A   B

time

FIGURE 6: A seismograph.

Detecting seismic waves

Figure 7 shows a simple seismograph or **seismometer**.

The device is used for recording the movement of the ground caused by seismic waves from an earthquake or an explosion. A pen at the end of a heavy pendulum is placed above a rotating paper drum. A trace (seismogram) is produced on the paper to show any tremors.

FIGURE 7: A simple seismometer used to predict earthquakes.

Modern seismometers have a magnet suspended within coils of copper wires (see Figure 8). Seismic waves make the coils move about. This movement induces a current in the coils. The size of the current depends on the amount of ground movement and the speed of the tremors. The electrical signals are either electronically stored or transmitted to the earthquake monitoring station.

QUESTIONS

5 An earthquake monitoring station picks up P and S waves from an earthquake 100 s apart. P waves travel at 10 km/s and S waves at 6 km/s. Calculate the distance in km of the earthquake from the station.

FIGURE 8: A modern seismometer used in remote parts of the world.

S and P waves   Seismometer   Longitudinal and transverse waves

Preparing for assessment: Applying your knowledge

To achieve a good grade in science, you not only have to know and understand scientific ideas, but you also need to be able to apply them to other situations. This task will support you in developing these skills.

✸ Telescopes: from Galileo to Hubble

Dave is on a school trip to a planetarium. There is a small exhibition showing replicas of Galileo's and Newton's telescopes.

Galileo's telescope consisted of an objective (converging) lens at the far end of a tube and an eyepiece (diverging) lens at the near end. The telescope was focused by changing the distance between the two lenses. Astronomers call these instruments refracting telescopes.

About 60 years after Galileo had made his first telescope, Isaac Newton thought about the disadvantages of refracting telescopes. Newton invented a reflecting telescope which used a curved mirror to focus the rays coming from an object in the sky.

The exhibition also contained photographs of some modern telescopes. Some of these telescopes were in observatories on the tops of mountains. Some telescopes were attached to satellites orbiting high above the atmosphere.

The was also a computer playing a video called *Hubble: 20 Years of Discovery*. The Hubble space telescope allows astronomers to see far into space, and has made many discoveries that could never have been made at ground level.

✸ Task 1

In the exhibition the display talked about Newton finding problems with refracting telescopes.

> Suggest what these may have been and how Newton overcame them in the telescope that he invented.

✸ Task 2

Dave has to write a homework assignment on how modern telescopes have developed. State three developments he should list and explain why.

✸ Task 3

The refracting telescope Dave saw at the exhibition was 250 cm long.

> Suggest the likely focal lengths for the lenses in this telescope. Explain your answer.

> Would this be the same in a reflecting telescope? If not, explain why.

✸ Task 4

The photographs show that both of the telescopes used for the Faulkes' Telescope Project were on the tops of mountains. Can you explain why this is a good location?

✸ Task 5

Write a short article describing some of the discoveries made by the Hubble space telescope and state why these discoveries could only be made from space.

✸ Maximise your grade

These sentences show what you need to include in your work to achieve each grade. Use them to improve your work and be more successful.

For grade E, your answers should show that you can:
> describe some disadvantages of early telescopes
> list some changes in telescopes since they were first used to look at the sky
> explain image blurring in terms of the variation of focal length or refractive index with colour.

For grades D, C, in addition show that you can:
> explain the role of lenses and mirrors in reflecting and refracting telescopes, respectively
> describe how the atmosphere hinders ground-based astronomy.

For grades B, A, in addition show that you can:
> explain the changes in telescopes and observatories in their ability to collect light and minimise the effects of the atmosphere
> describe in detail some of the discoveries made by the use of non-visible electromagnetic waves in examining the Universe.

191

Preparing for assessment: Analysis and conclusions

To achieve a good grade in science, you not only have to know and understand scientific ideas, but you also need to be able to apply them to other situations and investigations. This task will support you in developing these skills.

✳ Task

> Test the hypothesis that the focal length of a lens is less for thick lenses than for thin ones.

✳ Looking into converging lenses

Lenses are widely used in all sorts of optical devices: spectacles, telescopes, microscopes, cameras, your eyes, and so on. To select suitable lenses for a particular task, you need to know their focal lengths.

The focal length of a converging lens is the distance between the centre of the lens and its focal point (that is the point at which it brings parallel rays to a focus). Focal length depends on the curvature of the lens and the glass it is made from.

✳ Method and results

In an experiment, a student was given six lenses, each one being marked with the thickness of the lens at its centre.

The student used each lens to focus the image of a distant tree onto a screen. She noticed that the image was always upside-down.

The student measured the distance between the centre of the lens and the screen when the image was well focused. She carried out each measurement three times.

Lens used	Thickness (t) at centre (mm)	Distance from lens to screen (cm)	Average focal length (f, cm)
A	6.0	17.9 17.3 18.7	18.0
B	7.0	22.1 22.8 23.4	22.8
C	3.0	36.9 36.8 37.2	
D	2.3	47.8 48.3 46.9	
E	7.5	14.4 14.9 14.5	
F	4.0	27.5 28.2 28.0	

✳ Processing the evidence

1. Decide whether the images seen by the student are real or virtual. Give a reason for your decision.

2. Copy the table above and complete the column 'Average focal length' by calculating the average value of the focal length of each lens.

3. Display your results on a suitable graph.

4. The result from one of the lenses is anomalous. What does this mean? Identify the lens which has given the anomalous result.

5. Comment on the quality of the data obtained in this experiment.

> Ensure that the averages are given to an appropriate number of significant figures.

> Two continuous variables are best plotted as a line graph. Good line graphs show a line or curve of best fit; joining points one to another in a zig-zag will lose marks.

> Consider your scale carefully so you have a graph of appropriate size.

> How will you deal with this anomaly when forming your conclusions? Does this affect how you will view your hypothesis?

✺ Stating conclusions

1. Explain carefully what the graph shows.

2. Explain whether the results support the hypothesis. If so, use scientific ideas and appropriate mathematical relationships to explain why you could expect the results you got. If not, use scientific ideas to suggest why.

3. (**Higher tier only.**) Extend the results table to investigate further the relationship between the two variables (for example by calculating f^{-1}, f^2 or $f \times t$). Use this data to plot a further graph and improve your explanation in answer to question 1.

> Is the graph a straight line or curve? Does it pass through the origin? Can you describe the relationship between the two variables qualitatively (without using mathematical terms) and quantitatively?
>
> Remember to take into account the anomaly.

> Remember that a straight line through the origin shows a directly proportional relationship between the x and y variables.

✺ Evaluating the method

1. Describe the strengths of the investigation.

2. Suggest two possible reasons why one of the lenses gave the anomalous result even though the experiment was carried out carefully.

3. Suggest how the method might be improved to produce better quality evidence.

> Think about what factors can affect focal length.

✺ Evaluating the conclusion

1. How could you improve the evidence to better support your conclusion?

2. How might you reword your hypothesis in light of your conclusions?

> Remember that reliable evidence is repeatable evidence. Scientists generally expect to have six or more points close to a curve or line of best fit before drawing conclusions from a graph.

> Consider the hypothesis and scientific language used.

✺ Connections

How Science Works

> Collecting and analysing scientific data.

> Evaluating the best methods of data collection and considering their reliability.

> Presenting information and drawing a conclusion and stating this in a scientific way.

> Interpreting data qualitatively and quantitatively.

> Analysing, interpreting, applying and questioning scientific information.

Maths in Science

> Carrying out calculations.

> Substituting numerical values into simple formulae using appropriate units.

> Providing answers to correct number of significant figures.

> Using proportion and ratios.

> Calculating means.

> Drawing graphs with appropriate scales.

> Interpreting data from tables and graphs.

Infrared and ultraviolet

You will find out:
> about the discovery of ultraviolet
> about the discovery of infrared
> the effects of ultraviolet radiation

Sun rays

We all look forward to soaking in the rays of the Sun. The light from the Sun helps us to see the world around us. It also emits waves that we cannot see. The invisible infrared makes you feel warm and the invisible ultraviolet can give you sunburn.

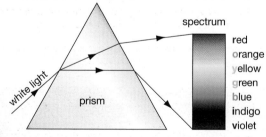

Remember!
Never look directly at the Sun. It can damage your eyes.

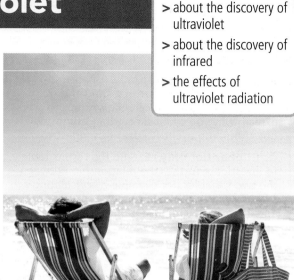

FIGURE 1: We cannot see all the waves coming from the Sun.

Visible light

Isaac Newton (1643–1727) showed that white light is made up of different colours. He passed a ray of white light through a glass **prism**. The prism split the light into a colourful rainbow. The splitting of white light into its colour components is known as dispersion.

The visible spectrum is shown in Figure 2.

white light — prism — spectrum: red, orange, yellow, green, blue, indigo, violet

FIGURE 2: The visible spectrum.

The colours in the visible spectrum, in order, are: **R**ed, **O**range, **Y**ellow, **G**reen, **B**lue, **I**ndigo and **V**iolet. You can remember these colours by forming the name **ROY G BIV** or from the saying **R**ichard **O**f **Y**ork **G**ave **B**attle **I**n **V**ain.

Figure 3 shows a rainbow in the sky. Tiny water droplets in the air produce this rainbow because each droplet behaves like a tiny prism.

The different colours in the visible spectrum have different wavelengths (red light has a longer wavelength than violet light).

FIGURE 3: A rainbow in the sky. How did the colours come about?

QUESTIONS

1 State how you can split up white light.

2 State the number of colours in the visible spectrum.

3 Use Figure 2 to state which colour of light is refracted the most.

Rainbow formation   Harmful effects of UV   Johann Ritter   Ozone layer

Beyond visible light

Infrared (IR) radiation

William Herschel (1738–1822) not only discovered Uranus but also discovered **infrared** waves. In 1800 he was using thermometers to investigate the temperature of the different colours of the visible spectrum. He found that the temperature increased towards the red end of the spectrum. To his surprise, the *hottest* part was beyond the red end where there was no visible colour at all. This invisible region is known as the infrared region.

> The wavelength of infrared is *longer* than visible light.

FIGURE 4: A country view photographed using an infrared camera.

QUESTIONS

4 Two identical thermometers are placed in the yellow and infrared parts of the spectrum. Explain which would show a lower temperature.

5 Ultraviolet and infrared waves travel at the same speed of 300 million m/s. Explain which one has the higher frequency.

Ultraviolet (UV) radiation

In 1801, Johann Ritter (1776–1810) was experimenting with silver chloride. This chemical turns black when exposed to sunlight. Ritter placed silver chloride in each colour of the visible spectrum. The rate of reaction of silver chloride increased from red to violet. He then decided to see what would happen just beyond the violet end of the visible spectrum. The rate of reaction of silver chloride was greatest in this invisible region. We know this region as the ultraviolet region.

> The wavelength of ultraviolet is *shorter* than visible light.

As you will see on the next page, both ultraviolet and infrared waves are **electromagnetic waves**.

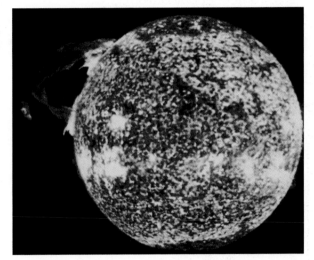

FIGURE 5: An extreme UV image of a giant loop prominence on the Sun, recorded by the Skylab space station.

Is ultraviolet radiation dangerous?

Ultraviolet from the Sun is harmful. It will damage skin (surface) cells and the eyes if we do not have protection. Applying sunscreen lotion and wearing dark sunglasses is the best way to protect our skin and eyes from harm.

There are three types of UV waves: UV-A, UV-B and UV-C.

QUESTIONS

6 A scientist detects UV waves of frequency 1.0×10^{15} Hz. Identify the type of UV wave. The speed of UV waves is 3.0×10^8 m/s.

Type	UV-A	UV-B	UV-C
Wavelength range (10^{-7} m)	3.2–4.0	2.8–3.2	<2.8
Effects on the body	Causes premature wrinkling of the skin	Causes sunburn Can trigger skin cancer Can cause eye conditions such as cataracts Can also destroy proteins in the eye lens Produces vitamin D in our body	This is the most damaging; fortunately most is stopped by the ozone layer in the atmosphere

Q UV-A, UV-B and UV-C   How do we get vitamin D?   William Herschel

Electromagnetic waves

You will find out:
> about electromagnetic waves
> about the continuous electromagnetic spectrum
> about the properties of electromagnetic waves

Strange sunlight

If you were a bee, you would see things differently to a human as bees' eyes have evolved to detect pollen in ultraviolet light.

The Sun emits a range of electromagnetic radiation. (Physicists use the term *radiation* to mean *waves* that can travel through empty space.) Your eyes, unlike those of a bee, see just the visible part of the electromagnetic spectrum.

Did you know?

The Sun releases more energy per second than people on the Earth would use in a million years.

FIGURE 1: Two pictures of a flower: the one on the left shows a human view and the one on the right a bee's-eye view. Which one shows the pollen grains more clearly?

Electromagnetic (EM) waves

Both ultraviolet and infrared waves were discovered at the extreme ends of the visible spectrum. Is the visible spectrum, together with ultraviolet and infrared waves, just a part of a much bigger spectrum? The answer is yes. This larger spectrum is known as the **electromagnetic spectrum**. As you will see later, this spectrum has other **electromagnetic (EM) waves** such as microwaves and X-rays.

Properties of EM waves

All EM waves:

> are **transverse waves**

> can travel through a **vacuum**

> travel at the same speed of 300 000 000 m/s in air or vacuum.

Like all other waves, EM waves:

> transfer energy

> can be reflected, refracted and **diffracted** (diffraction is the *spreading* of a wave at an opening or a gap)

> obey the wave equation:
   wave speed = frequency × wavelength.

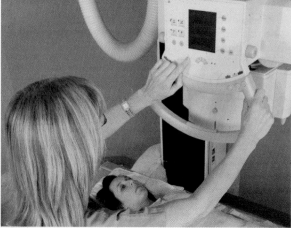

FIGURE 2: A microwave oven (above) and an X-ray machine (below) both use EM waves.

QUESTIONS

1 It takes radio waves about 1 s to travel from the Earth to the Moon. How far is the Moon?

2 Explain why all electromagnetic waves from the Sun take the same time to reach the Earth.

The EM spectrum

Microwaves and X-rays are essentially the same type of wave. The only differences between them are their wavelength and frequency.

The continuous EM spectrum is shown in Figure 3.

The electromagnetic spectrum has different regions. The names of each region in order of *decreasing* wavelength or *increasing* frequency are:

Increasing frequency

Decreasing wavelength

> radio waves
> microwaves
> infrared
> visible
> ultraviolet
> X-rays
> gamma rays.

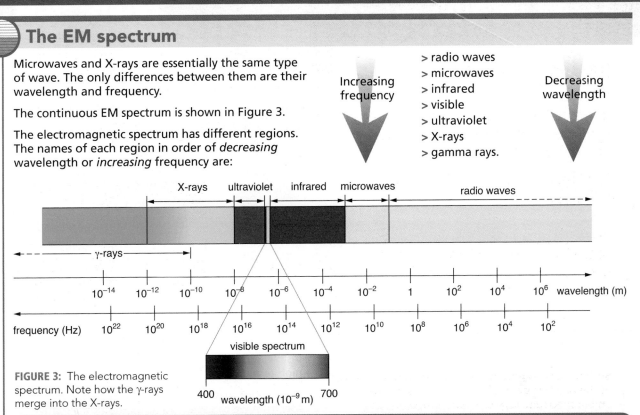

FIGURE 3: The electromagnetic spectrum. Note how the γ-rays merge into the X-rays.

QUESTIONS

3 Name all waves that have frequencies greater than ultraviolet.

4 Calculate how long it would take sunlight or a radio signal to travel the length of Great Britain; a distance of about 1100 km.

5 Use Figure 3 to identify the type of waves that have a wavelength of about 1 cm.

Why 'electromagnetic' waves?

An EM wave consists of two combined waves (see Figure 4). One of these waves consists of a vibrating *magnetic* field; the other is a vibrating *electric* field. The vibrations are *perpendicular* to the direction in which the wave travels (and to each other). Hence, EM waves are transverse waves. The wavelength of EM waves can be as small as 10^{-15} m (about the size of a nucleus of an atom) or as large as 1 km. In a vacuum, the electric and magnetic vibrations travel at the speed of 3.0×10^8 m/s.

QUESTIONS

6 The frequency of orange light is about 5.1×10^{14} Hz, with each vibration taking 2×10^{-15} s. Calculate the distance travelled by this light in one vibration of the wave.

7 A space probe close to Jupiter sends a radio signal. Calculate how long it would take the signal to reach us given Jupiter is 9.0×10^{11} m from the Earth.

8 Use the information given above to estimate how many times greater the frequency of gamma rays is compared to radio waves.

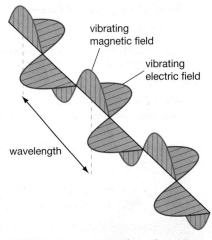

FIGURE 4: Can you see where the name 'electromagnetic' comes from?

Uses of EM waves

You will find out:
> the uses of radio waves, microwaves, infrared and visible light
> about optical fibres

Seeing infrared

Thermographs are special photographs taken of objects using infrared waves. Thermographs have many uses, for example they can be useful when you want to see how a house loses heat.

FIGURE 1: A thermograph of a building. Can you tell where most heat escapes from?

Helpful waves

Radio waves

Radio waves are produced and detected by *aerials*. Your favourite television and radio broadcasts are carried by radio waves. Emergency services also use radio waves for communications. Radio communications are extremely fast because all EM waves travel at the speed of light (3.0×10^8 m/s).

Microwaves

Microwaves are short wavelength radio waves.

Microwaves are used to cook your food in a microwave oven. Microwaves are absorbed by water and fatty molecules found in the food. This absorbed energy is turned into *heat*.

Microwaves are also used for communicating with your mobile phone.

Infrared

Any object above a temperature of –273 °C (absolute zero) will give out infrared waves – even you! Warmer objects emit greater amounts of infrared than cooler objects.

Rescue services use infrared cameras to find survivors buried under rubble. We also use infrared to cook food with kitchen appliances such as ovens, grills and toasters.

Visible light

Visible light is produced by anything that is at a very high temperature.

It is the only part of the electromagnetic (EM) spectrum we can see. Your eyes are most sensitive to yellow and green light. We also use visible light to take photographs and illuminate our homes, streets and towns.

QUESTIONS

1 Name two types of EM waves used to cook food.

2 List three things that produce visible light.

FIGURE 2: Imagine if all the lights were switched off.

Revisiting waves

Uses of radio waves

> Communications and broadcasts: medium-frequency radio waves (*sky waves*) reflect off the **ionosphere** and can therefore travel very long distances.

> Satellite transmissions: microwaves and high-frequency radio waves travel in straight lines (space waves) to geostationary satellites. Such waves are used for TV broadcasts and for communications.

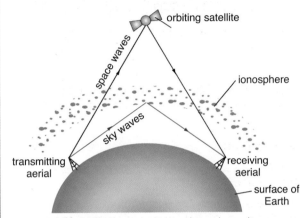

FIGURE 3: How radio waves can travel very long distances.

Uses of microwaves

> Cooking.

> Communications and satellite transmissions: just as with radio waves, you can communicate almost instantly with people across the world using satellite links.

Uses of infrared

> Cooking.

> Thermal imaging (**thermographs**).

FIGURE 4: A TV remote in action.

> Short-range communications: infrared waves cannot travel through walls, hence their range is limited. However, they still have uses (a cordless computer mouse, for example).

> Remote controls: these send coded information to your TV when you want to change the channel or adjust the sound.

> Optical fibres: these are fine glass threads (thinner than human hair) used by internet networks for sending lots of information at high speed. Both visible light and infrared can be sent along optical fibres.

> Security systems: some security alarms and lamps are switched on by detectors that pick up the infrared waves from an intruder.

QUESTIONS

3 Explain why you can still control your TV when pointing the remote control towards the wall opposite to the TV.

4 In 1901, well before satellites, Guglielmo Marconi was able to send coded radio signals from England to America. Explain how this was possible.

Optical fibres

Figure 5 shows infrared or light incident at different angles in a semi-circular glass block.

> When $i < c$, the light is refracted out from the block. There is also a weak reflection.

> When $i = c$, the light is refracted at an angle of 90°. There is also a weak reflection.

> When $i > c$, the light does not escape from the block. Instead, it undergoes **total internal reflection**.

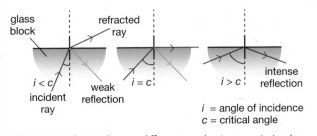

FIGURE 5: Light incident at different angles in a semi-circular glass block.

In an optical fibre, each ray is internally reflected and follows a zigzag path. Copper wires are being replaced by optical fibres in communication networks. Compared with copper wires, optical fibres are cheaper and lighter, do not corrode, carry information securely and transmit information at a speed of about 2×10^8 m/s.

FIGURE 6: The path of a ray inside an optical fibre.

QUESTIONS

5 Estimate the time taken for an infrared signal to travel along 1.0 km of optical fibre.

6 Explain why a ray following a zigzag path within a fibre takes longer to emerge than a ray travelling along the central axis of the fibre.

Further uses of EM waves

You will find out:

> about the uses of ultraviolet, X-rays and gamma rays
> how X-rays are produced

Glowing

Some chemicals glow or fluoresce when exposed to ultraviolet. Security pens have fluorescent ink. Writing your details 'invisibly' on expensive electrical items can help the police to return them if they get stolen. An example of fluorescence is shown in this photograph.

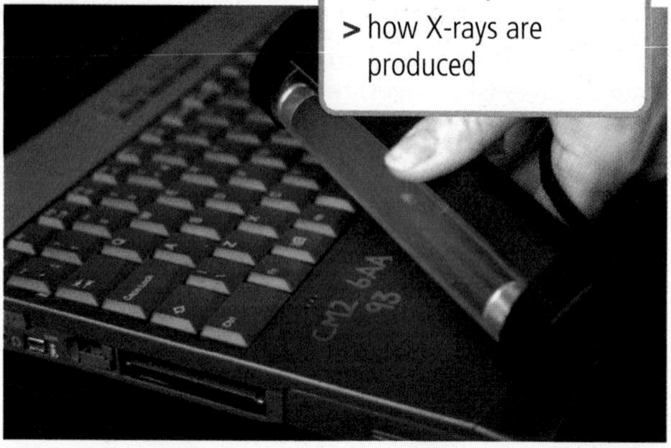

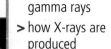

FIGURE 1: A postcode marked on a laptop helps it to be returned to its rightful owner in the case of theft.

Uses of ultraviolet radiation and X-rays

Ultraviolet

Ultraviolet can be produced by special ultraviolet lamps with mercury inside them.

A fluorescent lamp is a long glass tube containing mercury vapour. The inside of the tube is coated with fluorescent powder. The mercury emits ultraviolet when a current is passed through the tube. The ultraviolet makes the powder glow with intense white light (**fluoresce**).

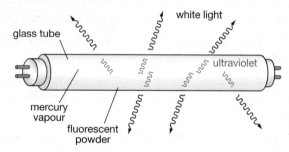

FIGURE 2: A fluorescent lamp.

Forged bank notes can be detected using ultraviolet. Most notes have fluorescent markings. Only a genuine note held under an ultraviolet lamp will show these markings.

Bottled water can be disinfected by exposing it to intense ultraviolet. This kills most of the germs and makes the water safe to drink.

X-rays

X-rays are produced when fast moving electrons hit a metal.

X-rays are easily absorbed by denser materials. Airport security scanners are X-ray machines. With the help of fast computers, these scanners can identify liquids, explosives and metallic objects.

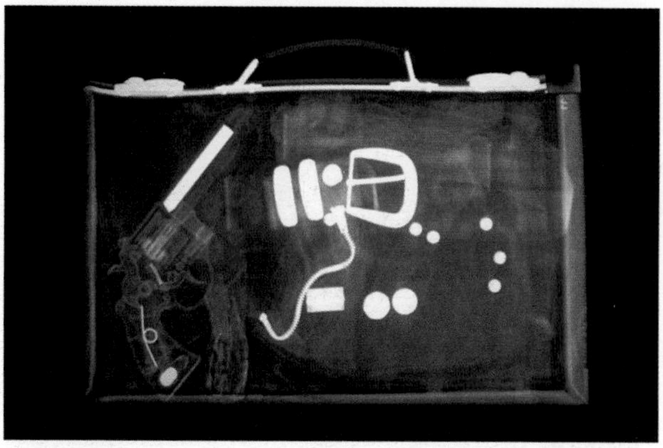

FIGURE 3: What can you identify in this X-ray image from an airport scanner?

Medical X-rays help doctors and dentists to check the condition of bones and teeth. X-rays pass easily through soft tissues like skin, but not through denser bone.

In some food factories, X-rays are used to detect unwanted metal or stones in the products. X-rays are also used to observe the internal structures of objects. For example, an X-ray image of a jet engine can help engineers to identify any loose components within the engine or to locate fine cracks.

QUESTIONS

1 Name the chemical that produces the ultraviolet in a fluorescent lamp.

2 Unscramble the letters 'retabaci' to identify what is killed off when sterilising water.

3 List three applications of X-rays. Using research can you find out about any other applications of X-rays?

Fluorescent materials Sterilising food Sterilising hospital equipment

Uses of gamma rays

Gamma rays are produced by radioactive substances (for example, cobalt-60) and have a number of uses.

Sterilisation

The life of food, especially vegetables and soft fruit, can be prolonged by irradiating it with intense gamma rays. The gamma rays kill off bacteria and mould spores within the food. This **disinfection** process is safe – it does not make the food radioactive.

In hospitals, metal instruments can be boiled to remove germs. The same cannot be done to syringes and bandages in sealed plastic bags. They are sterilised using gamma rays, making the package and its contents safe.

Detecting cancer

The patient is injected with a small amount of radioactive substance, known as a **tracer**. Technetium-99 is a popular tracer which emits gamma rays. The tracer is carried round the body by the blood. It builds up in the cancerous regions. The

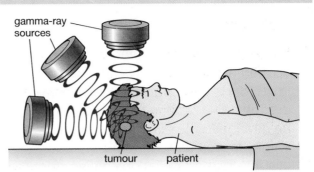

FIGURE 5: Radiotherapy uses gamma rays to kill off cancerous cells.

gamma rays from the technetium pass through the patient and are detected by a special gamma camera.

Treating cancer

Intense gamma rays can be used to destroy cancer cells in a technique known as **radiotherapy**. Radiation from a gamma-ray source is directed at the tumour. The source moves around the patient but is always focused on the cancer. This minimises the amount of radiation passing through the healthy cells. Nevertheless, the patient often feels unwell until the effects of the radiation have worn off.

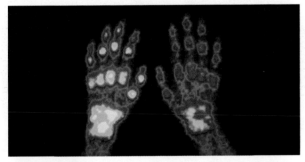

FIGURE 4: Images from a gamma camera of a patient with cancer (shown by the red colour).

QUESTIONS

4 Explain why sterilising strawberries can make them stay fresh for longer.

5 Explain why a moving source of gamma rays is used in radiotherapy rather than a single beam.

An X-ray machine

Figure 6 shows the main components of an X-ray machine.

A high voltage (100 000 volts) is applied between the cathode and the anode. The electrons from the hot filament are accelerated to high speeds towards the anode. The anode has a thick coating of tungsten. The accelerated electrons collide with the tungsten atoms, causing some of the atoms to emit X-rays. About 1% of the kinetic energy of the electrons is converted into X-rays; the rest is lost as heat.

The anode is rotated and also cooled with water to ensure that it does not melt.

QUESTIONS

6 Describe the energy transfer taking place in an X-ray machine.

7 Calculate the power lost as heat in a 60-watt X-ray machine.

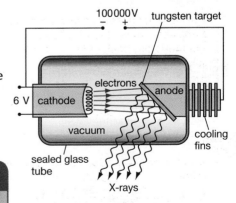

FIGURE 6: An X-ray machine.

Ionising radiation

You will find out:
> about ionising radiation from radioactive sources
> about the harm caused by electromagnetic waves
> about alpha and beta particles

Invisible

Figure 1 shows a fuzzy photograph accidentally produced by Henri Becquerel in 1896. He placed uranium salts on a photographic plate in his drawer. When he developed the plate, this unexpected image appeared. He had discovered invisible ionising radiation coming from the radioactive uranium.

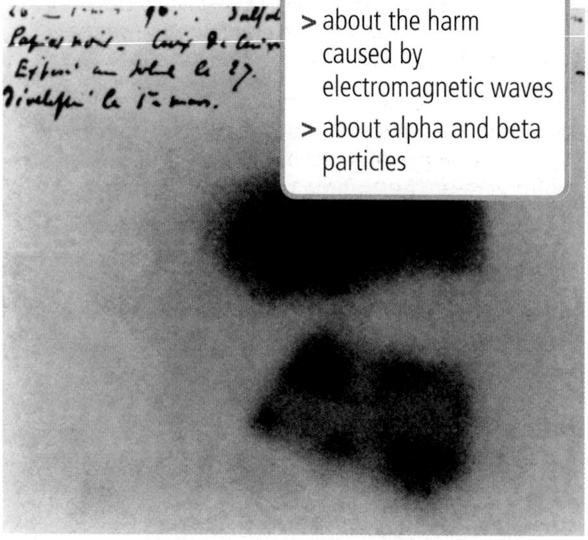

FIGURE 1: A fuzzy image that resulted in Henri Becquerel (1852–1908) receiving the physics Nobel Prize in 1903.

Radioactivity

A neutral atom has a tiny positively charged **nucleus** which is surrounded by a cloud of negatively charged electrons. Radioactivity is a term used to describe the natural and continuous breaking down (*disintegration*) of the *nuclei* of some atoms. As the nuclei disintegrate, they release enormous energy in the form of alpha (α) particles, beta (β) particles and gamma (γ) rays.

Radioactivity occurs naturally. It cannot be switched off and is not affected by temperature.

The timeline below shows some important discoveries.

1895	Wilhelm Röntgen discovers X-rays
1896	Henri Becquerel discovers mysterious 'rays' from uranium salts
1897	Márie Curie names Becquerel's mysterious rays 'radioactivity'
1898	*Gamma rays* are discovered by Paul Villard
	Ernest Rutherford discovers alpha and beta 'radiation'
	Beta radiation is identified as high-speed *electrons* by Fritz Geisel, Henri Becquerel and Marie Curie
1899	W.H. Rollins shows X-rays are dangerous to mammals
1907	Ernest Rutherford identifies alpha radiation as high-speed *helium nuclei*

The scientists with their names in colour were all awarded Nobel Prizes for their remarkable discoveries.

FIGURE 2: Marie Curie (1867–1934) is the only woman in history ever to get two Nobel Prizes.

QUESTIONS

1 Name the three 'radiations' emitted from radioactive materials.

2 According to a student, 'radioactivity can be destroyed by burning'. Explain whether or not this is true.

3 Name the radiation identified to be high-speed electrons.

Ionisation

The term *radiation* is confusing because physicists take it to mean either electromagnetic *waves* or alpha and beta particles from radioactive sources.

Radiation can transfer some or all of its energy to the atoms of the material it passes through. An atom gaining energy can eject an electron and become a positive atom (**ion**). This process is called **ionisation**. Ultraviolet, X-rays, gamma rays, beta particles and alpha particles carry enormous energy. They are all *ionising radiations*. Radioactive sources emit ionising radiation all the time.

Living cells have atoms. These atoms share electrons and are chemically bonded to each other. Hence, all ionising radiations will damage living cells.

QUESTIONS

4 List all cancer-causing radiations.

5 'Ionising radiations destroy living cells'. Explain this statement in terms of *electrons*.

6 Explain why gamma rays are more harmful than ultraviolet.

Harmful waves

Table 1 below shows the effects of excessive exposure to electromagnetic waves.

TABLE 1: Effects of excessive exposure to electromagnetic waves. Notice how the damage is more severe as the frequency and energy of the waves increase.

Waves	What they do
Radio waves	These are safe because they do not produce ionisation
Microwaves	Cause internal heating of body cells. (This is similar to cooking food with microwaves.)
Infrared	Can cause skin burns
Visible light	Intense light can cause permanent damage to the retina
Ultraviolet	Intense ultraviolet damages skin (surface) cells Can trigger skin cancer Can cause eye conditions such as cataracts Destroy proteins in the eye lens
X-rays and gamma rays	Can damage the DNA (deoxyribonucleic acid) of cells Can mutate cells Can trigger cancer

increasing energy and frequency

Detecting radiation

You can detect ionising radiations from radioactive substances in the laboratory using a Geiger–Müller (GM) tube. A single alpha or beta particle entering the tube causes the gas atoms inside the tube to *ionise*. This produces a burst of electrical charge which is detected by the counter connected to the GM tube. Each 'clicking sound' or 'count' represents the detection of a single particle.

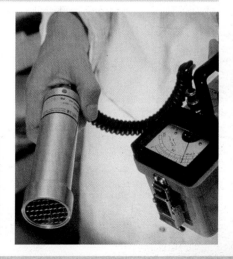

FIGURE 3: A GM tube connected to a portable counter.

QUESTIONS

7 A single alpha particle of kinetic energy 1.4×10^{-13} J travels a distance of 5 cm in air. It takes about 2×10^{-18} J of energy to ionise an air molecule. Estimate the number of molecules ionised per centimetre of air by this alpha particle.

Our place in the Universe

You will find out:
> about the content of the Universe
> about the relative sizes of objects in the Universe
> about the relative distances of objects in the Universe

What can you see?

This is a magnified image of the night sky from the Hubble space telescope. Each blob of light is not a star, but a galaxy. Each of these galaxies has about 100 billion stars!

FIGURE 1: How many galaxies can you see in this image from the Hubble telescope?

The Milky Way

A **galaxy** is a collection of stars held together by the force of gravity. Our galaxy is called the **Milky Way**. The **Universe** contains all of the galaxies and astronomers have estimated that there are about 200 billion galaxies in the Universe.

The stars we see in the night sky are those in our Milky Way. Our Sun is one of many typical stars in the Milky Way. The **Solar System** is a part of the Milky Way. It consists of the Sun, eight planets, asteroids and frozen objects in the Kuiper belt and Oort cloud (see pages 178–9).

Information about the Solar System

The objects in the Solar System vary greatly in size and the planets are at different distances from the Sun; see Table 1 below.

TABLE 1: Objects in the Solar System. 1 AU (astronomical unit) = mean distance between the Sun and the Earth. 1 AU = 1.5×10^{11} m.

Object	Average distance from the Sun (AU)	Diameter relative to Earth
Sun	–	110
Mercury	0.39	0.38
Venus	0.72	0.95
Earth	1.00	1.00
Moon	1.00	0.27
Mars	1.52	0.53
Jupiter	5.20	11.20
Saturn	9.54	9.44
Uranus	19.20	3.69
Neptune	30.10	3.48

If the diameter of the Sun was represented by this page of the book, then the Earth would a single letter on this page and Neptune would be 1.5 km away!

Figure 3 shows a helpful way of visualising the relative distances of the planets in our Solar System.

FIGURE 2: You can see the Milky Way on a clear night.

QUESTIONS

1 List the objects in the table on the left in order of *increasing* size.

2 Which of these items are within our Milky Way?

  Stars   Universe   Solar System   Galaxies

3 A student thinks that 'Mars gets closer to the Earth than Venus'. Explain whether or not the student is right.

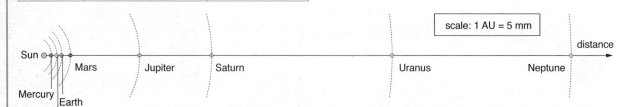

FIGURE 3: Visualising the scale of the Solar System. On this scale, the nearest star will be 1.3 km away. (The Sun and planets are shown much enlarged.)

scale: 1 AU = 5 mm

The scale of things

The Universe is enormous in size. It would take light 100 billion years to cross it. This is a colossal distance of about 10^{27} m. Imagine the palm of your hand is the size of the Universe, then our Solar System would only be equivalent to the tiny nucleus of an atom.

> The Universe contains about 10^{11} galaxies.

> Each galaxy has about 10^{11} stars.

> A star may have its own planets, just like our Solar System.

Table 2 shows the distances between objects in the Universe and the size of the Universe.

Remember!

The speed of light is 3×10^8 m/s.

TABLE 2: The distances between objects in the Universe and the size of the Universe.

Object		Approximate distance (m)	Comments
Earth and Moon		3×10^8	Our nearest neighbour is about 30 Earth diameters away
Sun and Earth		1.5×10^{11}	It takes about 8 minutes for the light from the Sun to reach us
Solar System		4×10^{12}	The outermost planet Neptune is about 30 times further from the Sun than our Earth
Nearest star		4×10^{16}	Proxima Centauri is our nearest star beyond the Sun. No planets have been detected around this star
Closest galaxy		2×10^{22}	Andromeda is our nearest galaxy and is very similar to our own Milky Way. It is about 10^{21} m across
Size of the Universe		1×10^{27}	The Universe contains all the galaxies embedded in its space

QUESTIONS

4 Use Table 1 to calculate the *multiplying* factor as you go from one row to the next. For example, the multiplying factor is $\dfrac{1.5 \times 10^{11}}{3 \times 10^8} = 500$ as you go from the Earth–Moon distance to the Sun–Earth distance.

Light-years

In astronomy, distance is conveniently measured in light-years. A **light-year** (ly) is the distance travelled by light (in a vacuum) in 1 year. It is a bit easier to visualise the size of the Universe when given 100 billion light-years rather than 10^{27} m.

QUESTIONS

5 Show that 1 light-year is equal to 9.5×10^{15} m.

6 Show that Proxima Centauri is 4.2 light-years away.

7 Calculate the distance in metres from Earth to the stars shown in Figure 4.

8 Explain why the light-year is a sensible unit to use for astronomical distances.

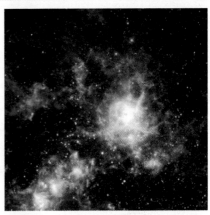

FIGURE 4: These stars are 400 ly from Earth.

Exploring the Universe

You will find out:
> how to observe the Universe with electromagnetic waves
> how evidence for life beyond Earth can be gathered

A little squirt

This photo shows the extraordinary image of Enceladus (a tiny moon of Saturn) taken from the Cassini space probe. The distant yellow blob is the Sun and it is illuminating giant water jets from Enceladus. At −180 °C, the surface of this moon is too cold to sustain life.

FIGURE 1: There is water on this moon. What about life?

Modern telescopes

Apart from visible light, other regions of the electromagnetic (EM) spectrum, such as X-rays, are used by modern telescopes to provide more information on objects in space. This helps astronomers to improve their understanding of the Universe.

Figure 2 shows images of the Milky Way with waves from the different regions of the electromagnetic spectrum.

The dark regions in the 'optical' image are cooler gas and dust clouds. These clouds absorb visible light but not radio waves, microwaves, infrared and gamma rays. The top image shows intense radio waves coming from behind these clouds. The white blobs in the X-ray image show the locations of dense stars emitting strong X-rays.

Here are three benefits of modern telescopes:

> The large image magnification helps astronomers clearly see objects such as galaxies.

> New objects, such as star formations, can be discovered from images taken using different EM waves that could not be seen using visible light.

> All modern telescopes are connected to computers. Computers are able to collect data over long exposure times. More data means that better quality images can be produced.

QUESTIONS

1 State what cooler gas and dust clouds do to visible light.

2 List three advantages of using modern telescopes.

FIGURE 2: This amazing tapestry shows the Milky Way photographed using different electromagnetic waves.

radio continuum (408 MHz)
atomic hydrogen
radio continuum (2.5 GHz)
molecular hydrogen
infrared
mid-infrared
near infrared
optical
x-ray
gamma ray

NASA **Multiwavelength Milky Way**

X-ray images of Universe   SETI project

Gathering information

The Universe has lots of galaxies and stars. A small number of the 10^{22} stars could have planets. There may be a very small chance that some other planets could have alien life forms or microorganisms.

Is there life in the Universe or are we all alone? Scientists are using three methods to gather evidence for life beyond our Earth.

Space probes

Water is important for life. Space probes are sent on fly-by missions to planets looking for the presence of water and other minerals necessary for life to exist. They collect samples and send back to Earth photographs and analyses of the data collected.

Soil experiments by landers

A small robotic **lander** on the surface of a planet can analyse the soil composition and search for life in the form of bacteria. Figure 4 shows the Sojourner rover vehicle on the surface of Mars sampling a large rock (called Yogi). It is solar powered and is controlled remotely from the Earth.

Analysis of soil shows that there was once water on Mars. Landers have so far been sent to the Moon, Venus, Titan (one of Saturn's moons) and Mercury.

Search for Extraterrestrial Intelligence (SETI) project

An advanced **extraterrestrial** civilisation could be using radio waves for communications – just as we do. These broadcasts could be detected here on Earth using large radio telescopes.

FIGURE 3: Sojourner rover vehicle on Mars. Can you see Yogi?

FIGURE 4: What are these radio telescopes waiting for?

> ### QUESTIONS
>
> **3** Discuss the advantages of using fly-by space probes and landers.
>
> **4** Suggest why astronomers think that extraterrestrial aliens would be using radio waves rather than light to communicate.

Jupiter in X-rays

Figure 5 shows Jupiter using X-rays taken from the Chandra X-ray telescope orbiting Earth.

Computer software transforms the intensity of the X-rays into colours that we can interpret. The image shows X-rays being emitted as charged particles from the Sun are trapped and accelerated by Jupiter's strong magnetic field. The data was collected over 17 hours. The white regions show the magnetic poles of Jupiter. Analysing images taken in different EM waves helps scientists to have a better understanding of this mysterious planet.

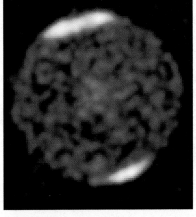

FIGURE 5: Jupiter in X-rays.

> ### QUESTIONS
>
> **5** What does the image in Figure 5 reveal that would otherwise be hidden using visible light?
>
> **6** Discuss why this image was only possible by taking a longer exposure.

Analysing light

You will find out:
> about a simple spectrometer
> about analysing common light sources
> why telescopes are located outside the Earth's atmosphere

A colourful DVD

You must have used a DVD to watch your favourite movie. The information on the disc is stored along closely spaced tracks. Light hitting the shiny surface of the DVD is diffracted (spread out) by these tracks and produces a colourful spectrum of colours. You can use a DVD to investigate light from different sources, including stars.

FIGURE 1: A DVD showing a diffracted spectrum of light.

Spectrometer

White light from a filament lamp can be split up into its component colours using a glass prism. You can also split up white light using a DVD by reflecting it off its shiny surface. A **spectrometer** is a device used for looking at the spectrum of light. You can think of a glass prism and a screen as a spectrometer. You can also make your own spectrometer using a DVD, which is much cheaper than a buying a glass prism.

Figure 2 shows the construction and details of a simple spectrometer made from a DVD and a cereal box.

You can get a clear image of the spectrum by:

> making the slit narrow

> looking at the light source in darkened conditions.

QUESTIONS

1 State two ways in which you can produce a spectrum.

2 Unscramble this meaningless word 'termetroceps' to identify the name of a device.

3 Explain how you would make a simple spectrometer.

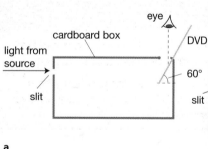

a

b

c

FIGURE 2: a The design of the spectrometer. **b** This is what the spectrometer looks like. **c** This is a typical spectrum.

Light from different sources

You can use a spectrometer to analyse the light from different sources. The spectrometer shown in Figure 2 could be used to investigate the light from the Sun, the Moon, a filament lamp, a fluorescent lamp, a sodium street lamp, a light-emitting diode, a candle, and so on.

Figure 3 shows the spectra produced by some light sources.

Earth's atmosphere and telescopes

The gases in the Earth's atmosphere absorb some electromagnetic (EM) waves more than others. Visible light is not easily absorbed. However, it is still sensible to have large optical telescopes on top of mountains where the air is thinner and there is less turbulence of air.

Q Build your own spectrometer   Optical spectrometers

Spectrum of white light from a filament lamp

Spectrum of the light from the Sun

Spectrum from a fluorescent lamp.

Spectrum from helium gas.

FIGURE 3: The spectra produced by various light sources.

Telescopes and spectrometers

Have a close look at the colours of the stars in the night sky. There is a lot of variety. The colour of a star depends on its surface temperature. In addition, astronomers can identify the chemical composition of the atmosphere of stars by examining the light they emit. Modern telescopes have built-in spectrometers for analysing the light from stars. These spectrometers are much more elaborate than the cereal box version shown in Figure 2.

Remember!
Never look directly at the Sun.

QUESTIONS

4 Compare the spectra from the filament lamp and the fluorescent lamp.

5 Explain why spectrometers are important in astronomy.

Did you know?

Helium was discovered not on the Earth but in the Sun. A spectrometer was used during a solar eclipse in 1868 to identify this new element.

Analysing data (Higher tier only)

When electromagnetic (EM) waves of various wavelengths pass through the Earth's atmosphere, some wavelengths are absorbed. Telescopes that use EM waves and are located outside the Earth's atmosphere, such as the Hubble space telescope, avoid the problem of the Earth's atmosphere absorbing energy.

Figure 4 shows the percentage of energy absorbed against the wavelength of EM waves.

Use the data provided in Figure 4 to answer the questions.

QUESTIONS

6 Identify the type of EM waves that can be used by telescopes on the Earth's surface.

7 Discuss the type of telescopes likely to be found on board satellites orbiting high above the Earth's atmosphere.

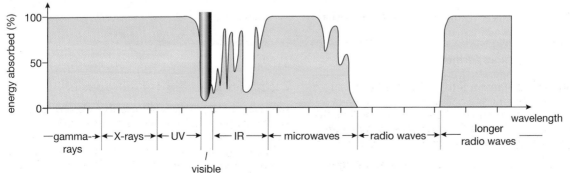

FIGURE 4: A graph showing the effect of the Earth's atmosphere on electromagnetic waves.

How stars are formed

You will find out:
> how stars, including our Sun, are formed
> how a stable Sun was formed

A stellar nursery

This huge cloud of dust and gas is in our Milky Way and is 1000 light-years across. It is a powerhouse for the production of young hot stars. You can see these stars as tiny specks of light.

FIGURE 1: How many clusters of stars can you see?

How stars are formed

The Sun is our local star. It was formed some 4.6 billion years ago from a thin cloud of dust, gas and ice called a **nebula**:

> The gas in this cloud was mostly hydrogen, with some helium.

> The particles in the cloud were attracted to each other by the **force of gravity**.

> After a very long time, the cloud began to contract slowly towards its centre and also started to spin.

> The temperature of the cloud increased as a result of this shrinking. The particles in the nebula began to move faster and bump into each other more frequently.

> As the temperature reached a few million °C, **nuclear fusion** reactions took place between hydrogen nuclei (see the next page). These reactions further increased the temperature and the rate of reaction of hydrogen nuclei.

> Most of the cloud material disappeared, leaving behind the hot ball of glowing gas we call a star.

FIGURE 2: Creation of a star from a dust cloud.

QUESTIONS

1 State what is meant by a nebula.

2 Sequence the stages of how a star is formed from a nebula.

Formation of stars from nebulae   Temperature of stars

Our local star – the Sun

Our Sun is an *average* star, often referred to as a **main sequence star**. It has a surface temperature of about 5500 °C, which makes it appear yellow. Its central core is much hotter at 14 million °C. Figure 3 shows the Orion constellation. The pink star at the top is Betelgeuse. Its surface is much cooler than the Sun at 3200 °C. The blue stars are much hotter than our Sun.

The energy from the Sun comes from nuclear reactions between hydrogen nuclei. These reactions produce vast amounts of energy, some as electromagnetic (EM) radiation.

FIGURE 3: The constellation of Orion. Not all stars are the same.

How is it that the Sun does not collapse under its own gravity? There is a delicate balance of forces at the surface of the Sun. The force of gravity is trying to pull all matter towards the centre of the Sun. This is balanced by the force produced by the EM radiation pushing its way out from the Sun. The Sun will continue to have a stable shape as long as the *inward* force of gravity is balanced out by the *outward* force from the radiation.

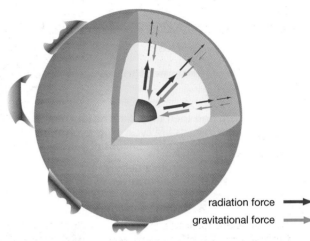

radiation force →
gravitational force →

FIGURE 4: What prevents the Sun from collapsing?

QUESTIONS

3 Explain the origin of the radiation from the Sun.

4 Suggest what might happen to the Sun if the nuclear reactions suddenly stopped.

5 Explain how the temperature of a star can be estimated.

Fusion reactions

All stars get their energy from nuclear fusion reactions. These reactions are quite complicated. The fast-moving hydrogen nuclei in the core of stars join together (*fuse*) and produce helium nuclei. In each reaction, some of the mass of the hydrogen nuclei is lost and this reappears as energy.

hydrogen → helium + energy

The reaction above is often referred to as **hydrogen burning**.

The Sun converts about 4 billion kilograms of matter into energy every second. It is amazing that it has been doing this for the last 4.6 billion years.

Did you know?

Scientists are trying to build fusion reactors that work like the reactions in the Sun as a way of producing large quantities of cheap, clean energy.

QUESTIONS

6 The mass of the Sun is 2×10^{30} kg. Predict how long the Sun will last. Clearly state any assumptions made.

7 Explain why fusion might offer a good source of energy. Use the internet to help you research your answer.

Evolution of stars

You will find out:
> about the evolution of the Sun
> about the evolution of massive stars

Supernovae

Figure 1 shows hot gases expanding from a star that was observed by Johann Kepler about 400 years ago. It is quite extraordinary that all the elements on Earth, such as the oxygen we breathe and the iron in our blood, originated from such exploding stars, known as supernovae.

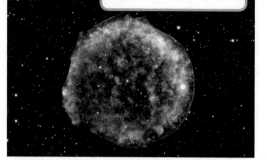

FIGURE 1: This is what an exploded star looks like.

Life cycle

Stars are born and then they die. The journey of a star in time is known as its **life cycle** or its evolution. This can last for millions or even billions of years.

The Sun was created from a nebula. It will spend most of its life as a stable star. However, when the Sun eventually runs out of hydrogen, it will start to use helium as fuel. The fusion of helium will produce elements such as carbon and oxygen, and this will cause a change.

QUESTIONS

1 Suggest how the mass of the star formed depends on the size of the nebula.

Evolution of stars with a similar mass to the Sun

As the Sun starts to use helium as a fuel, the following changes will happen:

> The outer layers of the Sun will expand and cool. It will become a **red giant**. As a red giant, the Sun will swallow up all the planets up to Mars. Do not worry; this is some 5 billion years into the future!

> Eventually, the central core of the Sun will run out of elements to fuse.

> The core of the Sun will shrink under its own force of gravity. It will become very hot and dense – becoming a **white dwarf**.

> The white dwarf will slowly cool and end its life as a **black dwarf**.

QUESTIONS

2 Name some of the elements found in the Sun.

3 Choose the appropriate words to describe a red giant:

   big, tiny, cool, hot, dense.

4 Describe the evolution of the Sun.

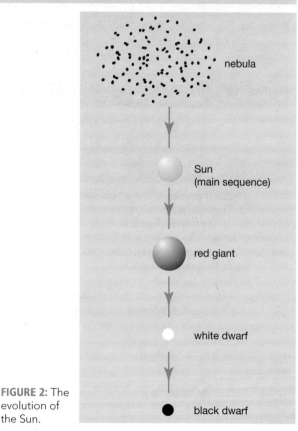

FIGURE 2: The evolution of the Sun.

nebula

Sun (main sequence)

red giant

white dwarf

black dwarf

Evolution of massive stars (Higher tier only)

Larger mass stars are created from larger nebulae. In the night sky, these massive stars appear blue in colour. Massive stars will, just like the Sun, eventually die. However, their evolution is very different:

> The outer layers of the star will expand and cool as it runs out of hydrogen. It expands into a **super red giant**.

> Within the central core of the star, the nuclear fusion reactions will produce heavier elements such as magnesium and iron. The core of the star has layers of elements, with iron in the middle.

> Eventually, the nuclear fusion reactions will suddenly stop when there is no more fuel left.

> The only force acting on the core will be the huge force of gravity. The shells of the core will suddenly shrink and bounce off violently against the solid iron core. This will eject the hot material of the shells into space. Even heavier elements, such as gold and uranium, are produced in this explosion. The exploding star is known as a **supernova**.

> The core of the star becomes a very dense **neutron star**. Neutron stars are so dense that a spoonful of their material would have a mass of more than a billion tonnes.

> For super-massive stars, the neutron star will collapse even further to become a **black hole**.

> A black hole has an extremely strong gravitational force around it; even light cannot escape it. Black holes also curve and distort the space around them.

> **Did you know?**
>
> The super red giant VY Canis Majoris is 2000 times bigger than the Sun. It would take 5000 years to travel round it on a high-speed train!

> **Did you know?**
>
> A white dwarf is a million times denser than water.

○ QUESTIONS

5 Describe the evolution of a star much larger in mass than the Sun.

6 Explain the origin of the elements ejected from a supernova.

7 Estimate the diameter of VY Canis Majoris if the Sun is represented by a dot of diameter 1 mm.

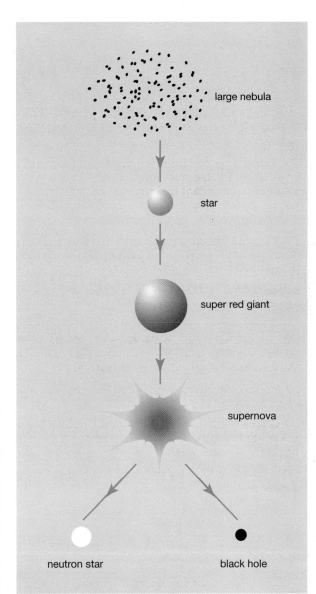

FIGURE 3: The evolution of a massive star.

Steady State and Big Bang

You will find out:
> about the Steady State theory of the Universe
> about the Big Bang theory of the Universe
> about cosmic microwave background radiation and red-shift

Creation from empty space

Imagine if hydrogen atoms were created out of nowhere right in front of you; this extraordinary idea was proposed by Fred Hoyle in his Steady State theory of the Universe. As you will see here, this theory lost out in favour of the Big Bang theory of the Universe.

FIGURE 1: Fred Hoyle (left) showing Prince Charles a telescope in 1974.

Theories about the Universe

Steady State theory of the Universe

The **Steady State theory** was proposed by Fred Hoyle, Hermann Bondi and Thomas Gold in 1946. According to this model, the Universe:

> is expanding

> has unchanging density

> spontaneously created matter, especially hydrogen, from empty space to keep the density the same

> had no beginning and will have no end.

Big Bang theory of the Universe

The main contributions to this theory came from George Gamov in 1948. According to this model, the Universe:

> is expanding

> is finite and ever changing

> was created some 14 billion years ago from an event known as the **Big Bang**

> may have an end depending on its density.

QUESTIONS

1 State one in thing common between the Steady State and Big Bang theories.

2 Give two pieces of supporting evidence for the Big Bang theory.

You can think of the Big Bang as a hot explosion from which *space* and *time* began. The Big Bang caused the Universe to expand and made every galaxy in the Universe move away from each other.

The currently accepted model of the Universe is the Big Bang theory because it explains the existence of **cosmic microwave background (CMB) radiation**.

This is an example of how scientists use evidence to prove, or disprove, a theory.

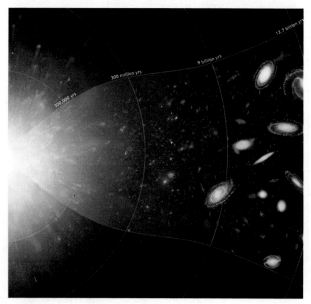

FIGURE 2: Radiation thought to come from the Big Bang still fills the Universe today.

Evidence for the Big Bang theory

Cosmic microwave background (CMB) radiation

One of George Gamov's predictions about the Universe was that it would be flooded with microwaves. These microwaves may be considered as the 'left-over radiation' from the Big Bang. We refer to these microwaves as CMB radiation. It can be detected by radio telescopes on Earth. The strength of this radiation is the same in all directions. The origin of these microwaves is explained on pages 216–17.

Red-shift

The spectrum of light from the Sun has dark lines set against a continuous spectrum of colours. These lines are caused by the Sun's cooler atmosphere absorbing specific colours of light. The spectrum of light from the stars of a distant galaxy is almost identical to that of the Sun, but with one major difference. The dark lines are all shifted towards longer wavelengths. This is called red-shift because the lines are shifted towards the red end of the spectrum. The significance of red-shift is explained on pages 216–17.

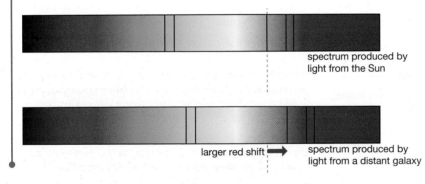

spectrum produced by light from the Sun

larger red shift → spectrum produced by light from a distant galaxy

FIGURE 3: Each dark line is red-shifted.

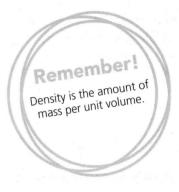

Remember!
Density is the amount of mass per unit volume.

QUESTIONS

3 Make a list of facts about CMB radiation.

4 Explain what is meant by red-shift.

Did you say bird poo?

The existence of CMB radiation was predicted by Gamov, but it was accidentally discovered by two radio astronomers 30 years later. Arno Penzias and Robert Wilson were trying to communicate with orbiting satellites and ran into technical problems.

They were continuously detecting some sort of 'static' coming from all directions of space. When they noticed a pigeon's nest, they tried, without success, to remove this annoying problem by clearing bird droppings from their telescope dish. It was only through chance conversations with other physicists that they realised they had discovered CMB radiation. Both received the physics Nobel Prize in 1978.

QUESTIONS

5 The strength of the 'static' picked by the astronomers was the same in all directions. Suggest the significance of this.

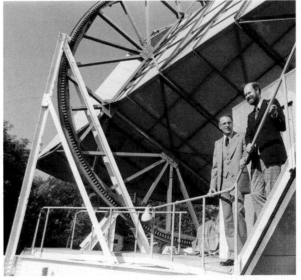

FIGURE 4: Penzias and Wilson in front of their 'clean' telescope dish in 1978.

The expanding Universe

You will find out:
> about the red-shift of light from galaxies
> about the evidence supporting the Big Bang theory
> why the Steady State theory was rejected

Looking back in time

Andromeda is our closest galaxy. The light from this galaxy takes 2.3 million years to reach us. The galaxy we see through our telescopes must be 2.3 million years in the past. So, someone looking at the Earth from this galaxy would see a time when our ape-like ancestors roamed the planet.

FIGURE 1: How old is this picture?

Evidence of an expanding Universe (Higher tier only)

Stretching and squeezing waves

You may have noticed the change in the pitch of sound when a wave source such as a siren on a police car passes you. The sound waves are *squeezed* together when the car is approaching and *lengthened* when it recedes. The relative motion of the car changes the wavelength and frequency of the sound. This effect is known as the **Doppler effect**.

The Doppler effect is also observed with light emitted from a moving source, such as a star:

> The wavelength of light *decreases* and frequency *increases* when the light source is moving towards an observer. This is known as blue-shift.

> The wavelength of light *increases* and frequency *decreases* when the light source is moving away from an observer. This is known as red-shift.

Light from distant galaxies

The light from all galaxies in the Universe is red-shifted. They must therefore be moving away from us and each other. The Universe must be expanding.

The further the galaxy, the greater the red-shift. This must mean that the more distant galaxies are moving away *more quickly*.

QUESTIONS

1 Explain the significance of red-shift of light from galaxies.

2 State how the distance of a galaxy affects its red-shift.

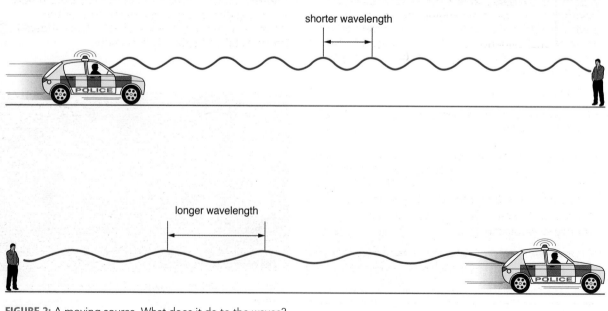

shorter wavelength

longer wavelength

FIGURE 2: A moving source. What does it do to the waves?

Big Bang (Higher tier only)

The further you look into space, the further back in time you go. Imagine how the Universe would have been in the past. This is like running a movie backwards in your mind. The Universe must have had a beginning. The Universe came into existence some 14 billion years ago. All the space, matter and radiation we see today originated from an event we call the Big Bang.

The Big Bang was very hot and extremely dense. In the first few seconds, matter in the form of hydrogen and helium nuclei was produced in abundance. About 25% of the matter in the Universe is helium. During the expansion which followed the Big Bang, the Universe cooled. After billions of years, atoms, then stars and then galaxies were formed.

There is strong evidence for the Big Bang theory:

> All galaxies show red-shift; the Universe must therefore be expanding.

> The temperature of the Universe was predicted to be −270 °C (3 kelvin). This was first confirmed by the COBE satellite in the 1990s.

> The original radiation formed in the Big Bang would have been short wavelength gamma rays. The expansion of the Universe, and of space itself, *stretched out* this electromagnetic radiation. We now observe this remnant radiation as cosmic microwave background (CMB) radiation. The CMB radiation has a wavelength of about 1 mm.

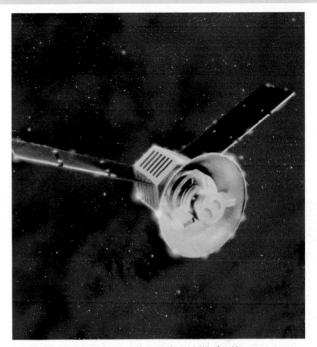

FIGURE 3: The COBE satellite. What did it find?

QUESTIONS

3 Sequence the key events after the Big Bang.

Big Bang or Steady State? (Higher tier only)

In both the **Big Bang theory** and the **Steady State theory** the Universe is expanding; hence both would predict red-shift of light from galaxies. Based on the observational evidence, the Big Bang theory is the accepted theory. The Steady State theory is rejected because it cannot explain:

> the existence of CMB radiation

> the abundance of light elements, especially the 25% helium in the Universe.

QUESTIONS

4 State the evidence for the Big Bang theory and explain why the Steady State theory was rejected.

5 Describe the two predictions made by the Big Bang theory about the temperature of the Universe.

Another amazing prediction of the Big Bang theory was the slight variation in temperature of the Universe. These tiny 'ripples' of 10^{-4} °C are shown in Figure 4, taken by the COBE satellite.

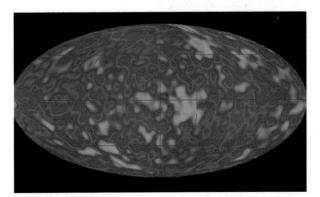

FIGURE 4: Our Universe in colour. The pink regions are warmer.

Q Closest galaxy   COBE satellite

P1 checklist (Topics 1–3)

To achieve your forecast grade in the exam you'll need to revise

Use this checklist to see what you can do now. Refer back to pages 176–217 if you're not sure.

Look across the rows to see how you could progress – **bold italic** means Higher tier only.

Remember you'll need to be able to use these ideas in various ways, such as:
> interpreting pictures, diagrams and graphs
> applying ideas to new situations
> explaining ethical implications
> suggesting some benefits and risks to society
> drawing conclusions from evidence you've been given.

Look at pages 270–92 for more information about exams and how you'll be assessed.

To aim for a grade E	To aim for a grade C	To aim for a grade A
recall the key features of the two models of the Solar System: geocentric and heliocentric	describe and apply the structure of the geocentric and heliocentric models	provide the evidence for the heliocentric model and understand the social and scientific context in which it developed
recall the methods (the naked eye, photography and telescopes) used to observe the Universe and the Solar System and understand the role of light in these methods	compare the methods used to observe and find out information about the Universe	explain the advantages and disadvantages of the methods used to observe the Universe and how they developed
understand that all waves can be reflected and refracted	describe what happens to waves at a boundary	*explain refraction in terms of change of speed of a wave at a boundary*
describe what happens to light when it passes through a converging lens	explain how to measure the focal length of a converging lens	apply information about the focal length to magnification and investigate factors affecting magnification
recall how Galileo's and Newton's telescopes worked	outline the timeline in the development of the telescope and how both reflecting and refracting telescopes work	explain how telescopes magnify the image formed by the objective lens (or mirror) *and analyse data about telescopes*

To aim for a grade E | To aim for a grade C | To aim for a grade A

To aim for a grade E	To aim for a grade C	To aim for a grade A
recall and define the following terms: frequency, wavelength, amplitude and speed	use the wave equation to solve problems	interpret and apply the terms frequency, wavelength, amplitude and speed to solve problems rearrange the wave equation to solve problems
recall the parts of the visible spectrum recall the properties of electromagnetic (EM) waves	describe the discovery of EM waves and list EM waves in order of decreasing (or increasing) wavelength and frequency	explain what EM waves consist of
recall that some EM waves and radioactivity are dangerous	describe in detail the harmful effects of EM radiation and radioactivity	
recall some of the uses of EM waves	describe in detail the uses of radio waves, microwaves, infrared, visible light, ultraviolet light, X-rays and gamma rays	
recall that radioactivity occurs naturally	explain ionising radiation in terms of particles, rays and energy	
recall that the Universe contains galaxies and our Solar System is part of the Milky Way	compare and contrast the relative sizes of objects in the Universe	
recall the methods used to explore the Universe using EM waves	explain the methods used to explore the Universe	evaluate data to explain the methods used to explore the Universe
recall the evolution of the Sun from a nebula	describe the evolution of the Sun from a nebula	*describe the evolution of massive stars and understand the importance of fusion reactions in stars*
demonstrate an understanding of the main concepts of the two models of the Universe: Steady State and Big Bang	describe the Steady State and Big Bang models of the Universe and understand that there is evidence to support them	*provide evidence to support the Big Bang model of the Universe: red-shift of galaxies, CMB radiation and the abundance of light elements*

AO1 **1** **a** A long time ago, astronomers believed in the geocentric model of the Solar System. In the geocentric model, what did all the objects in the Solar System move round?

    A Moon   C Sun

    B Earth   D Milky Way.   [1]

AO1 **b** Which one of the following is a correct statement of the geocentric model of the Solar System?

    A the Earth was stationary

    B the Sun was stationary

    C the planets moved in oval-shaped orbits

    D the Moon went round the Sun.   [1]

c Colin uses a telescope to see Jupiter and its moons. The diagram below shows his observations over two days. The moons of Jupiter are shown by dots.

·   · O ·   · | · O ·   · ·   ·

AO3 **i** Explain what you can conclude about the motion of the moons of Jupiter from the diagram.   [2]

AO3 **ii** Galileo carried out observations similar to Colin more than 500 years ago. Explain how Galileo's observations of the Solar System provided evidence for the heliocentric model of the Universe.   [2]

AO2 **iii** Colin used a telescope to make his observations. Explain the advantages to Colin of using a telescope rather than the naked eye to observe the moons of Jupiter.   [2]

                            [Total: 8]

2 The list below shows the electromagnetic spectrum.

Radio waves	Microwaves	Infrared	Visible light	Ultraviolet	X-rays	Gamma rays

AO1 **a** Name two waves in this spectrum that are used in long-distance communication.   [2]

AO1 **b** State one difference and one similarity between radio waves and gamma rays.   [2]

AO2 **c** Explain why gamma rays are more harmful than visible light.   [1]

AO2 **d** The speed of radio waves is 300 000 000 m/s. Calculate the wavelength of radio waves of frequency 200 000 Hz. State the unit.   [3]

                            [Total: 8]

3 **a** Our Sun was formed a long time ago from a dust cloud called a nebula.

AO1 **i** State the attractive force that pulled together the matter of the nebula.   [1]

AO1 **ii** Describe the likely evolution of the Sun.   [3]

AO1 **b** Explain what is meant by the Big Bang theory.   [2]

AO1 **c** State two pieces of supporting evidence for the Big Bang theory.   [2]

                            [Total: 8]

4 **a** The diagram below shows the path of light rays through a lens.

AO1 **i** State the name given to the type of lens shown in the diagram.   [1]

AO1 **ii** Explain what is meant by the focal length of the lens.   [1]

AO1 **iii** Describe how the shape of the lens affects the focal length.   [2]

AO1 AO3 **b** You are given a converging lens, a screen and a ruler. Your teacher wants you to measure the focal length of the lens. Describe how you would accurately determine the focal length of the lens. Discuss how you could improve the quality of your results.   [6]

                           [Total: 10]

AO1 recall the science   AO2 apply your knowledge   AO3 evaluate and analyse the evidence

✳ Worked example

a The photograph shows our closest galaxy called Andromeda.

AO1 i Explain what is meant by a galaxy. [1]

A galaxy has lots of stars held together by the force of gravity. ✔

AO2 ii Name two objects that lie in the space between our Sun and Andromeda. [2]

Galaxies and space. ✘ ✘

AO1 iii The light from Andromeda shows red-shift. Explain what is meant by red-shift. [2]

Red-shift means light's wavelength is changing. It becomes redder. ✔ ✘

AO1 b Astronomers have now rejected the Steady State theory of the Universe in favour of the Big Bang theory. Describe the Steady State theory and state one piece of evidence that led to its rejection. [3]

In the Steady State model, matter is created from space. It was red-shift that led to the rejection of Steady State theory. ✔ ✘ ✘

How to raise your grade

Take note of the comments from examiners – these will help you to improve your grade.

This is an excellent start with a very clear answer.

Since Andromeda is our closest galaxy, there cannot be galaxies between the Sun and Andromeda. 'Space' is not an object. The examiners were looking for planets and stars as the answers.

The candidate was awarded a mark for recognising that it was the wavelength of the light that was affected. Stating that the light becomes 'redder' is unscientific – all wavelengths become longer.

The candidate has not given a detailed answer or expanded on their first sentence. Examiners would have allowed an additional mark for 'the density of the Universe remained constant'. Red-shift is accounted for in both Big Bang and Steady State theories; the examiners were looking for cosmic microwave background (CMB) radiation as evidence.

This candidate scored 3 marks out of a possible 8. This is below a grade C. Extra marks could have been gained in **aiii** and **b** by carefully reading the question and providing greater depth in the answers. This would have lifted the performance to a grade C.

1 a The diagram below shows the heliocentric model of the Solar System.

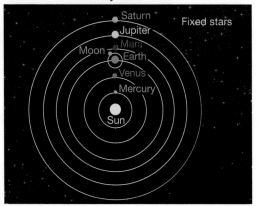

AO1 **i** Apart from the Sun at the centre, state two other assumptions of the heliocentric model of the Solar System. [2]

AO1 **ii** Explain why the heliocentric model was as inaccurate as the geocentric model of the Solar System at predicting the positions of the planets. [1]

b Galileo used a telescope made from lenses to observe the Solar System. With this telescope he could see more detail than by the naked eye. The diagram below shows a modern telescope with an objective lens and an eyepiece.

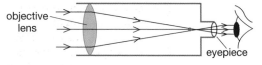

AO1 **i** What do both lenses do to the light? [1]

A make the light brighter C magnify the light
B refract the light D reflect the light.

AO1 **ii** Explain the purpose of the objective lens. [2]

AO2 **iii** Newton developed a telescope that used a concave mirror in place of the converging objective lens. Suggest an advantage of Newton's reflecting telescope over Galileo's refracting telescope. [2]

[Total: 8]

2 The diagram below shows radio waves used for communications between America and England.

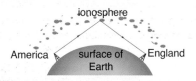

AO1 **a** Radio waves are electromagnetic waves. State two properties of all electromagnetic waves. [2]

AO2 **b** Explain why the radio waves sent between America and England have a small time delay. [2]

AO2 **c** The radio waves sent between America and England have a frequency of 200 kHz. The speed of radio waves is 3.0×10^8 m/s. Calculate the wavelength of the radio waves. State the unit. [4]

[Total: 8]

3 a The diagram below shows an object placed close to a converging lens.

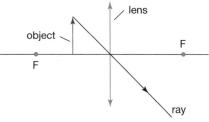

The focal point of the lens is shown by the letter F. The path of one ray of light from the top of the object is shown.

AO2 **i** On a copy of the diagram, draw another ray from the top of the object and locate the position of the image. [2]

AO1 **ii** State two properties of the image formed by the lens. [2]

b A camera uses a converging lens to form an image of a tall building on a film.

AO1 **i** State one property of the image formed by the lens. [1]

AO2 **ii** Image magnification = $\dfrac{\text{image height}}{\text{object height}}$

The image has a magnification of 4×10^{-4} and a height of 1.2 cm. Calculate the height of the object in metres (m). [3]

[Total: 8]

AO1 **4 a** Our Milky Way has stars that are much more massive than our Sun. All stars are created from dust clouds. Describe and explain the evolution of such a star after it has fused most of its hydrogen. [4]

AO1 **b** The Big Bang theory is the currently accepted
AO2 model used to explain the origin of the Universe. Explain how the Big Bang theory developed and came to be accepted by the scientific community as the most appropriate model for the evolution of the Universe. [6]

[Total: 10]

AO1 recall the science   AO2 apply your knowledge   AO3 evaluate and analyse the evidence

✳ Worked example

a The light from a distant galaxy is red-shifted.

AO1 **i** Explain what is meant by red-shift. [1]

Red-shift is when the wavelengths get longer for the entire spectrum. ✔

AO3 **ii** Explain how the red-shift from a more distant galaxy will be different and explain what astronomers have concluded from this about the Universe. [3]

More distant galaxies show greater red-shift. The Universe must therefore be expanding. ✔ ✔

AO2 **b** A particular galaxy is 100 million light-years away. The speed of light in a vacuum is 3.0×10^8 m/s. Use the information below to calculate the time in seconds it would take for the light from this galaxy to reach us. Show your working and give the unit. [4]

$$\text{speed} = \frac{\text{distance}}{\text{time}}$$

1 million light-years = 1.5×10^{17} m

distance = $100 \times 10^6 \times 1.5 \times 10^{17} = 1.5 \times 10^{25}$ m. ✘

time = $\dfrac{\text{distance}}{\text{speed}}$ ✔

time = $1.5 \times 10^{25} / 3.0 \times 10^8$ ✔ (error carried forward)

time = 5.0. ✘

How to raise your grade

Take note of the comments from examiners – these will help you to improve your grade.

> This is a clear answer from the candidate.

> The candidate's first statement is accurate but brief, as 3 marks are available. The examiners were looking for statements that suggested that the universe had a beginning. A mention of the Big Bang would have secured an additional mark.

> There was no need to include the factor of 10^6 because the conversion from 1 million light-years was given.

> The candidate's incorrect value has been used in a correct method of calculation. The examiner will not penalise the same mistake again and so the candidate receives marks for completing the correct method. Sadly, the candidate has not given the correct powers of ten in the final answer and so has lost one further mark.

This candidate scored 5 marks out of a possible 8. This is below a grade A. The candidate could have easily secured a grade A by carefully using the formula in **b**. Misreading the calculator and missing the unit is uncharacteristic of A-grade candidates.

P1 Universal physics (Topics 4–6)

What you should know

Sound and waves

Sound waves travel through media.

We can hear sound using our ears.

- Which of the following can sound waves travel through: solids, liquids or gases?

Magnetism and electricity

Fossil fuels and renewable sources are used to provide energy.

How power stations work.

Electric current and voltage can be used to explain circuits.

Electrical symbols can be used to draw series and parallel circuits.

Magnets and electromagnets create a magnetic field.

The strength of an electromagnet depends on the size of the current.

- Draw and name two symbols used in electrical circuits.

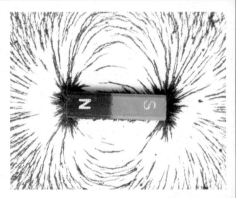

Energy

Energy is always conserved.

Energy can be transformed into heat.

Thermal energy is transferred by conduction, convection and radiation.

- What type of energy do objects in motion have?

You will find out about

> infrasound and ultrasound

> the uses of infrasound and ultrasound

> how earthquakes are created by seismic waves and how we can locate earthquakes

> how seismic waves are reflected and refracted by the inside of the Earth

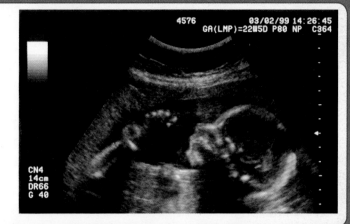

> electrical current and voltage in circuits

> using non-renewable and renewable resources to generate electricity in power stations

> how generators and transformers work

> how electricity is transported using the National Grid

> electrical power and payback times

> low-energy devices

> determining the efficiency of electrical items

> conservation of energy

> energy transfers

> the factors that affect the absorption and emission of infrared radiation

Ultrasound and infrasound

You will find out:
> about ultrasound and infrasound
> about uses of ultrasound and infrasound

Your first picture

Your first picture was probably taken by a hospital radiographer when you were still inside your mother's womb. Figure 1 shows an ultrasound scan. This image is produced using inaudible high-frequency sound waves. Unlike X-rays, they are very safe.

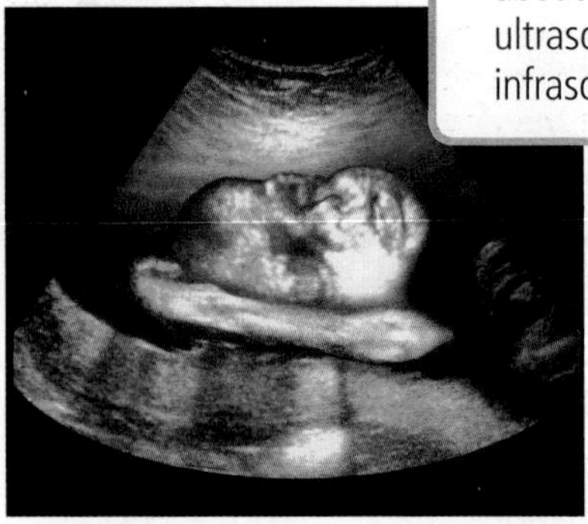

FIGURE 1: An ultrasound scan. Have you seen your first photograph?

What you can and cannot hear

Human hearing

Humans can hear sounds in the frequency range of 20 Hz to 20000 hertz (Hz). This range is not the same for everybody. For example, younger people can hear higher frequencies much more than older people.

Did you know?

Some dogs can hear up to 48000 Hz.

Ultrasound

Sound with frequencies greater than 20000 Hz is known as **ultrasound**. We cannot hear or feel these vibrations. This is different for some animals. Dolphins use ultrasound for communicating with each other, as do some moths, mice, rats, grasshoppers and frogs.

Infrasound

Sound with frequencies lower than 20 Hz is known as **infrasound**. We cannot hear infrasound, but we can feel these slow vibrations. It gives humans a sensation of unease, which is exploited by some film soundtracks.

Whales use infrasound to communicate with each other over long distances (several hundred kilometres). Hippopotamuses, rhinoceroses, elephants, okapis, giraffes and alligators also use infrasound to communicate.

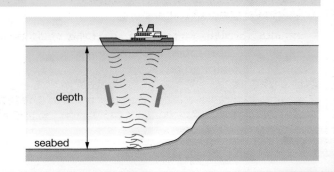

FIGURE 2: Humpback whales. How do they communicate?

QUESTIONS

1 Identify the sound signals we cannot hear from this list: 10 Hz; 100 Hz; 1000 Hz; 10000 Hz; 100000 Hz.

2 State one similarity and one difference between infrasound and ultrasound.

3 State which type of sound wave travels longer distances.

Sound waves

Ultrasound is used by some animals for communication. It is also used for **sonar** and foetal scanning. The speed of sound varies depending on the material it travels through, and so it will be different for a solid, a liquid or a gas. The closer the molecules are in a substance, the faster the sound waves travel.

depth

seabed

FIGURE 3: Ships use sonar to find the depth of water.

Sonar – Sound Navigation And Ranging

This is a technique used by ships to determine the depth of water. Pulses of ultrasound are reflected off the bottom of the seabed. The time delay between receiving the echo and sending the ultrasound can be used to determine the depth of the water.

Dolphins and bats also use ultrasound to navigate and find their prey. The technique is called **echolocation** rather than sonar. Bats can identify the shape and texture of their surroundings.

Foetal scanning

Ultrasound is used for safely examining the inside of the body. Different tissues reflect ultrasound by different amounts. Echoes from the inside of the body are used to create an image. In order to see fine details, the frequency of the ultrasound has to be very high, typically 1.5 MHz.

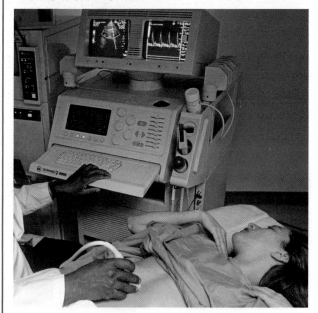

FIGURE 4: A woman having a foetal scan in a hospital.

Uses of infrasound

Infrasound is produced naturally by volcanoes, avalanches, ocean waves, hurricanes, earthquakes, meteorite explosions and movement of animals on the ground. It can also be produced by human activity such as drilling for oil, and nuclear and chemical explosions. Infrasound can travel hundreds of kilometres through air and ground. Animals are more responsive to these waves than humans.

Infrasound is used by humans to detect and monitor:

> animal movement in remote locations

> volcanic eruptions

> meteorite explosions.

FIGURE 5: Birds can hear infrasound. Are these birds flying away from a natural disaster?

QUESTIONS

4 List six naturally occurring sources of infrasound.

5 Describe the common features of sonar and foetal scans.

Deep waters

Sonar can be used to determine the depth of water. This is illustrated with the following example.

The delay time between receiving an echo and sending a burst of ultrasound is 0.60 s. The velocity of ultrasound in water is 1500 m/s. Calculate the depth of water:

distance travelled by ultrasound = velocity of ultrasound × delay time

= 1500 × 0.60

= 900 m

The total distance travelled by the wave is 900 m. This is twice the depth of the water because the wave has to travel to the seabed and then back up to the ship. Therefore:

depth of water = $\frac{900}{2}$ = 450 m

QUESTIONS

6 A boat on Loch Ness is using sonar. The depth of Loch Ness is about 220 m. Calculate the delay time for the ultrasound.

7 The speed of ultrasound in the body is about 1500 m/s. Calculate the wavelength of ultrasound of frequency 1.5 MHz.

The Earth and earthquakes

You will find out:
> about the interior structure of the Earth
> about tectonic plates

Something strange about this Earth

This drawing shows how it is thought the Earth looked some 250 million years ago. All the continents were bunched together. The movement of the molten magma beneath the ground slowly moved the continents apart.

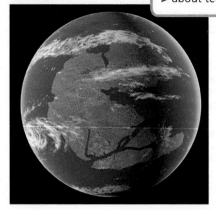

FIGURE 1: Can you spot South America and Africa?

The Earth

Figure 2 shows that the Earth is not a solid ball; it has several layers:

> Inner core – very hot, very dense and solid iron.

> Outer core – very hot, dense and liquid, mostly iron.

> Mantle – hot, less dense and a mixture of solid and hot molten rocks.

> Crust – very thin layer, like the shell of an egg and made up of plates.

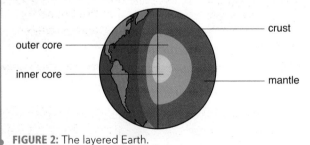

FIGURE 2: The layered Earth.

crust

outer core

inner core

mantle

The material underneath the crust is a hot sludgy liquid called **magma**. Magma is known as lava when it spills on to the surface of the Earth from volcanoes and cracks in the Earth's crust. The magma under the crust is constantly moving. Its motion is similar to convection currents in water that is being heated, but much slower. The crust, with its continents and oceans, sits on top of the magma. The motion of the magma in the mantle makes the thin crust drift slowly at a rate of about 1–3 cm per year.

QUESTIONS

1 Name the thin outermost layer of the Earth.

2 State the material at the centre of the Earth.

3 Explain what makes the Earth's crust move slowly.

Tectonic plates

The Earth's crust is divided into several solid pieces known as **tectonic plates**. These solid rocky plates float and move on top of the magma due to convection currents in the mantle. The arrows in Figure 3 show the direction of the movements of these plates. The plates move very slowly, so you do not notice this movement.

Like the pieces of a jigsaw, the east coast of South America and the west coast of Africa were once joined together. In 250 million years they have drifted apart to their current positions.

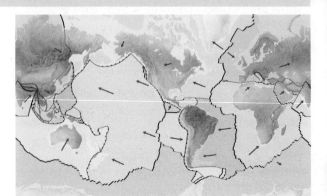

FIGURE 3: How many moving plates can you see?

Earthquakes

An earthquake is a shaking of the ground caused by the sudden movement of tectonic plates. Figure 4 shows two tectonic plates pushed in opposite directions.

At first the frictional force between the plates at the plate boundary prevents them from moving. There comes a time when the frictional forces are not strong enough to keep the plates still and they suddenly slip. This sudden movement of the plates releases the immense energy stored in the compressed plates as **seismic waves**. Seismic waves cause serious damage over vast areas.

An earthquake can be thought of as similar to snapping your fingers. Before the snap, your fingers push in opposite directions. The friction between the fingers prevents them from moving. As you push harder, the fingers overcome the friction and they suddenly move. The energy in this case is released as sound.

FIGURE 5: Snapping your fingers. What is the connection with earthquakes?

FIGURE 4: What happens at the boundary between these rubbing plates?

QUESTIONS

4 Explain what tectonic plates are and why they move.

5 Explain how seismic waves are created at the boundary between two tectonic plates.

Evidence for moving plates

The idea that the ground beneath us was moving, be it very slowly, was suggested as long ago as 1915 by Alfred Wegener. In science, ideas have to be backed up by evidence. The strongest evidence is provided by the east coast of South America and the west coast of Africa:

> The ancient rocks found in both regions are identical.

> Several kinds of fossils, including those of an aquatic reptile, *Mesosaurus tenuidens*, were found to be present in matching regions of South America and Africa.

Mountains are formed by tectonic plates as they collide head-on, lifting up the Earth's crust. Sea shells are found on the top of mountains, even Mount Everest. This shows that the mountains of today must have been seabeds millions of years ago.

FIGURE 6: Why do we find *Mesosaurus* fossils in America and Africa?

QUESTIONS

6 Discuss the evidence that supports the idea of moving tectonic plates.

Seismic waves and the Earth

Ring of fire

Figure 1 shows that the majority of the world's earthquakes (yellow) and volcanoes (red) are found at the boundaries between the tectonic plates. The large plate at the centre is the Pacific plate. It is surrounded by a ring of fire made up of volcanoes and earthquakes.

You will find out:

> why predicting earthquakes is difficult

> how seismometers are used to locate earthquakes

> about the reflection and refraction of seismic waves

FIGURE 1: Where do volcanoes and earthquakes occur?

Seismic waves

Earthquakes, and man-made explosions, create three types of seismic waves. You have already met two of these, S and P waves, on pages 188–9. The third type is called **L** waves; these are *long* wavelength surface waves. L waves from earthquakes cause the most destruction. They are the slowest of the seismic waves. They are very complicated because they are neither longitudinal nor transverse waves.

Figure 2 is a reminder of the key ideas of S and P waves.

reflected and refracted at the boundaries between crust, mantle and core

can travel through solid

S wave

tranverse wave

cannot travel through liquid

slower than P waves

QUESTIONS

1 List the S, P and L waves in order of decreasing speed.

2 Explain why S waves cannot travel through liquids.

3 Explain why P waves can travel through liquids and solids.

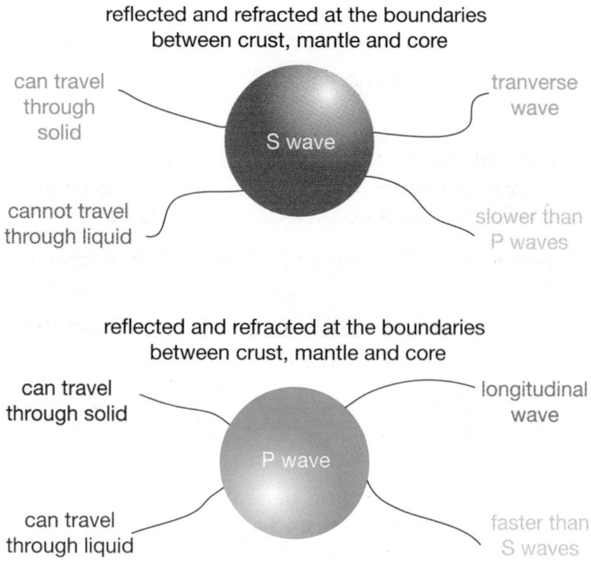

reflected and refracted at the boundaries between crust, mantle and core

can travel through solid

P wave

longitudinal wave

can travel through liquid

faster than S waves

FIGURE 2: A summary of P and S waves.

Predicting earthquakes and tsunamis

Earthquakes happen when rocks break or when tectonic plates collide. When an earthquake occurs on or under the seabed, it can start a tsunami (sometimes called a tidal wave), which can travel for hundreds, or even thousands, of kilometres across an ocean.

It is difficult to predict earthquakes and tsunamis because:

> Scientists cannot measure the pressure between the tectonic plates.

> The faults in the plates often lie deep in the Earth's crust.

However, scientists can sometimes make long-term predictions based on the earthquake history of a particular area. For example, there is a 67% chance of an earthquake in San Francisco, USA, in the next 30 years.

You can investigate the unpredictability of earthquakes using sliding blocks and weights in the laboratory.

Did you know?

Scientists are investigating whether a sudden increase in radon gas released from cracks in the Earth's crust could indicate that an earthquake is likely to occur.

Locating earthquakes

Seismic waves are monitored constantly around the world using a network of **seismometers**. These pinpoint the locations of 150 000 earthquakes occurring every year. Figure 3 shows a typical trace, a seismograph, from a seismometer.

A seismograph can be used to locate the source of the earthquake. The distance D (in kilometres) of an earthquake from a monitoring station can be calculated using the following equation:

$$D = (v_P - v_S) \times t$$

where v_P = speed of P wave, v_S = speed of S wave and t = delay time (in seconds) of the S wave compared with the P wave. The speed of P waves is typically 10 km/s and for S waves it is about 7 km/s.

By measuring the time difference t for waves arriving at seismometers located at three different places on the Earth's surface, scientists are able to pinpoint the exact location of an earthquake.

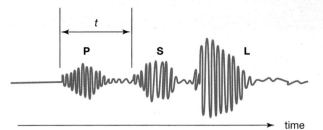

FIGURE 3: A seismograph showing S, P and L waves.

> ## QUESTIONS

4 Give one reason why it is difficult to predict where an earthquake is going to occur.

5 Calculate the distance of an earthquake using the information given above when the delay time t is 5.0 minutes.

S and P waves through the Earth (Higher tier only)

Like all waves, seismic waves show **reflection** and **refraction**. The evidence of the layered structure of the Earth comes from the different paths taken by S and P waves as they travel through the Earth.

Figure 4 shows the paths of S and P waves from an earthquake.

> The transverse S waves cannot travel through the *liquid* outer core of the Earth.

> The longitudinal P waves can travel through solids and liquids. They can travel through all layers of the Earth.

> The density of the rock deeper in the mantle increases because of higher pressures. Hence, the speed of both S and P waves increases with depth. This makes the paths of the S and P waves *curve*. The waves are *refracted*. The P waves are refracted within the core for the same reasons.

> There is a sudden change in the path of the P waves at the boundary between the mantle and outer core.

> At the boundaries between the layers, the S and P waves are *reflected*.

The earthquake monitoring stations are A, B, C, D and E:

> A, B, D and E detect both S and P waves.

> There are no S waves between B and D – the S wave shadow zone.

> Only the refracted P waves are detected between B and D.

Scientists can locate earthquakes from the data collected from all the monitoring stations.

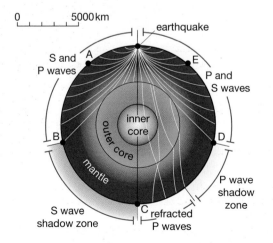
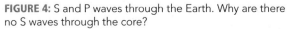

FIGURE 4: S and P waves through the Earth. Why are there no S waves through the core?

> ## QUESTIONS

6 Explain why S and P waves are refracted within the mantle.

7 Discuss how geologists know that the outer core of the Earth is liquid.

Preparing for assessment: Planning an investigation

To achieve a good grade in science, you not only have to know and understand scientific ideas, but you also need to be able to apply them to other situations and investigations. This task will support you in developing these skills.

✹ Investigating the unpredictability of earthquakes

Despite the progress in understanding plate tectonics, scientists still find it very difficult to predict earthquakes. They know *where* they are likely to occur, but predicting *when* they will occur is very hard.

Earthquakes happen when pieces of the Earth's crust (tectonic plates) suddenly move past each other along a plate boundary. One factor that determines when an earthquake will occur is the amount of friction between the rocks on the two sides of the fault.

Factors that influence friction at a plate boundary include:

> the area of contact between the two plates

> the size of the force pushing the two plates together.

Two ways of investigating the effect of these factors on friction are to:

a measure the force (**F**) needed to cause a block to move or keep moving on a horizontal surface

b measure the angle of tilt (θ) needed for a block to move or keep moving.

✹ Task

A student makes two predictions:

> **1** doubling the area of contact in **a** doubles the force needed to move the block

> **2** there is no direct relationship between θ and the surface area of the block in **b**.

Select one prediction to investigate.

✸ Planning

1. Choose one hypothesis to investigate. State the hypothesis clearly.

2. Decide which of the methods (**a** or **b**) you will use to investigate the hypothesis. State the equipment you will need to carry out your hypothesis.

3. State the independent and dependent variables that you will measure. Decide on a suitable range of values for the independent variable.

4. List the things that you need to keep the same in order to make it a fair test.

5. Write a detailed method to show exactly how you plan to carry out your experiment.

6. Think carefully about the method you have described. Is it likely to include some potential hazards? List all the significant hazards in your experiment and state how each one can be controlled so that the experiment can be carried out safely.

State what the student predicts will happen and the scientific reasons for this. Remember to state clearly the expectation and support this (using appropriate scientific terms) to gain Quality of Written Communication marks.

Explain your choice of method, thinking about the benefits and possible reliability.

Explain your choice of equipment.

The independent variable is what you will change to test the hypothesis. The dependent variable is what you will measure to find the result.

Remember that for an experiment to be fair, you can only change one thing at a time and you must control certain factors. State the values you will use for your controls.

Make sure that your method is a logical sequence of steps. A list of numbered steps or bullet points helps communicate your method clearly.

Hazards are things which could cause harm. Significant hazards are ones where there is a reasonable chance of their occurring and causing injury or damage.

✸ Processing evidence

1. Draw a results table with suitable columns for the independent and dependent variables.

2. Decide how you will analyse your results by indicating what form of graph will be most suitable. How will you label each axis?

3. Think about how you will interpret your graph so that you can describe the trends shown by your results.

4. Do your results support your original hypothesis? Do you need to reword it now that you have the results? What does tell you about the factors that influence friction at a plate boundary?

Remember to include the name and units of each variable.

Don't forget that each axis will need units as well as a name.

Remember, direct proportionality is only indicated by a straight line graph passing through the origin. Curves indicate more complex relationships.

Consider the hypothesis and the scientific language used.

✸ Connections

How Science Works

> Planning to test a scientific idea.

> Planning an experiment and answering a scientific problem.

> Collecting and analysing scientific data.

> Recognising science still cannot answer or address certain questions.

> Assessing methods of data collection.

> Collecting data accurately and safely, taking into account potential hazards.

> Presenting information and making conclusions and stating the results in a scientific fashion.

Maths in Science

> Understanding direct proportionality and simple ratios.

> Selecting the most appropriate type of graph for the experiment and appropriate scales for the axes.

Charge, current and circuits

You will find out:
> about charge
> about electric current
> about simple circuits

What a flash!

The photo shows a flash of lightning. During the flash, the current can be as high as 30 000 A and yet last for only one-hundredth of a second. Lightning can cause the temperature of the air to rise to 50 000 °C, which is hotter than the Sun. Currents in circuits are much smaller and less harmful.

FIGURE 1: A lightning flash.

Electrical circuits

A simple circuit

Figure 2 shows a battery, a lamp and a switch all connected together by wires in a single loop (series). Drawing an accurate picture of this circuit is quite difficult and very time consuming. It is much easier to draw the circuit using symbols for the components; this is shown in Figure 3.

Charge and current

The lamp in the circuit shown in Figure 3 will be lit when the switch is closed. We say that there is an electric **current** in the circuit. The current will exist as long as there are no gaps in the circuit:

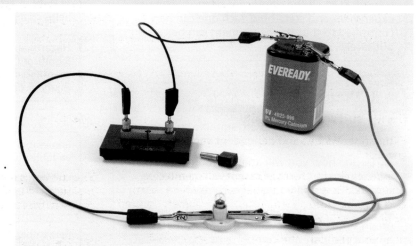

FIGURE 2: A photograph of a simple circuit.

> Electric current is caused by the *flow* of **charge**.

> This charge is due to negative particles called **electrons** which move in the circuit.

> Even with the most powerful microscope in the world, these electrons are too small to be seen. But they do exist.

QUESTIONS

1 Explain what is meant by electric current.

2 Name the particles responsible for current in a circuit.

3 Draw a circuit with a battery, a switch and two lamps all connected in series.

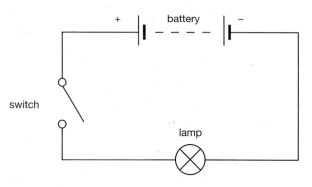

FIGURE 3: A circuit diagram. Can you see why this is easier?

Series circuits   Parallel circuits   Currents in circuits

Conventional current and electron flow

An **ammeter** is a device used to measure the current in a circuit. It is always connected in **series** with a component, see Figure 4.

Current is measured in **amperes** (A); this is often abbreviated to just amps.

The electrons in the circuit are repelled by the negative terminal of the chemical cell and attracted towards the positive terminal. They travel from the negative to the positive. The first scientists working with circuits thought that the charges moving in a circuit were positive and they drew arrows to show this. Unfortunately, we have kept this convention:

> **Conventional current** is the flow of (imaginary) positive charges.

> Electron flow is the flow of electrons.

> The directions of conventional current and electron flow are *opposite*.

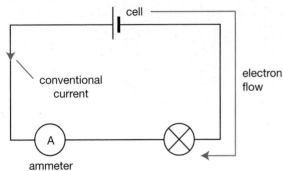

FIGURE 4: A circuit diagram showing an ammeter connected in series.

QUESTIONS

4 Explain what is meant by conventional current.

5 An arrow is drawn on a circuit to indicate the direction of the conventional current. Explain how you can deduce the direction of the flow of electrons.

Circuits and currents

Series and parallel circuits

Figure 5 shows two basic circuit types: series and **parallel**.

In a series circuit, the components are connected end-to-end in a single loop. The current in a series circuit is the same all way round. An ammeter placed at point **A** or **B** will show the same reading.

In a parallel circuit, the components are connected across each other. The current splits at the junction **X**. The total current leaving the junction is equal to the total current entering this junction.

More on current

You can think of current as the flow of charge. However, current does have a rigorous interpretation:

> Current is defined as the *rate* of flow of charge.

That is:

$$\text{current} = \frac{\text{charge}}{\text{time}}$$

The current is measured in amperes (A), the charge is measured in **coulombs** (C) and time is in seconds (s). An electron carries a tiny charge of -1.6×10^{-19} C.

QUESTIONS

6 In the parallel circuit shown in Figure 5, explain what happens to the current at junction Y.

7 Calculate the flow of charge in a time of 1.5 minutes in a circuit with a current of 2.0 A.

Did you know?

One ampere is equivalent to about 6 250 000 000 000 000 000 electrons per second.

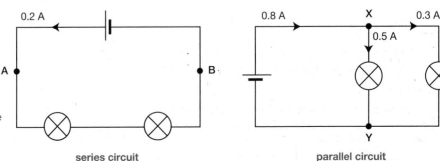

FIGURE 5: In the series circuit, the current is 0.2 A in each lamp. In the parallel circuit, the currents in the lamps add up to 0.8 A.

series circuit

parallel circuit

Voltage

You will find out:
> about voltage
> about simple circuits

Baghdad battery

Some people claim that these 2000-year-old objects dug up near Baghdad in Iraq in the 1930s may have been an early form of battery. Their use is not known, but replicas have been able to produce up to 2 volts.

FIGURE 1: The battery consisted of a terracotta jar about 13 cm tall containing a copper cylinder, which houses a single iron rod.

Understanding voltage

FIGURE 2: Modern cells and batteries. Without these there would be no current.

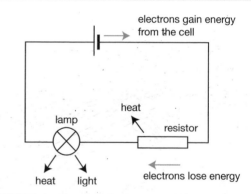

electrons gain energy from the cell

heat

lamp

resistor

heat   light

electrons lose energy

FIGURE 3: An electrical circuit.

To produce a current in a circuit you need a cell. You can also use a battery, which consists of several cells connected in series, or a mains power supply.

A cell is like a pump that pushes electrons around a circuit. The electrons have *electrical energy* as they move around the circuit. The electrons gain this energy from the *chemical energy* of the cell. As the electrons travel through the components, they give up some, or all, of their energy as *heat* and *light*.

Figure 4 shows a circuit with a lamp connected to a cell. A **voltmeter** is placed across, or in parallel with,

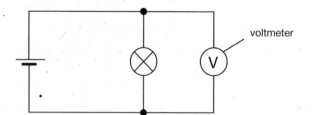

voltmeter

FIGURE 4: How is the voltmeter connected to the lamp?

the lamp. It measures the **voltage** across the lamp. Voltage is measured in **volts** (V).

Voltage is a difficult concept and to confuse matters further, it is also called **potential difference**. It may help to think of:

> voltage as electrical pressure that gives a measure of the energy transferred in a component (for example, a lamp)

> a voltmeter as an 'energy-measuring' device.

QUESTIONS

1 Copy and complete this sentence:
A v_____ is used to measure the v_____ across a component.
V _____ is also called _____.

2 Two lamps A and B are connected in series. The voltage across A is 4.0 V and the voltage across B is 6.0 V. Explain which transfers a greater amount of energy.

Voltage and circuits

Series circuits

Two lamps in **series** are connected to a variable power supply, see Figure 5. A voltmeter is used to measure the voltage V across the combination, the voltage V_1 across lamp 1 and the voltage V_2 across lamp 2. The results are shown in Table 1.

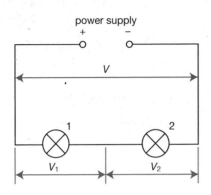

FIGURE 5: A series circuit.

TABLE 1: Voltages in series circuits.

Voltage V (volts)	Voltage V_1 (volts)	Voltage V_2 (volts)
10.2	6.0	4.2
8.4	5.0	3.4
5.0	3.0	2.0
2.8	1.8	1.0

The voltages V_1 and V_2 are related to total voltage V by the equation:

$$V = V_1 + V_2$$

Use Table 1 to check this rule.

Parallel circuits

Two lamps in **parallel** are connected to the variable power supply, see Figure 6. A voltmeter is used to measure the voltage V across the combination, the voltage V_1 across lamp 1 and the voltage V_2 across lamp 2. The results are shown in Table 2.

In a parallel circuit, the voltage across each lamp is the same. You can see why from Figure 6; all voltages are measured across the same points X and Y.

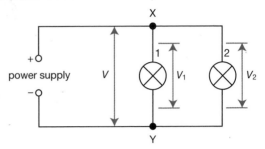

FIGURE 6: A parallel circuit.

TABLE 2: Voltages in parallel circuits.

Voltage V (volts)	Voltage V_1 (volts)	Voltage V_2 (volts)
10.0	10.0	10.0
7.5	7.5	7.5
5.0	5.0	5.0
3.5	3.5	3.5

QUESTIONS

3 A buzzer and a lamp are connected in series to a 10 V supply. The voltage across the buzzer is 3.5 V. Calculate the voltage across the lamp.

More on potential difference

Potential difference across a component is defined as the energy transferred per unit charge. That is:

$$\text{potential difference} = \frac{\text{energy}}{\text{charge}}$$

The potential difference is measured in volts (V), energy in joules (J) and charge in coulombs (C):

A potential difference of 1 volt is defined as 1 J of energy transferred per unit coulomb.

A voltmeter measures 3.0 V across a lamp. This means that every coulomb of charge passing through the lamp loses 3 J of energy as heat and light.

QUESTIONS

4 Express 1 V in terms of joules (J) and coulombs (C).

5 A charge of 3 C transfers 18 J of energy in a lamp. Calculate the potential difference across the lamp.

Electrical power

You will find out:
> about electrical power
> how to determine electrical power of electrical items

Did you say watt?

The photos show lamps connected to a meter. The meter displays the electrical power of each lamp. Power is measured in watts (W). The 10 W energy-saving lamp on the right is much more economical than the 61 W filament lamp. Electrical work requires a good understanding of power.

FIGURE 1: What are the numbers on the meters showing?

Electrical power

Electrical appliances in your home will have labels showing the voltage and power. Figure 2 shows an example label from a microwave oven.

Electrical power has a very precise meaning in physics:

> Electrical power is defined as the rate of energy transfer per second.

It is easier to see power written as a word equation:

$$\text{electrical power (watt, W)} = \frac{\text{energy used (joule, J)}}{\text{time taken (second, s)}}$$

Using P for power, E for energy transfer and t for time taken, we can also write:

$$P = \frac{E}{t}$$

> The unit for power is the **watt (W)**.

> 1 watt = 1 joule per second.

Understanding power

If a lamp is marked as 10 W, it means that it will transfer 10 joules of electrical energy into heat and light per second. The lamp will transfer more energy if it is used for a longer period of time. You can calculate the energy transferred using the equation:

energy (joule, J) = power (watt, W) × time (second, s)

In 60 seconds, the 10 W lamp will transfer 600 joules of energy.

Taste-e-Wave 🚮

Microwave Oven
Model No. R9-K105MB ABC

Voltage 230 V ~ 50 Hz

Power 800 W (IEC-60705)

Bob's Electricals (UK) Ltd

FIGURE 2: What important quantities can you see on this label?

Did you know?

If everyone in Indonesia switched to low-energy light bulbs, it could cut the country's greenhouse gas emissions by 8 million tonnes a year, the equivalent of taking two million cars off the road.

◯ QUESTIONS

1 State one difference between energy and power.

2 A heater is marked as 2200 W. Calculate the heat energy produced by the heater in 1 second and in 10 minutes (600 seconds).

Calculating and determining power

Calculating electrical power

The electrical power of a device is related to the current it carries and the voltage (potential difference) across it. You can use the word equation below to calculate the electrical power:

$$\text{electrical power (watt, W)} = \text{current (ampere, A)} \times \text{potential difference (volt, V)}$$

Using P for power, I for current and V for potential difference, we can also write:

$$P = I \times V$$

Determining electrical power

Figure 3 shows a circuit that you can use to determine the electrical power of an electrical item (component).

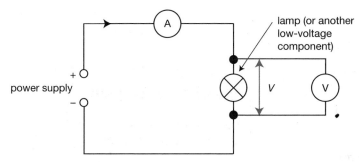

FIGURE 3: A circuit for determining electrical power.

> The ammeter measures the current I in the component.

> The voltmeter measures the potential difference V across the component.

> To find the electrical power P in watts, you simply multiply I and V.

The table shows typical results from a laboratory investigation.

Electrical item	I (A)	V (V)	P = I × V (W)
Filament lamp	2.0	12	24
Resistor	1.2	10	12
Buzzer	0.20	9.0	1.8
Heater	8.0	20	160

QUESTIONS

3 Describe how the meters are connected in the circuit shown in Figure 3.

4 A table lamp connected to a 230 V supply draws a current of 0.20 A. Calculate the electrical power of the lamp and the energy transferred in 1 hour.

Check your fuse

A **fuse** is an important safety item in a mains plug. It is a thin wire, made from tin which has a low melting point. If a fault occurs, a large current passes through the fuse. The fuse melts and stops the current. This prevents further damage or a fire.

The *fuse rating* is the maximum current that the fuse can carry without melting. Only certain values are available, for example, 1 A, 3 A, 5 A, 13 A.

Consider a 1100 W toaster connected to a 230 V supply. To find the correct fuse, you have to first calculate the current:

$$\text{Power (W)} = \text{current (A)} \times \text{potential difference (V)}$$
$$1100 = I \times 230$$
$$I = \frac{1100}{230} = 4.8\,A$$

The fuse rating must be greater than 4.8 A so a 5 A fuse would be adequate.

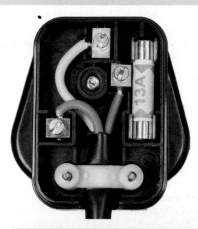

FIGURE 4: Is this the correct fuse for this plug?

QUESTIONS

5 Select a suitable fuse for a 12 V, 30 W heater.

6 Suggest why a 13 A fuse is not advisable for a 230 V, 100 W television.

Generating current

You will find out:

> how electric current is induced

> about generators

> about direct and alternating currents

Thank goodness for Faraday

A magnet is surrounded by a magnetic field. You can see this when you sprinkle iron filings around a magnet. In 1820 Hans Christian Ørsted demonstrated that an electric current in a wire produced a magnetic field. About a decade later, Michael Faraday showed that electricity could be generated using magnetism. Without his pioneering work we would not have mains electricity.

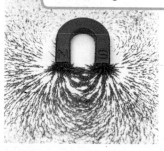

FIGURE 1: What is the link between magnets and Faraday?

Inducing a current

A cell or a battery can produce a current in a circuit. The electrical energy of the current comes from the chemical energy of the cell.

Is there another way of producing current? Yes. A current can be created, or **induced**, in a circuit using magnets.

Magnet and wire (Figure 2)

> The ammeter shows no current when the wire is held still between the poles of the magnet.

> A current is induced in the wire when it is moved up and it *cuts* the magnetic field lines of the magnet. This is called *electromagnetic induction*.

> The direction of the induced current is *opposite* when it is moved down.

> The induced current is larger when the wire is moved more quickly.

Magnet and coil of wire (Figure 3)

> A current is induced in the coil whenever there is relative motion between it and the magnet.

> Moving the magnet towards the coil induces a current in the coil.

> Moving the magnet away from the coil induces the current in the *opposite* direction in the coil.

> The induced current is larger when the magnet is moved more quickly.

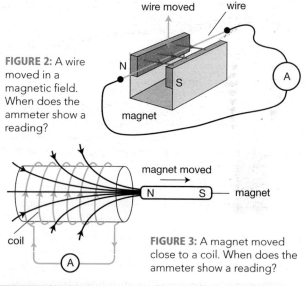

FIGURE 2: A wire moved in a magnetic field. When does the ammeter show a reading?

FIGURE 3: A magnet moved close to a coil. When does the ammeter show a reading?

QUESTIONS

1 Complete this sentence: A current is only i_____ in a coil when there is r_____ motion between it and a m_____.

2 Describe what determines the direction of the induced current in a coil.

Making bigger currents

The induced current in the coil of Figure 3 can be increased by:

> increasing the *speed* of the magnet

> increasing the number of turns of wire

> using a stronger magnet.

Generators

A **generator** is used to produce electricity. Figure 4 shows a simple electrical generator.

As the coil is rotated, it *cuts* the magnetic field lines of the magnet. This induces a current in the coil. The ends of the coil are attached to the inside of two slip

Q Induced currents using magnets   How does a generator work?

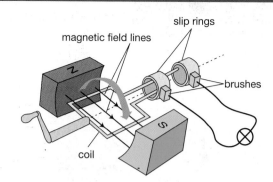

FIGURE 4: A simple generator. What type of current does this produce?

rings. The slip rings rotate with the coil. The rings are in contact with two brushes. The lamp is connected to the brushes. The current from the brushes and in the lamp is an **alternating current**.

Where does the energy for the induced current come from? Some of the kinetic energy of the coil is converted into the electrical energy of the moving charges.

FIGURE 5: A 350 million watt generator.

Practical generators

In a power station, **generators** produce the electrical energy for our mains supply. The coils of such generators are rotated by turbines. In oil- or coal-burning power stations, the turbines are rotated by high-pressure steam from boilers. You can think of these turbines as windmills driven by steam. Commercial generators are huge – see Figure 5.

Direct and alternating currents

A cell produces a **direct current** (d.c.). The current travels in the same direction.

A generator produces an **alternating current** (a.c.). The current changes direction at a frequency determined by the rotating coil.

QUESTIONS

3 Explain how a current is induced in a generator.

4 Explain why the graphs A and B in Figure 6 show direct currents.

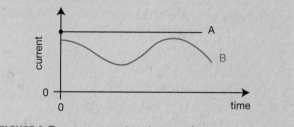

FIGURE 6: Two current against time graphs.

Current from generators

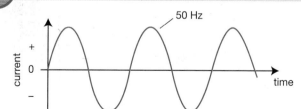

FIGURE 7: Typical alternating current from a mains generator.

Figure 7 shows the variation of current with time from a generator used to produce mains supply.

Because of its shape, this is known as a sinusoidal graph. The size of the current changes with time. The frequency of the mains current is 50 Hz.

Remember!
Frequency is number of cycles per second.

QUESTIONS

5 Use Figure 7 to answer these questions:

a Explain the significance of negative current.

b Determine the time for one revolution.

6 The UK demand for electricity is about 60 GW. Estimate the number of 350 MW generators required to meet this demand. (1 GW = 10^9 W and 1 MW = 10^6 W.)

Q Alternating current   Direct current

Non-renewable resources

You will find out:
> about large-scale electricity production
> about non-renewable resources

Bright lights

Figure 1 shows a satellite image of Europe at night. The energy for the city lights mostly comes from burning fossil fuels in power stations. There is a limited supply of these buried fuels. How long will these lights keep burning?

FIGURE 1: Europe by night.

Non-renewable energy resources

Coal, natural gas and oil are called fossil fuels because they were formed from the organic remains of prehistoric plants and animals. Fossil fuels are **non-renewable resources**. This means that:

> they cannot be replaced

> they will eventually run out.

Nuclear fuel, such as uranium, is also a non-renewable resource.

Producing electricity from fossil fuels

Fossil fuels are used in power stations to generate electricity (see Figure 2).

> Fossil fuels are burned to release heat (thermal) energy.

> The heat energy boils water to produce high-pressure steam.

> The steam rotates turbines, which are attached to electrical generators.

> The generators produce electrical energy.

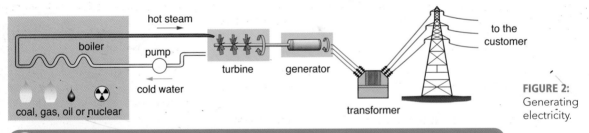

FIGURE 2: Generating electricity.

QUESTIONS

1 Explain what is meant by a non-renewable resource.

2 Explain the purpose of the high-pressure steam in a coal-burning power station.

Non-renewable resources: advantages and disadvantages

Table 1 summarises the advantages and disadvantages of power stations using different non-renewable energy resources.

Did you know?

It takes 5 million joules of energy to make one fizzy drink can.

The effects of CO_2 on Earth   Non-renewable resources

TABLE 1: Advantages and disadvantages of using non-renewable energy resources.

Resource	Advantages	Disadvantages
Coal	Fuel is cheap Coal-burning power stations have quick start-up time There is enough coal for at least 200 years	Burning coal releases CO_2 and SO_2 SO_2 produces acid rain. It is very expensive to remove Mining coal can be difficult and dangerous A stockpile of coal is needed to meet demand
Natural gas	Gas-fired power stations are very efficient They have the quickest start-up time, hence are flexible at meeting demand for power There is enough gas left to last for at least 50 years It does not produce SO_2	Burning gas releases CO_2 (although it is less than coal and oil) The network of pipelines for transporting gas is expensive
Oil	Oil-burning power stations have quick start-up time There is enough oil left for at least 50 years	Burning oil releases CO_2 and SO_2 Oil prices can be extremely variable Oil is transported by road, sea and rail. There is a chance of spillage and pollution
Nuclear	Nuclear power stations are located away from populated areas It does not produce CO_2 and SO_2	Building and decommissioning a power station is very expensive Start-up time is the longest Radioactive waste can remain dangerous for thousands of years

Did you know?

Using a single 100 W light bulb is responsible for 500 kg of CO_2 produced at the power station per year.

QUESTIONS

3 Name a gas that is released by all fossil fuels.

4 Discuss why coal-fuelled power stations are still being built around the world instead of nuclear power stations.

Greenhouse effect

The **greenhouse effect** is a process by which the infrared radiation emitted by the surface of the Earth is absorbed by some of the gases in the atmosphere. These gases are known as **greenhouse gases**, and they include carbon dioxide (CO_2) and methane. The atmosphere warms up. It re-radiates energy as infrared radiation in all directions, including back towards the surface of the Earth. This helps to warm up the Earth. The average temperature of the Earth is 14 °C, which is much higher than the −19 °C predicted if there was no atmosphere.

Figure 3 shows the flow of energy from the Sun, the ground and the atmosphere. The numbers represent the energy in 1 second over an area of 1 square metre.

Burning fossil fuels is increasing the levels of CO_2 in the atmosphere. Some scientists predict that this will increase the average temperature of the world in the future.

QUESTIONS

5 Use the information given in Figure 3 to explain why the average temperature of the Earth's surface remains constant.

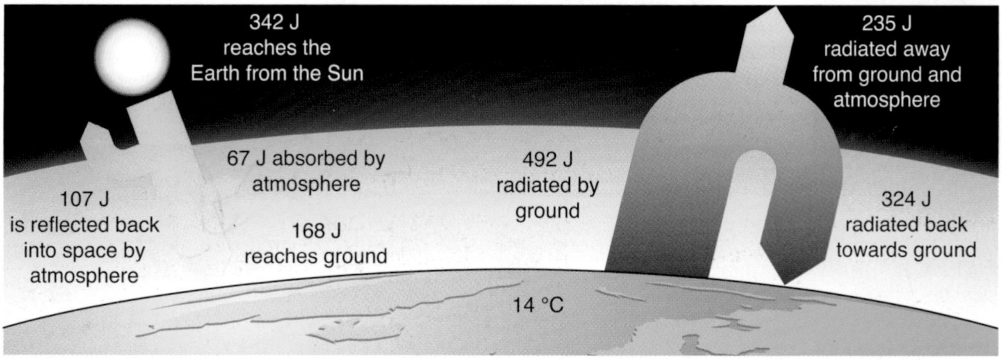

342 J reaches the Earth from the Sun

235 J radiated away from ground and atmosphere

67 J absorbed by atmosphere

492 J radiated by ground

107 J is reflected back into space by atmosphere

168 J reaches ground

324 J radiated back towards ground

14 °C

FIGURE 3: Greenhouse effect. Why is the Earth not much colder?

Renewable resources

Wind power is clean

This photo shows the UK's first offshore wind farm, located off the coast of north Wales. It has 30 wind turbines, each producing 2 MW of electrical power. This wind farm will offset the release of 160 000 tonnes of carbon dioxide every year.

FIGURE 1: Windmills that produce electricity.

Renewable energy resources

On pages 242–3, you learned about how fossil fuels can be burned to generate electricity in a power station. We can also use **renewable energy resources** to create electricity:

> A renewable resource is defined as one that will not run out.

Table 1 shows some details of the renewable energy resources used in the UK.

FIGURE 2: A float turning wave energy into electricity.

TABLE 1: Renewable energy resources available to the UK.

Resource	How it works	Is a turbine used?	Is a generator used?
Solar	The light energy from the Sun is turned directly into electrical energy by solar cells	No	No
Wind	The wind rotates the huge propeller blades. The rotating blades are used to generate electricity	No	Yes
Wave	Large 'floats' containing coils and magnets move up and down with the waves (see Figure 2)	No	Yes
Hydro-electric	Water stored in a reservoir above the power station flows through pipes. The fast-moving water is used to generate electricity (see Figure 3)	Yes	Yes
Tidal	The seawater from the incoming and outgoing tides is used to generate electricity (see Figure 4)	Yes	Yes
Biomass and wood	Biomass is an organic material used as fuel. It can be decaying plant or animal waste, for example, crop stalks, lawn trimmings and agricultural waste. A biomass or wood power station is identical to a fossil-fuel power station	Yes	Yes

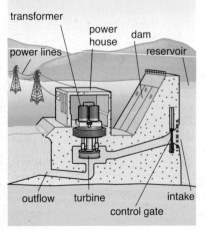

FIGURE 3: A hydroelectric power station.

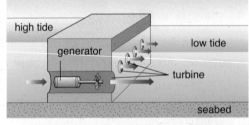

FIGURE 4: Using tides to generate electricity.

QUESTIONS

1 Name a resource that can be used to produce electrical energy without turbines or generators.

2 Explain why wind and wave power stations do not need turbines.

Where does the energy come from?

The Sun and the Moon are the source of many renewable energy resources:

> The Sun heats up the Earth's atmosphere and this creates wind and waves. The Sun also evaporates water and this creates rain and the flow of water in our rivers. The energy from the Sun is also stored by plants and animals as chemical energy.

> The gravitational pull of the Moon creates tides on the surface of the Earth.

Renewable energy: advantages and disadvantages

The main advantages of renewable resources, apart from biomass and wood, are that they cost nothing and produce no greenhouse gases. The main disadvantage is the cost of building renewable power stations.

Table 2 shows some other advantages and disadvantages of renewable resources used in the UK.

TABLE 2: Advantages and disadvantages of using renewable energy resources.

Resource	Advantages	Disadvantages
Solar	Useful in remote areas Single homes can have their own electricity supply	No power at night-time or when cloudy
Wind	Can be built offshore	Can cause noise and visual pollution The amount of electricity is dependent on the weather
Wave and tidal	Ideal for an island country	May be opposed by local or environmental groups
Hydro-electric	Creates water reserves as well as energy supplies	Can cause the flooding of surrounding communities and landscapes
Biomass and wood	It is a cheap and readily available source of energy If replaced, biomass can be a long-term, sustainable energy source	When burnt, it gives off CO_2 and SO_2 Biomass and wood are only renewable resources if crops and trees are replanted

QUESTIONS

3 Explain which energy resources will cause similar environmental problems to fossil fuels.

4 Most renewable energy resources cost nothing. Explain why some people can claim they are too expensive.

Did you know?

It would take 40 km^2 of solar cells to produce power equal to one oil-fuelled power station.

Using solar power

Figure 5 shows a solar power plant in the Alps. The solar panels change sunlight into electrical energy; one square metre produces about 14 W of power. The size of the plant shown is similar to the size of a football pitch, about $7.3 \times 10^3 \text{ m}^2$. Our climate in the UK is not ideal for solar power. However, solar panels can be used to provide some of the energy needs for homes.

QUESTIONS

5 In some remote places, solar panels are used in conjunction with rechargeable batteries. Explain a possible benefit of this system.

6 Estimate how many solar power plants like the one shown in Figure 5 will be needed to produce the same power as a 3.0 MW coal-fired power station.

FIGURE 5: Solar panels spread out in the Alps.

Transformers and the National Grid

High voltage!

Electricity is generated on a large scale at power stations. The electricity is transmitted from power stations to our homes, offices and factories along high-voltage cables. Figure 1 shows the pylons and cables used in the transmission of electricity.

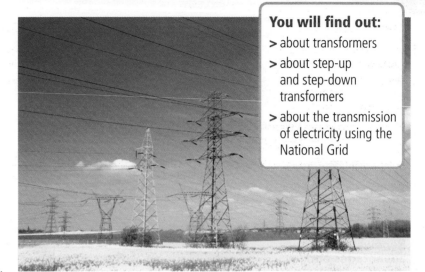

You will find out:
> about transformers
> about step-up and step-down transformers
> about the transmission of electricity using the National Grid

FIGURE 1: Electrical pylons.

Transformers

A **transformer** is a device used to change the size of an *alternating* voltage. Figure 2 shows a simple transformer.

> The transformer has two coils of wire wrapped around a soft-iron core.

> The alternating voltage supply is connected to the **primary coil**.

> The new voltage (lower or higher) is across the ends of the **secondary coil**.

> The *input* voltage is applied to the primary coil and the *output* voltage is taken from the secondary coil.

A **step-down transformer** is used to make the voltage smaller. It has *fewer* turns in the secondary coil than in the primary coil. Your phone charger has an inbuilt step-down transformer. It changes the mains voltage of 230 V to about 9 V for your phone's battery.

A **step-up transformer** is used to make the voltage bigger. It has *more* turns in the secondary coil than the primary coil. The generators in a power station are connected to step-up transformers. Each transformer increases the 23 000 V from the generator to 400 000 V for the cables of the National Grid.

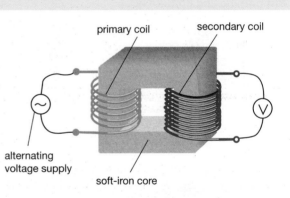

primary coil   secondary coil

alternating voltage supply

soft-iron core

FIGURE 2: A simple transformer.

Remember!
An alternating voltage supply gives an alternating current.

QUESTIONS

1 State the type of input voltage used in a transformer.

2 Describe a step-down transformer.

3 Explain why generators in a power station use step-up transformers.

Did you know?

To get power to the London Olympic Games site, cables 6 km long are housed in a 4 m diameter tunnel at a depth of 15 to 30 metres.

Transmitting electricity

The National Grid

In the UK there are over 2200 pylons supporting the high-voltage cables (or lines) transmitting the electrical energy from power stations to millions of users. The network of pylons and cables is known as the **National Grid**.

Figure 3 shows how transformers are used in the transmission of electricity.

> Step-up transformers are used to increase the 23 kV output from power station generators to high voltages (275 kV or 400 kV) for transmission.

> The current in the transmission cables is smaller when higher voltages are used. This reduces the heat losses in the cables. This improves the efficiency of transmitting the electricity. Less wastage of energy also saves money.

> Step-down transformers are used to lower the voltage to a safer value of 230 V for homes.

Hazards of electricity transmission

The high-voltage overhead cables are not insulated with rubber or plastic. Touching the cables is extremely dangerous. The high voltage across your body is likely to kill you. Accidental contact with high-voltage cables is a frequent cause of *injury* and *death*. The risks of electrocution can be minimised by burying the cables underground. Unfortunately, burying cables is costly and maintenance is difficult because roads have to be dug up. Suspending cables from pylons is a cheaper option.

QUESTIONS

4 Explain what is meant by the National Grid.

5 Explain why electricity is transmitted at high voltage.

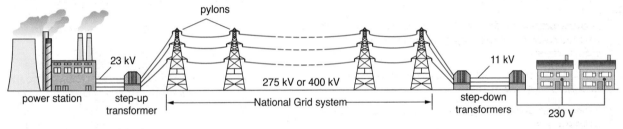

FIGURE 3: The National Grid system.

More on transformers (Higher tier only)

How does a transformer work?

The alternating voltage supply in Figure 2 produces an alternating current in the primary coil. The alternating current in the primary coil produces a changing magnetic field in the soft-iron core. The secondary coil is linked by this changing magnetic field; hence a voltage is induced across the ends of the secondary coil.

Turns ratio equation

You can calculate the size of the output voltage at the secondary coil using the turns ratio equation:

$$\frac{\text{output voltage at secondary coil}}{\text{input voltage at primary coil}} = \frac{\text{number of turns on secondary coil}}{\text{number of turns on primary coil}}$$

or

$$\frac{V_s}{V_p} = \frac{N_s}{N_p}$$

QUESTIONS

6 Explain why a battery connected to the primary coil will give a zero voltage at the secondary coil.

7 A transformer has 2000 turns on the primary coil and 500 turns on the secondary coil. Calculate the output voltage from the secondary coil when an alternating voltage of 230 V is applied at the primary coil.

Kilowatt-hours and payback times

The energy label

All electrical retailers use labels to tell us about the energy efficiency of a mains appliance. An appliance is rated from A to G, with A being the most efficient. You can compare appliances and save on your fuel bills.

You will find out:
> about the kilowatt-hour
> how to calculate the cost of electricity
> about payback times

Energy

Washing machine

Manufacturer
Model

More efficient

A
B
C
D
E
F
G

A

Less efficient

Energy consumption kWh/cycle (based on standard test results for 60°C cotton cycle)		0.95
Actual energy consumption will depend on how the appliance is used		
Washing performance A: higher G: lower	A	B C D E F G
Spin drying performance A: higher G: lower	A	B C D E F G
Spin speed (rpm)		1400
Capacity (cotton) kg		5.0
Water consumption l		55
Noise (dB(A) re 1 pW)	Washing	5.2
	Spinning	7.0
Further information is continued in product brochures		

FIGURE 1: What does this label tell you?

Energy in joules or kilowatt-hours?

Energy in joules

The power rating in watts (W) and kilowatts (kW) of mains appliances used in the home varies widely, see Table 1.

TABLE 1: Power ratings of some appliances.

Appliance	Power
Energy-saving bulb	10 W = 0.01 kW
Filament bulb	100 W = 0.1 kW
TV	150 W = 0.15 kW
Vacuum cleaner	500 W = 0.5 kW
Electric cooker	2500 W = 2.5 kW

The energy in joules used by an appliance can be calculated using the equation:

energy (joule, J) = power (watt, W) × time (second, s)

Low-power appliances use less energy in a given time and hence they cost less to run. For example, in a given time, a 10 W bulb will cost 10 times less than a 100 W lamp.

Kilowatt-hour (kW h)

How much energy in joules is used by a 2000 W heater in 1.5 hours (5400 s)?

energy = 2000 × 5400 = 10 800 000 J

The number 10 800 000 is large. The joule is not a practical or a convenient unit for electrical companies to use for the mains supply of electricity. They prefer to use the **kilowatt-hour** (kW h) instead on electricity bills:

> One kilowatt-hour (kW h), is the energy used by an appliance of power 1 kW used for 1 hour.

> The kilowatt-hour is a unit for energy, not power.

> The energy used in kW h is calculated using the equation:

energy   =   power   ×   time
(kilowatt hours, kW h)   (kilowatts, kW)   (hours, h)

> The cost of electricity is calculated using the equation:

cost   =   power   ×   time   × cost of 1 kW h
 (p)   (kilowatts, kW)   (hours, h)   (p/kW h)

The 2.0 kW heater operated for 1.5 hours uses 3.0 kW h. This value is much easier to handle than 10 800 000 J.

QUESTIONS

1 Show that 1 kW h is equal to 3 600 000 J.

2 The cost of 1 kW h of energy is 15p. Using the appliances listed in Table 1, calculate the cost of using each appliance for 2 hours.

Saving energy and money

Wasted energy

Using energy-efficient appliances in our homes will waste less energy. Using less energy has an environmental benefit and may reduce pollution from greenhouse gases and conserve fossil fuels. Here are some energy-saving devices and methods:

> energy-saving light bulbs

> motion-activated lights

> standby-detection devices that switch an appliance off when it enters standby mode

> fitting home insulation.

While there are many benefits in using energy-saving devices, there are also disadvantages that need to be considered:

> the high initial cost of purchasing and installing certain energy-saving methods can be prohibitive, for example double glazing is expensive to buy and install.

> disposal issues can still be a problem for energy-saving technologies, for example energy-saving bulbs contain a small amount of mercury, which is poisonous and needs careful handling

> energy-saving bulbs cannot always used with dimmer switches – perhaps using more electricity than is always needed and affecting the functionality and desirability of the product.

FIGURE 2: Do these light bulbs look different from standard light bulbs?

Payback times

Is it worth insulating your home? It depends on the initial cost of the insulation method and how much money you will save. One way of deciding whether an energy-saving method is cost-effective is to calculate the **payback time**.

The payback time is defined as the number of years it takes to get back the cost of an energy-saving method. It is calculated as follows:

$$\text{payback time} = \frac{\text{initial cost}}{\text{annual saving}}$$

Double glazing a house costs £5000. In one year, it saves £250 on electricity bills, so the payback time is 20 years.

Did you know?

The joule is the unit of energy. A chocolate bar can provide about 2 million joules of chemical energy.

QUESTIONS

3 List the advantages and disadvantages of using energy-saving devices.

4 It costs £60 to draught-proof a house and this cuts the electricity bill by £40 per year. Calculate the payback time.

Cost-effectiveness

You can decide whether an energy-saving method is cost-effective by calculating the payback time and the savings made over a period of time. Use the data provided in Table 2 to answer the questions.

TABLE 2: Cost-effectiveness.

Energy-saving method	Initial cost (£)	Annual saving (£)
Insulating hot water cylinder	10	20
Energy-saving bulb	3	9
Loft insulation	250	50
Cavity wall insulation	400	150
Double glazing	5000	250
Solar water heating	5000	150

QUESTIONS

5 Calculate the payback time for each method in Table 2.

6 Discuss the cost-effectiveness of each method by calculating the savings made after 10 years.

Understanding energy

You will find out:
> about conservation of energy
> about transfer of energy

What a jump!

This is the path of a snowboarder after taking off from a ramp. During the flight the snowboarder has different forms of energy, but his total energy remains the same. Energy can take many different forms and understanding it is an important part of physics.

FIGURE 1: What types of energy does this snowboarder have?

Energy

Energy exists in many different forms. The different forms (or types) of energy are summarised in Table 1.

TABLE 1: A summary of different types of energy.

Name	Description	Some examples
Thermal (heat) energy	An object at a higher temperature has greater thermal energy	A heater, the Sun and hot water
Light energy	Light is a wave that is emitted from anything at a very high temperature	Lamp, stars and fire
Electrical energy	This is usually associated with electric current	Mains supply, overhead high-voltage cables and output from a transformer
Sound energy	An object vibrating will emit sound	Buzzer, bell, siren and talking
Kinetic (movement) energy	This is energy due to movement	Person running, high-speed train and planet orbiting the Sun
Chemical energy	This is energy stored by atoms	Food, chemical cell and coal
Nuclear energy	This is energy stored by the nuclei of atoms	Nuclear power station, radioactivity and nuclear bombs
Elastic potential energy (the word 'potential' means *stored*)	An object that is pulled or squashed has this type of energy	A stretched rubber band and the cables supporting a bridge
Gravitational potential energy	This is energy due to an object's position in the Earth's gravitational field. An object lifted higher will have greater gravitational potential energy	An aeroplane in the sky and a person up a ladder

QUESTIONS

1 In each case below, state and explain the different types of energy that the object has or produces.
   a A stretched catapult.
   b An aeroplane flying overhead.
   c An electric generator.

What happens to energy?

Energy transfer chains

A firework exploding in the night sky will emit light energy, get very hot and produce a loud bang. Where does all the energy come from? It comes from the chemicals in the firework. The energy changes taking place for the exploding firework are shown below:

$$\text{chemical energy} \rightarrow \text{thermal energy} + \text{light energy} + \text{sound energy}$$

When one form of energy is changed into another form, we say that energy is *transferred*. Energy transfers are quite common. For example, if you want to go somewhere, you can catch a bus. The bus transfers chemical energy into kinetic energy. When it gets dark, you switch on the lights. The light bulb transfers electrical energy into light and heat.

When water cascades over a waterfall, its gravitational potential energy at the top is changed into kinetic energy as it falls and then into heat and sound when it hits the rocks at the bottom.

FIGURE 2: Exploding fireworks. What are the energy changes taking place?

Conservation of energy

Energy is measured in joules (J). When energy is transferred, the total amount neither increases nor decreases. The total amount of energy remains the same. This is a very important idea in physics and is known as the **principle of conservation of energy**.

According to this principle, energy cannot be created or destroyed. It can simply be transferred from one form to another.

QUESTIONS

2 Describe the energy changes taking place for:

a A car.

b A burning coal.

c An electric buzzer.

3 In the exploding firework in Figure 2, the thermal energy is 15 J, light energy is 2 J and sound energy is 0.5 J. Calculate the chemical energy of the firework.

Analysing heat

All matter is made up of atoms. In a solid, the atoms are held together in a lattice structure by electrical forces. The atoms jiggle about fixed points. The atoms have both potential (electrical) energy and kinetic energy due to the vibrations. Heating the solid increases the temperature of the solid. Microscopically, the atoms have greater kinetic energy. In a gas, the atoms move around and bump into each other; they have kinetic energy.

The heat energy of a substance is the total kinetic energy and potential (electrical) energy of all the atoms in that substance.

QUESTIONS

4 A student suggests that electrical energy and sound energy are both really kinetic energies. Discuss whether or not you agree with the student.

FIGURE 3: What kind of energy do hot coals have?

Efficiency of devices

Choosing bulbs

This photo shows a collection of light bulbs. Which one would you choose? Your decision might depend on the appearance of the bulb or its cost-effectiveness. These bulbs produce light, but sadly the majority of the energy is wasted as heat. A light bulb is really a small heater!

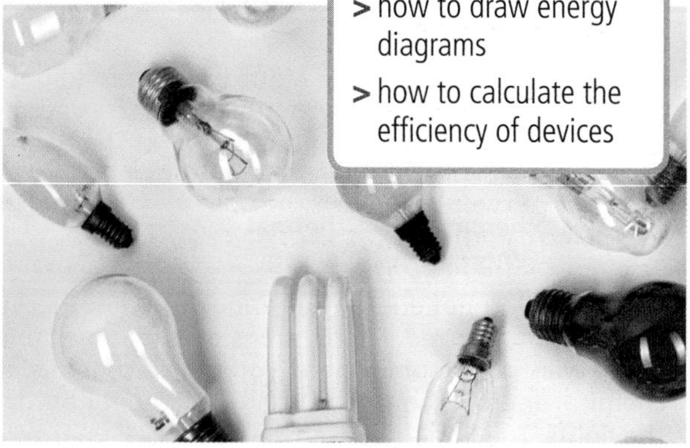

FIGURE 1: Can you identify the different types of light bulb?

Useful energy

In order to decide how effective a light bulb is, you have to consider how much useful energy is being produced. The purpose of a light bulb is to produce light and not to heat your room!

The useful energy depends on the device. This is shown in Table 1.

TABLE 1: Energy from various equipment.

Device	Input energy	Useful energy	Wasted energy
Loudspeaker	Electrical	Sound	Heat in the wires
Electric heater	Electrical	Thermal (heat)	None
Torch	Chemical	Light	Heat from the bulb
Solar panel	Light	Electrical	Heat in the wires and solar panel
Car	Chemical (from fuel)	Kinetic	Heat and sound
Generator	Kinetic	Electrical	Heat (due to friction)

For most devices, apart from the electric heater, heat is considered as wasted energy. Heat is produced by:

> an electric current in the wires and the device

> frictional forces between two objects rubbing together.

FIGURE 2: A fast-moving train. What is its useful energy?

QUESTIONS

1 Draw a table to show the input energy, the useful energy and the wasted energy for the following:

a Battery-powered radio.

b Television.

c Coal-fired power station.

2 Where do cars get chemical input energy from?

Efficiency

The equation

Efficiency is a measure of how well a device transfers energy into the form we want. It is the proportion of the input energy that is transferred to the useful form. The efficiency of a device, as a percentage, can be calculated using this equation:

$$\text{efficiency} = \frac{\text{(useful energy transferred by the device)}}{\text{(total energy supplied to the device)}} \times 100\%$$

Q Efficiency of devices   Efficiency and energy-saving lamps

Consider an energy-saving bulb. For every 60 J of electrical energy supplied to the bulb, 45 J is wasted as heat and 15 J is transferred into light. The efficiency of this bulb is:

$$\text{efficiency} = \frac{15}{60} \times 100\% = 25\%$$

The bulb transfers 25% (a quarter) of the input energy into useful energy. If the bulb was being used as a heater (perhaps in an experiment), then its efficiency would be 75%.

Sankey diagrams

Figure 3 shows an energy-transfer diagram, also known as a **Sankey diagram**, for the energy-saving bulb considered above.

In a Sankey diagram:

> The thickness of the arrow is drawn to scale to show the amount of energy.

> Energy is always conserved.

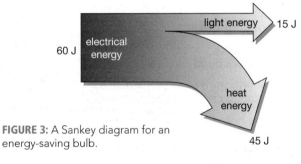

FIGURE 3: A Sankey diagram for an energy-saving bulb.

Figures 4 and 5 show Sankey diagrams for an iPod and a car's petrol engine.

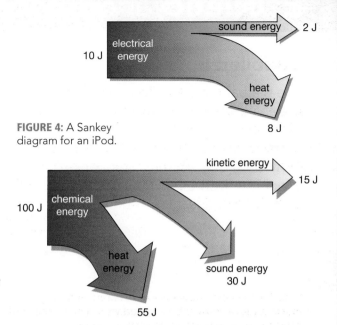

FIGURE 4: A Sankey diagram for an iPod.

FIGURE 5: A Sankey diagram for a car's petrol engine.

QUESTIONS

3 Use Figures 4 and 5 to calculate the efficiencies of the iPod and the car's petrol engine.

4 An electric motor is 30% efficient. The wasted energy is heat in the motor and the wires. The input electrical energy is 50 J. Draw a labelled Sankey diagram for this motor.

Back to the National Grid

Electricity is transported around the country at high voltages along a network of cables – the National Grid. High voltage is used in order to minimise the thermal losses in the cables.

Figure 6 shows a graph of heat energy lost in the cables against transmission voltage when the input electrical energy to the cables is 2.0×10^6 J.

Use the information provided in this graph to answer the questions.

QUESTIONS

5 Calculate the efficiency when electricity is transported at 50 kV.

6 High-voltage transmission is dangerous because of potential injuries that can be caused by electrocution or sparks flying between the cables and objects. The dangers can be minimised by using lower voltages. Discuss whether or not this is a viable suggestion, calculating the efficiencies at 100 kV and 200 kV.

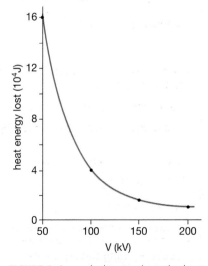

FIGURE 6: A graph showing how the heat energy lost in the cables depends on the transmission voltage.

Radiated and absorbed energy

All foiled up!

This is a baby in a thermal blanket. The shiny blanket is made of fabric and aluminium foil. Have you ever wondered why these blankets are shiny and not dull? The shiny blanket is highly reflective and insulates the body from heat losses due to radiation.

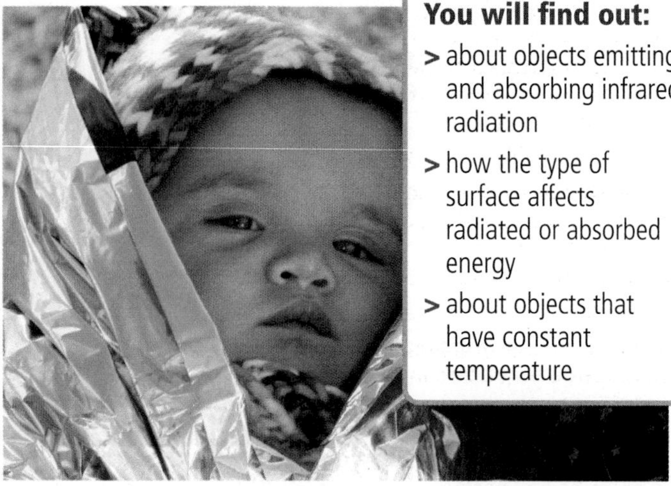

FIGURE 1: Why is it important to have a shiny blanket?

You will find out:

- about objects emitting and absorbing infrared radiation
- how the type of surface affects radiated or absorbed energy
- about objects that have constant temperature

Infrared radiation

An object can:

- emit (give out) infrared radiation
- absorb (take in) infrared radiation
- reflect (bounce off) infrared radiation.

Different objects emit different amounts of radiation depending on their *temperature* and their *surface*.

Emitting infrared radiation

- All objects above –273 °C (absolute zero) give out infrared radiation.
- The hotter the object, the greater the amount of power it radiates. For example, a hot oven will emit greater amounts of infrared radiation per unit time than when it is cooler.
- A dull, black surface loses energy more quickly. It is a good radiator of heat.
- A bright, shiny surface loses energy more slowly. It is a poor radiator of heat.

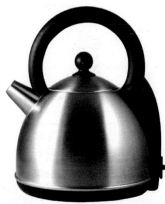

FIGURE 2: Some kettles are shiny to reduce heat loss by radiation. What effect does this have?

Absorbing infrared radiation

- A dull, black surface is a good absorber of radiation (as well as a good radiator).
- A bright, shiny surface is a poor absorber of radiation. It reflects radiation away.

In some hot countries, people wear bright white clothes and paint their houses white to reduce absorption of infrared radiation from the Sun.

- Objects hotter than their surroundings emit more infrared energy per unit time (power) than they absorb from their surroundings.
- Objects cooler than their surroundings absorb more infrared energy per unit time (power) than they emit.

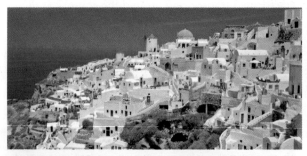

FIGURE 3: A Greek village in the Mediterranean. Why are all the houses painted white?

QUESTIONS

1 Explain why a shiny teapot is preferable to a dull-coloured one.

2 Explain why some fire-fighters wear bright shiny suits when tackling fires.

Absorption of infrared radiation   Infrared radiation and type of surface

Staying at the same temperature

Imagine that you have taken a ball from your cool room out in the Sun on a hot summer's day. The ball will absorb infrared radiation from the Sun and get hot. After some time, the temperature will remain steady. Why does the ball not get hotter and hotter as it absorbs energy from the Sun?

Apart from absorbing radiation, the ball is also emitting radiation. It reaches a steady temperature when the ball radiates away the same power as it absorbs. The same idea can be applied to explain the following:

> A hot filament of a lamp reaches a steady temperature when the input electrical power is equal to the power radiated away from the filament.

> The Earth is constantly absorbing power from the Sun. The Earth maintains a steady average temperature because it radiates away the same amount of power.

> The temperature of food in a microwave oven will eventually become constant when the absorbed power from the microwaves is equal to the power radiated away by the food.

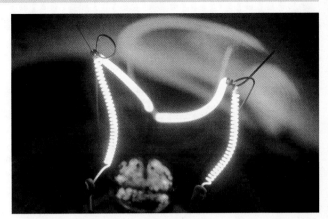

FIGURE 4: A hot filament of a lamp.

Did you know?

The Earth receives about 10^{16} J/s of infrared radiation from the Sun.

QUESTIONS

3 The input electrical power to a heater is 120 W. The temperature of the heater stays constant. State the amount of power radiated from the heater. Explain your answer.

4 The bulb of a table lamp is at room temperature. The lamp is switched on. Explain why its temperature initially increases and then levels off.

Experimenting with radiation

How can you investigate the effects of different surfaces on their ability to absorb and emit infrared radiation?

Figure 5 shows two beakers, A and B, containing hot water. The outside of beaker A is painted silver and beaker B is painted matt black. The temperature of the water in A and B is recorded at regular intervals. The water in B cools more rapidly because the black surface radiates a greater amount of power.

Figure 6 shows two identical metal plates, X and Y, placed on opposite sides of a heater. Plate X is painted silver and plate Y is painted matt black. Both plates have a cork attached to them using melted wax. The cork stuck to plate Y drops off first because the matt black surface absorbs a greater amount of radiation from the heater than the silver surface. As a result, the wax on plate Y melts sooner.

QUESTIONS

5 Discuss the factors you need to control in order to make each of the experiments shown in Figures 5 and 6 fair.

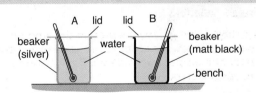

FIGURE 5: A cooling experiment with shiny and black beakers. The thermometers in each beaker will indicate the amount of thermal energy radiated.

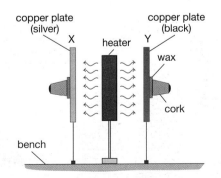

FIGURE 6: An absorption experiment with shiny and black metal plates. The melting wax is an indicator of the amount of thermal energy absorbed.

Preparing for assessment:
Applying your knowledge

To achieve a good grade in science, you not only have to know and understand scientific ideas, but you also need to be able to apply them to other situations. This task will support you in developing these skills.

✳ Radiation: warming up and cooling down

The Smith family is preparing for their summer holidays. The family is going to one of the Greek islands and the weather is going to be very hot and sunny. Tom teases his fashion-conscious sister Lili for packing mostly black clothes.

'Everyone knows that you should wear white clothes to keep cool', he tells her.

Lili explains that he is wrong.

When the Smith family arrive in Greece they notice that many of the houses are painted white and some of the people wear dark clothes. This really confuses Tom.

✳ Task 1

Tom thought that Lili should pack white clothes

> Explain what is wrong with this idea.

✳ Task 2

Many of the houses in the village where the Smith family stayed are painted white. Suggest why this may be.

✳ Task 3

Arrange the following four items of clothing in order of increasing heat-absorbing ability, starting with the worst absorber:

A Black swimsuit
B White swimsuit
C Denim jeans
D Shiny, metallic-style jacket

Which of the clothes listed above would be best for each of the following? Explain your answers.

> A holiday somewhere hot and sunny.

> Swimming in the heated pools of Iceland.

> A dull day in Manchester.

✳ Task 4

A friend mentions that she is going on a beach holiday and she is taking a black swimsuit as 'black will attract the Sun's rays and help me tan more quickly'. What is wrong with the statement 'A black swimsuit attracts the Sun's rays'?

> Explain to your friend why this is not the case.

> Rewrite your friend's statement so that it is scientifically correct.

✳ Maximise your grade

These sentences show what you need to include in your work to achieve each grade. Use them to improve your work and be more successful.

E

For grade E, your answers should show that you can:
> identify the surfaces which are the best absorbers, emitters and reflectors of radiant heat.

C

For grades D, C, in addition show that you can:
> know that an object reaches a steady temperature.

For grades B, A, in addition show that you can:
> critically evaluate scientific statements and apply your knowledge of science to identify misconceptions and correct them
> explain why an object reaches steady temperature in terms of power radiated and power absorbed.

A

P1 checklist (Topics 4–6)

To achieve your forecast grade in the exam you'll need to revise

Use this checklist to see what you can do now. Refer back to pages 224–57 if you're not sure.

Look across the rows to see how you could progress – **_bold italic_** means Higher tier only.

Remember you'll need to be able to use these ideas in various ways, such as:
> interpreting pictures, diagrams and graphs
> applying ideas to new situations
> explaining ethical implications
> suggesting some benefits and risks to society
> drawing conclusions from evidence you've been given.

Look at pages 270–92 for more information about exams and how you'll be assessed.

To aim for a grade E	To aim for a grade C	To aim for a grade A
recall the frequencies of ultrasound and infrasound	outline and explain the uses of ultrasound and infrasound	
recall that seismic waves are created by explosions and earthquakes	describe how earthquakes are created by the movement of tectonic plates and explain why earthquakes are unpredictable	evaluate evidence for the movement of tectonic plates
recall that P waves are longitudinal and S waves are transverse	explain how seismometers can be used to locate earthquakes	**_understand how P and S waves are reflected and refracted by the layers inside the Earth_**
recall that current is due to the flow of charge and voltage is a measure of energy transferred define power as the energy transferred per second	use the equation $P = I \times V$ to solve problems and investigate how to determine the power of an electrical item	
recall what is meant by renewable and non-renewable resources and give examples of these resources	discuss the advantages and disadvantages of large-scale electrical production using renewable and non-renewable resources	
recall how current can be induced	explain how generators produce alternating and direct electric currents explain how the size and direction of current can be changed	

To aim for a grade E	To aim for a grade C	To aim for a grade A
recall what transformers do	understand step-up and step-down transformers and describe how the National Grid works	*use the turn-ratio equation for transformers* and explain why high voltages are used for the transmission of electricity in terms of heat losses in the overhead cables
recall that the kilowatt-hour (kW h) is a unit of energy	use the equation: cost = power (kW) × time (hours) × cost (p) and calculate payback time	use data to compare and contrast the advantages and disadvantages of energy-saving devices
give examples of different types of energy and understand that devices can never be 100% efficient	understand that energy is conserved and how it is transformed interpret and explain energy-flow (Sankey) diagrams interpret data and information in order to determine the efficiency of a device: $\text{efficiency} = \dfrac{(\text{useful energy transferred})}{(\text{total energy supplied})} \times 100\%$	
recall that dark surfaces are good emitters and absorbers of infrared waves and shiny surfaces are poor emitters and absorbers of infrared waves	know that an object reaches a steady temperature	explain why an object reaches a steady temperature in terms of power radiated and power absorbed and design experiments to support this

259

Exam-style questions: Foundation

AO1 **1 a** A sound wave with frequency less than 20 Hz is called … [1]

    A transverse
    B ultrasound
    C infrasound
    D longitudinal.

b Copy and complete the sentences below by choosing from the following words: sound, refract, light, wavelength, frequency, speed, reflect, transverse and longitudinal.

AO1 **i** Ultrasound is a ____ wave. [1]

AO1 **ii** We cannot hear ultrasound because it has a very high ____. [1]

AO1 **iii** Ultrasound is used by dolphins to locate fish. The fish ____ the ultrasound. [1]

c $\text{speed} = \dfrac{\text{distance}}{\text{time}}$

A ship uses ultrasound to find the depth of water by bouncing ultrasound off the bottom of the seabed. The depth of the water is 120 m.

AO2 **i** Explain why the distance travelled by the ultrasound is 240 m. [1]

AO2 **ii** The time taken for the ultrasound to travel a distance of 240 m is 0.16 s. Calculate the speed of the ultrasound. State the unit. [3]

[Total: 8]

2 The output voltage from generators in a coal-fired power station is 23 000 V. Transformers are used to change the voltage to 400 000 V for cables in the National Grid.

AO1 **a** State one major disadvantage of coal-fired power stations. [1]

AO1 **b** State the type of transformer used in the power station to increase the size of the voltage. [1]

AO1 **c** Explain why electricity is transported at high voltage. [2]

AO1 **d** State one hazard of transporting electricity at high voltage. [1]

AO2 **e** Energy can also be produced by wind, solar and hydroelectric power. A coastal town relying on coal-fired power stations is researching new sources of energy. Discuss the advantages and disadvantages of wind, solar and hydroelectric power, compared to coal-fired power stations, for the community. [6]

[Total: 11]

3 The diagram below shows how the Earth might have looked some 250 million years ago.

AO2 **a** Explain why the positions of the land masses are now different. [3]

AO1 **b** State the names of the two types of seismic waves created by earthquakes. [2]

AO1 **c** Which statement below is correct about seismic waves? [1]

    A all seismic waves are transverse waves
    B seismic waves cannot be created by explosions
    C all seismic waves can be reflected
    D all seismic waves travel at the same speed through the Earth.

AO2 AO3 **d** An earthquake creates S waves and P waves. The diagram shows the chart from a seismometer. How can evidence from the trace be used to predict the likelihood of an earthquake? [2]

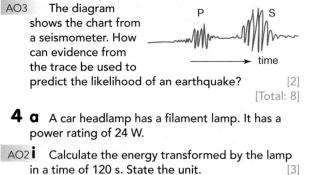

[Total: 8]

4 a A car headlamp has a filament lamp. It has a power rating of 24 W.

AO2 **i** Calculate the energy transformed by the lamp in a time of 120 s. State the unit. [3]

AO2 **ii** State why the lamp is not 100% efficient. [1]

b A generator consists of a coil that is moved in a magnetic field. As the coil is rotated it produces an electrical current.

AO1 AO2 **i** State the type of current produced by the generator and the energy changes taking place in the generator. [2]

AO1 AO2 **ii** Discuss two factors that affect the size of the current from the generator. [4]

[Total: 10]

AO1 recall the science   AO2 apply your knowledge   AO3 evaluate and analyse the evidence

✱ Worked example

AO1 a Complete the sentences below about an electrical circuit. Select from the following words: energy, frequency, power, charge, watts, amperes and volts. [2]

Current is the flow of _charge_ in a circuit. ✔

Voltage is a measure of _power_ in a circuit. ✘

AO2 b A lamp carries a current of 1.2 A when it is connected to a 9.0 V supply. Calculate the electrical power of the lamp and state the unit. [3]

power = 9.0 × 1.2 ✔

= 10.8

power = _10.8_ ✔ unit: _joules_ ✘

AO2 c i Complete the energy flow (Sankey) diagram for the lamp in **b**. [1]

electrical energy
40 J

light

_70_ J ✘

heat (thermal) energy
30 J

ii Use the following equation to calculate the efficiency of the lamp in **b**:

$$\text{efficiency} = \frac{\text{useful energy transferred by the device}}{\text{total energy supplied to the device}}$$ [2]

$\frac{30}{40}$ = 0.75

efficiency = _0.75_ ✘ %

AO2 d Which of these two devices involves the transfer of more energy: a 2 kW kettle running for 30 seconds or a 50 W light bulb running for 15 minutes? Show your working. [2]

kettle: E = P × t 2 × 1000 × 30 = 60 000 J

light: E = P × t 50 × 15 × 60 = 45 000 J

The kettle transfers more energy than the light does. ✔ ✔

This candidate scored 5 marks out of a possible 10. This is below a grade C. Extra marks gained in **b** and **c** by looking carefully at the units used and extracting the correct data would have lifted the performance to a grade C.

How to raise your grade

Take note of the comments from examiners – these will help you to improve your grade.

This is a good start from the candidate.

The answer should have been 'energy'. Watch out – in exams, candidates often mix up energy and power.

This is a well-structured answer by the candidate with clear workings shown.

The candidate has lost an easy mark here. Power is measured in *watts* (W), not joules (J).

The correct answer is 10 joules. The candidate has added the energies instead of subtracting them. Remember, the thickness of the line in a Sankey diagram represents the amount of energy. Here the line for light is thinner, so the energy should have a lower value in joules.

The useful energy for a lamp is light. The candidate should have divided the 10 J by 40 J. The answer would have been 25%.

The candidate has remembered to convert the data into the units. The equation requires power in watts and time in seconds. Kilowatts has been converted to watts, and minutes has been converted to seconds. You will not be awarded any marks if you do not show your working.

AO1 **1** **a** Which of the statements is correct about ultrasound? [1]

    A ultrasound is an electromagnetic wave
    B ultrasound has frequency less than 20 kHz
    C ultrasound can be refracted
    D ultrasound can travel through a vacuum.

b A pulse of ultrasound is sent into a patient. This pulse is reflected by the internal organ of the patient.

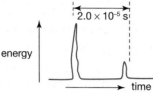

AO2 **i** The speed of ultrasound in the patient is 1500 m/s and the frequency of the ultrasound is 1.5×10^6 Hz. Calculate the wavelength of the ultrasound. State the unit. [4]

AO2 **ii** The time delay between the pulse sent into the patient and receiving the pulse is 2.0×10^{-5} s. The speed of the ultrasound is 1500 m/s. Calculate the distance in metres travelled by the ultrasound in this time delay. [2]

AO2 **iii** Explain why the reflected pulse is smaller than the pulse sent into the patient. [1]

[Total: 8]

2

AO1 **a** Explain how an earthquake is caused at the boundaries between tectonic plates. [3]

b An earthquake creates S waves and P waves. The diagram shows the chart from a seismometer.

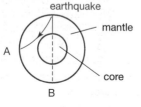

AO2 **i** Use the diagram above to explain which of these two waves travels more slowly. [1]

AO1 **ii** State one property of S waves. [1]

c The diagram below shows the possible paths of two S waves through the Earth.

AO2 **i** Explain why the path of the S wave arriving at point A is curved inside the Earth. [2]

AO2 **ii** Explain why no S waves are detected at point B. [1]

[Total: 8]

3

AO2 **a** **i** A student wants to determine the power of a lamp. Copy and complete the circuit below to show how she should measure the potential difference across the lamp. [1]

AO2 **ii** The potential difference across the lamp is 6.0 V and its power rating is 0.36 W. Calculate the current in the lamp when operating at 6.0 V. Show your working and state the unit. [4]

AO1 **b** Define a kilowatt-hour. [1]

AO2 **c** An electric kettle of power rating 2.0 kW and a 60 W lamp are operated for a time of 5 minutes. Without doing any calculations, explain which of these two devices would cost more to use. [2]

[Total: 8]

4 **a** The diagram below shows a transformer used in a domestic appliance.

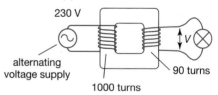

AO2 **i** Use the information given in the diagram to calculate the output voltage V in volts from the transformer. Show your working. [3]

AO2 **ii** Explain the output voltage from the transformer when the alternating supply of 230 V is replaced by a battery. [1]

b Describe the effect on the brightness of the lamp when:

AO2 **i** there are fewer turns on the output [2]

AO3 **ii** the lamp is far away from the transformer and longer cables are required. [4]

[Total: 10]

AO1 recall the science   AO2 apply your knowledge   AO3 evaluate and analyse the evidence

✺ Worked example

AO1 **a** Define current. [1]

Current is how quickly charges move in a circuit. ✗

AO1 **b** Define power. [1]

Power is energy divided by time. ✔

AO2 **c** A small buzzer has a power rating of 200 mW when connected to a 4.0 V supply. Calculate the current in the buzzer. Show your working and give the unit:

200 = 4.0 × current ✗

Current = 200/4.0 ✔ (error carried forward)

Current = 50

Current = *50* ✔ unit: *amps* ✔ [4]

AO2 **d** An energy-saving lamp has an efficiency of 18%. Calculate the input electrical energy in joules when the output light energy is 10 J. Show your working:

electrical energy = $\dfrac{10}{0.18}$ ✔

energy = *55.6* ✔ joules [2]

How to raise your grade

Take note of the comments from examiners – these will help you to improve your grade.

A-grade candidates cannot afford to get definitions wrong. Current is the rate of flow of charge. This statement is too vague.

This is a perfect answer. The alternative definition is 'power is the rate of transfer of energy'. Remember the term *rate* means 'divide by time'.

The candidate has failed to change the power from mW to W. The correct value for the current is 0.20 A.

The examiner has applied the 'error carried forward rule' here. The correct answer is 1000 times smaller; i.e. current = 0.05 A.

A very clear solution. The candidate has changed the efficiency from a percentage to 0.18.

This candidate scored 6 marks out of a possible 8. Getting the definition correct in **a** or changing mW correctly into W in **c** would have earned the candidate extra marks and a grade A.

Bad Science for Schools

When the evidence doesn't add up.

Sometimes people use what sound like scientific words and ideas to sell you things or persuade you to think in a certain way. Some of these claims are valid, and some are not. The activities on these pages are based on the work of Dr Ben Goldacre and will help you to question some of the scientific claims you meet. Read more about the work of Ben in his *Bad Science* book or at badscience.net.

How much to look younger?

There are many ways to make yourself look younger if you're an adult. These include the style and colour of your hair, the texture of your skin, your body shape and the clothes you wear. Manufacturers and retailers know this and recognise where there's money to be made.

Which of these do you think is more effective?

Are there other ways for adults to make themselves look younger?

How are these age-defying products promoted?

✳ YOUNG SKIN FROM OLD?

Skin changes in appearance as people get older. These photographs show how older skin looks different to young skin.

> Examine the photographs. What are the differences?

> How might an anti-ageing skin cream work on the old skin? What would it need to do?

 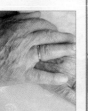

Young skin   Old skin

✳ THE SCIENCE BEHIND THE CLAIM

As you get older you may not like the appearance of wrinkles and crows feet. You can spend quite a lot of money on anti-ageing skin creams. Creams are advertised with appealing images and lavish claims, but do they really work?

One immediate gain from a cream is rehydration. Dried out skin doesn't look good so we can make it look better by moisturising it. This is easy and the active ingredients are really cheap. However something more is needed to make someone genuinely look younger.

These are three types of active ingredient commonly used:

> Alphahydroxy acids, such as vitamins A and C, are used to exfoliate the skin. Some of these work at high doses, but they are also irritants, so they can only be sold at low doses.

> Vegetable proteins, which are long chain molecules. As the cream dries on the skin the chain molecules tighten, applying tension and temporarily tightening it.

> Hydrogen peroxide, which is corrosive and will lightly burn the skin.

Why might someone who uses a cream with these ingredients think that it is working? Will the effects last?

We are learning to:
> find out how anti-ageing skin creams work
> examine claims that are made for them

NEW AND IMPROVED! ADVERTISER'S CLAIMS

Many anti-ageing skin creams are sold on the basis that there is a scientific reason that they work. Some claims are justified but others are pretty dubious, even if they look persuasive at first glance. You should think critically about what you are told by the advertisers.

> Claims sound more convincing if they are based on tests and if scientists have been involved. Powerful scientific words include *conclusive tests*, *laboratory*, *cleanse*, *purify* and *health*.

> They may claim to make you feel better, look younger, have more energy and be healthier. Some of the claims may be difficult to prove; they should have been tested, the full results published and independently checked in a scientific way. There are very few cases of anti-ageing skin creams being proved to get rid of wrinkles. Why do you think this is?

> Watch out for claims such as 'eight out of ten users said that…' if it's not clear what kind of people and how many were asked. What do you think ten company employees might say about their product and would this be representative of all their consumers?

✳ THE PSYCHOLOGY OF COSMETICS

You can buy very cheap creams in the shops. You can even make your own skin cream using simple ingredients. If you did, it would be pretty good at moisturising, so your skin would feel soft and maybe a little smoother. It wouldn't, however, make you look younger for long.

Why do you think anti-ageing skin creams are sometimes quite expensive?

Do you think people who buy anti-ageing skin creams

a) genuinely believe that they make them look younger?

b) hope that they might but don't really believe it?

c) do it because it makes them feel good?

Bad Science for Schools

When the evidence doesn't add up.

Sometimes people use what sound like scientific words and ideas to sell you things or persuade you to think in a certain way. Some of these claims are valid, and some are not. The activities on these pages are based on the work of Dr Ben Goldacre and will help you to question some of the scientific claims you meet. Read more about the work of Ben in his *Bad Science* book or at badscience.net.

What we'll look like in the future

Here are some questions to get you thinking about the future of the human race.

> How do you think humans have evolved over the last few millions of years?

> What changes have taken place in the way we look and move?

> How might evolution affect us over the next few million years?

News stories that sound like they are about science can come from a number of different places. Sometimes they are fair reports of real scientific research, but sometimes they are just good stories.

The story opposite featured in a number of news reports, including The Times, where this version was printed, BBC, Daily Telegraph and The Sun. Your task is to work out if this story is good science or bad science.

You are going to investigate the predictions reported in this article. First you need to identify the predictions. This is the first one – that humans will evolve into two separate species. To decide whether you think this is good or bad science think about what you have learnt about evolution. Do you think this likely to happen?

From **THE TIMES**
October 17, 2006

The future ascent (and descent) of man

Within 100,000 years the divide between rich and poor could lead to two human sub-species

By Mark Henderson, Science Editor

The mating preferences of the rich, highly educated and well-nourished could ultimately drive their separation into a genetically distinct group that no longer interbreeds with less fortunate human beings, according to Oliver Curry.

Dr Curry, a research associate in the Centre for Philosophy of Natural and Social Science of the London School of Economics, speculated that privileged humans might over tens of thousands of years evolve into a "gracile" subspecies, tall, thin, symmetrical, intelligent and creative. The rest would be shorter and stockier, with asymmetric features and lower intelligence, he said.

THE BRAVO EVOLUTION REPORT

People today are taller and live longer than people a few hundred years ago. Why do you think this has happened? Do you think that trend will continue?

Dr Curry is a research associate, but is this story based on scientific research? Why do you think Bravo asked Dr Curry to write this piece? Do you know if Bravo usually take an interest in stories about science?

Dr Curry's vision echoes that of H. G. Wells in *The Time Machine*. He envisaged a race of frail, privileged beings, the Eloi, living in a ruined city and coexisting uneasily with ape-like Morlocks who toil underground and are descended from the downtrodden workers of today.

Dr Curry also said that today's concept of race would be gone by the year 3000, relationships between people with different skin colours producing a "coffee-colour" across all populations.

In Brazil, the black African, white European and native American populations have been having children together for hundreds of years but there is still a lot of diversity in physical appearance. Can you think of any other examples that you know of that either back up the idea about the whole population being "coffee-coloured" or make you think it might not happen that way?

With improvements in nutrition and medicine, people would routinely grow to 6ft 6in and live to the age of 120, he said.

Genetic modification, cosmetic surgery and sexual selection — whereby mate preferences drive evolution — meant that people would tend to be better-looking than today.

Otherwise, humans will look much as they do now, with one exception: Dr Curry also suggested that increased reliance on processed food would make chewing less important, possibly resulting in less developed jaws and shorter chins. Ten thousand years from today this effect could be compounded as human faces grow more juvenile in appearance.

This effect — neotony — is known from domestic animals: dogs resemble young versions of wild relatives such as wolves.

Dr Curry raised the worrying possibility that reliance on technology could erode social skills and even health. As deaths from

How have we ended up with a huge variety of breeds of domestic dog? Could the same happen with humans?

genetic diseases such as cancer are prevented, the genes themselves might become more common, no longer being "weeded out" of the gene pool. Increased use of medicine as a means of treating disease could lead to the deterioration of the body's immune system.

Dr Curry's predictions were commissioned by the television channel Bravo to celebrate its 21st anniversary on air.

"The Bravo Evolution Report suggests that the future of man will be a story of the good, the bad and the ugly," he said. "While science and technology have the potential to create an ideal habitat for humanity over the next millennium, there is the possibility of a genetic hangover due to an over-reliance on technology reducing our natural capacity to resist disease or get along with each other.

"After that, things could get ugly, with the possible emergence of genetic 'haves' and 'have-nots'."

Do you think that the "genetic 'haves' and 'have-nots'" is a likely future for our race? Is a world with two species of humans likely? What evidence would you use to support your claim?

1,000 YEARS//
The peak of human enhancement – average height 6.5 feet, life expectancy of 120 years, coffee coloured, symmetrical features, athleticism, large clear eyes and smooth hairless skin. Humans will have less developed jaws and shorter chins.

100,000 YEARS//
Mankind will be divided into two distinct sub-species – the genetic 'haves' and the genetic 'have nots.' The 'haves' will be tall, thin, symmetrical, clean, healthy, intelligent and creative. The 'have nots' will be short, stocky, asymmetrical, grubby, unhealthy and less intelligent.

Bad Science for Schools

When the evidence doesn't add up.

Sometimes people use what sound like scientific words and ideas to sell you things or persuade you to think in a certain way. Some of these claims are valid, and some are not. The activities on these pages are based on the work of Dr Ben Goldacre and will help you to question some of the scientific claims you meet. Read more about the work of Ben in his *Bad Science* book or at badscience.net.

Keeping your brain fit

In science you learn about ideas that scientists have developed by collecting evidence from experiments; you are also learning to collect and evaluate evidence yourself. You can use this outside of the laboratory to weigh up information you come across everyday. Let's look at this example about how to prepare for exams.

When it comes to exam season you will get lots of different tips from teachers, other students and companies that all claim to help you do better in exams but who is right? If you had an important exam coming up, what would be a good way of making sure that your brain was going to function well?

✳ GOOD ADVICE?

Here are three pieces of advice offered to students before exams. For each one:

> suggest why it might be true;

> suggest why you might be dubious about it;

> decide whether you think it's good advice and explain why.

Before sitting an aural exam (a listening test) spin round three times clockwise and three times anticlockwise. This stimulates the semicircular canals which are located in the inner ear, thus stimulating the cochlea.

A drink with caffeine in it is a good idea as it acts as a stimulant and will cause your brain to work quicker.

Before doing an exam in the morning make sure you have a good breakfast. Something like porridge is good as the energy is released slowly during the morning, so you don't get tired towards the end.

✴ THE SCIENCE BEHIND THE CLAIM

Let's look in more detail at some activities that some schools have used to try to improve students' concentration and learning. Your task is to work out which bits of science are good science and which are bad. To help you decide whether you think your activity is good or bad try discussing these questions:

> What *advice* is being given?

> What *claim* is being made?

> What *scientific ideas* are being used to justify that claim?

> What *scientific ideas* do you have that may tell you something about this topic?

> Is the advice *sound*?

This is the advice.

This is the claim.

Interlock the fingers of both your hands, holding your elbows out at the sides. This completes a circuit and allows positive energy to flow. Positive energy creates positive thoughts, stimulating the brain, stilling anxieties and clearing the way for a free flow of logical thought.

These are the scientific ideas used to back up this claim. Forming the arms in a loop creates no circuit that any kind of energy 'flows around' and 'positive energy' is a meaningless term.

So can you think of any reason why this might work? You know that regular exercise is good and could help to refocus on ideas and mental activities.

Is the advice sound? Well, it won't do you any harm and may even improve concentration, but not for the reasons claimed.

Now you have a go. Are these good or bad science?

Water is a vital ingredient of blood and blood is essential to transport oxygen to the brain. For the brain to work well you have to ensure your blood is hydrated. This needs water, little and often. The best way of rehydrating the blood taking oxygen to the brain is to hold water in the mouth for up to half a minute, thus allowing direct absorption.

Your carotid arteries are vital to supplying your brain with richly oxygenated blood. Ensure their peak performance by pressing your brain buttons. These are just below the collar bone, one on either side. Make 'C' shapes with forefinger and thumb to place over the brain buttons and gently massage.

✴ WOULD YOU PAY MONEY FOR THIS?

Many products or services are sold on the basis that there is a scientific reason that they work. Some claims are justified but some are pretty dubious, even if they look persuasive at first glance. You should think critically about what you are told.

> Claims might sound more convincing if they use technical scientific terms, but sometimes they are used incorrectly, to make something sound scientific when it's not.

> Powerful scientific words include 'conclusive tests', 'energy', 'cleanse', 'purify' and 'health'.

> They may claim to make you feel better, look better, have more energy and be healthier.

> The claims may be true but they should have been tested, the full results published and independently checked.

Carrying out practical investigations in GCSE science

Introduction

As part of your GCSE science course, you will develop practical skills and carry out investigative work as part of the scientific process.

Your investigative work will be divided into several parts:

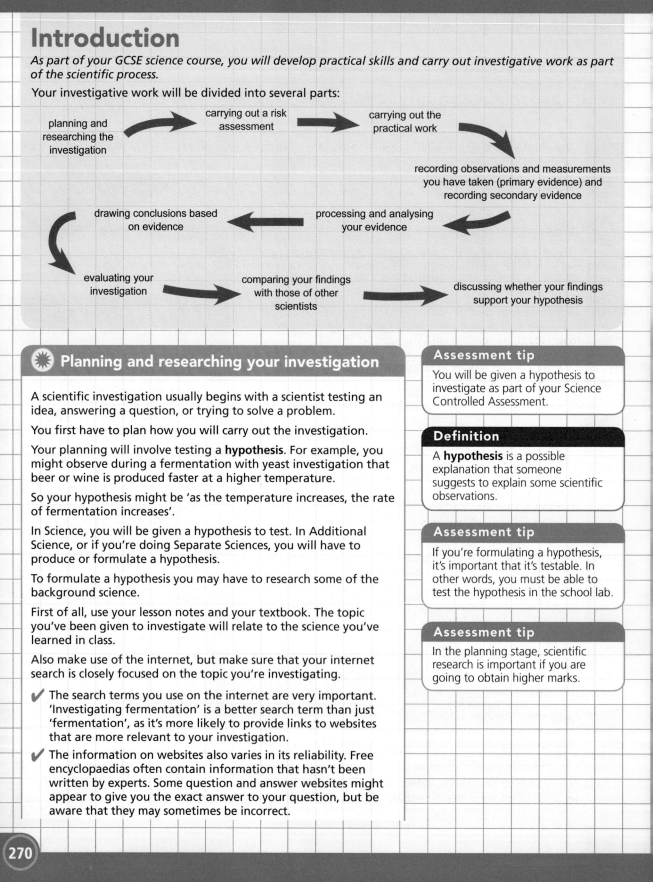

planning and researching the investigation → carrying out a risk assessment → carrying out the practical work → recording observations and measurements you have taken (primary evidence) and recording secondary evidence → processing and analysing your evidence → drawing conclusions based on evidence → evaluating your investigation → comparing your findings with those of other scientists → discussing whether your findings support your hypothesis

✳ Planning and researching your investigation

A scientific investigation usually begins with a scientist testing an idea, answering a question, or trying to solve a problem.

You first have to plan how you will carry out the investigation.

Your planning will involve testing a **hypothesis**. For example, you might observe during a fermentation with yeast investigation that beer or wine is produced faster at a higher temperature.

So your hypothesis might be 'as the temperature increases, the rate of fermentation increases'.

In Science, you will be given a hypothesis to test. In Additional Science, or if you're doing Separate Sciences, you will have to produce or formulate a hypothesis.

To formulate a hypothesis you may have to research some of the background science.

First of all, use your lesson notes and your textbook. The topic you've been given to investigate will relate to the science you've learned in class.

Also make use of the internet, but make sure that your internet search is closely focused on the topic you're investigating.

✔ The search terms you use on the internet are very important. 'Investigating fermentation' is a better search term than just 'fermentation', as it's more likely to provide links to websites that are more relevant to your investigation.

✔ The information on websites also varies in its reliability. Free encyclopaedias often contain information that hasn't been written by experts. Some question and answer websites might appear to give you the exact answer to your question, but be aware that they may sometimes be incorrect.

Assessment tip
You will be given a hypothesis to investigate as part of your Science Controlled Assessment.

Definition
A **hypothesis** is a possible explanation that someone suggests to explain some scientific observations.

Assessment tip
If you're formulating a hypothesis, it's important that it's testable. In other words, you must be able to test the hypothesis in the school lab.

Assessment tip
In the planning stage, scientific research is important if you are going to obtain higher marks.

✔ Most GCSE science websites are more reliable, but, if in doubt, use other information sources to verify the information.

As a result of your research, you may be able to extend your hypothesis and justify it using scientific ideas.

Example 1

Investigation: Plan and research an investigation into the activity of enzymes.

Your hypothesis might be 'When I increase the temperature, the rate of reaction increases'.

You may be able to add more detail, 'This is because as I increase the temperature, the frequency of collisions between the enzyme and the reactant increases'.

Assessment tip

Based on your scientific research, it may also be possible to predict how much you expect this rate of reaction to increase. For example your hypothesis may be 'I expect that the reaction rate will double for every 10 °C rise in temperature'.

✳ Choosing a method and suitable equipment

As part of your planning, you must choose a suitable way of carrying out the investigation.

You will have to choose suitable techniques, equipment and technology, if this is appropriate. How do you make this choice?

You will have already carried out the techniques you need to use during the course of practical work in class (although you may need to modify these to fit in with the context of your investigation). For most of the experimental work you do, there will be a choice of techniques available. You must select the technique:

✔ that is most appropriate to the context of your investigation, and

✔ that will enable you to collect valid data; for example, if you are measuring the effects of light intensity on photosynthesis, you may decide to use an LED (light-emitting diode) at different distances from the plant, rather than a light bulb. The light bulb produces more heat, and temperature is another independent variable in photosynthesis.

Your choice of equipment, too, will be influenced by measurements you need to make. For example:

✔ you might use a one-mark or graduated pipette to measure out the volume of liquid for a titration, but

✔ you may use a measuring cylinder or beaker when adding a volume of acid to a reaction mixture, so that the volume of acid is in excess to that required to dissolve, for example, the calcium carbonate.

Assessment tip

Carrying out a preliminary investigation, along with the necessary research, may help you to select the appropriate technique to use.

Assessment tip

You should always be ready to explain your choice of equipment.

Assessment tip

Technology, such as data-logging and other measuring and monitoring techniques – for example, heart sensors – may help you to carry out your experiment.

✳ Variables

In your investigation, you will work with independent and dependent variables.

The factors you choose, or are given, to investigate the effect of are called **independent variables**.

What you choose to measure, as affected by the independent variable, is called the **dependent variable**.

✳ Independent variables

In your practical work, you will be provided with an independent variable to test, or will have to choose one – or more – of these to test. Some examples are given in the table.

Investigation	Possible independent variables to test
activity of yeast	> temperature > sugar concentration
rate of a chemical reaction	> temperature > concentration of reactants
stopping distance of a moving object	> speed of the object > the surface on which it's moving

Independent variables can be **discrete** or **continuous**.

> When you are testing the effect of different disinfectants on bacteria you are looking at discrete variables.

> When you are testing the effect of a range of concentrations of the same disinfectant on the growth of bacteria you are looking at continuous variables.

Range

When working with an independent variable, you need to choose an appropriate **range** over which to investigate the variable.

You need to decide:

✔ what you will test, and/or

✔ the upper and lower limits of the independent variable to investigate, if the variable is continuous.

Once you have defined the range to be tested, you also need to decide the appropriate intervals at which you will make measurements.

The range you would test depends on:

✔ the nature of the test

✔ the context in which it is given

✔ practical considerations, and

✔ common sense.

Example 2

1 Investigation: Investigating the factors that affect how quickly household limescale removers work in removing limescale from an appliance.

You may have to decide on which acids to use from a range you're provided with. You would choose a weak acid, or acids, to test rather than a strong acid, such as concentrated sulfuric acid. This is because of safety reasons, but also because the acid might damage the appliance you were trying to clean. You would then have to select a range of concentrations of your chosen weak acid to test.

> **Definition**
>
> Variables that fall into a range of separate types are called **discrete** (also known as **categorical**) **variables**.

> **Definition**
>
> Variables that have a continuous range are called **continuous variables**.

> **Definition**
>
> The **range** defines the extent of the independent variables being tested.

> **Assessment tip**
>
> Again, it's often best to carry out a trial run or preliminary investigation, or carry out research, to determine the range to be investigated.

Concentration

You might be trying to find out the best, or optimum, concentration of a disinfectant to prevent the growth of bacteria.

The 'best' concentration would be the lowest in a range that prevented the growth of the bacteria. Concentrations higher than this would be just wasting disinfectant.

If, in a preliminary test, no bacteria were killed by the concentration you used, you would have to increase it (or test another disinfectant). However, if there was no growth of bacteria in your preliminary test, you would have to lower the concentration range. A starting point might be to look at concentrations around those recommended by the manufacturer.

✴ Dependent variables

The dependent variable may be clear from the problem you're investigating; for example, the stopping distance of moving objects. But you may have to make a choice.

> *Example 3*
>
> 1 Investigation: Measuring the rate of photosynthesis in a plant.
>
> There are several ways in which you could measure the rate of photosynthesis in a plant. These include:
>
> > counting the number of bubbles of oxygen produced in a minute by a water plant such as *Elodea* or *Cabomba*
>
> > measuring the volume of oxygen produced over several days by a water plant such as *Elodea* or *Cabomba*
>
> > monitoring the concentration of oxygen in a polythene bag enclosing a potted plant using an oxygen sensor
>
> > measuring the colour change of hydrogen carbonate indicator containing algae embedded in gel.
>
> 2 Investigation: Measuring the rate of a chemical reaction.
>
> You could measure the rate of a chemical reaction in the following ways:
>
> > the rate of formation of a product
>
> > the rate at which the reactant disappears
>
> > a colour change
>
> > a pH change.

✴ Control variables

The validity of your measurements depend on you measuring what you're supposed to be measuring.

Some of these variables may be difficult to control. For example, in an ecology investigation in the field, factors such as varying weather conditions are impossible to control.

> **Assessment tip**
>
> The value of the *depend*ent variable is likely to *depend* on the value of the independent variable. This is a good way of remembering the definition of a dependent variable.

> **Definition**
>
> Other variables that you're not investigating may also have an influence on your measurements. In most investigations, it's important that you investigate just one variable at a time. So other variables, apart from the one you're testing at the time, must be controlled, and kept constant, and not allowed to vary. These are called **control variables**.

> **Assessment tip**
>
> Always identify all the variables to be controlled and how you will control them.

Experimental controls

Experimental controls are often very important, particularly in biological investigations where you're testing the effect of a treatment.

Example 4

Investigation: The effect of disinfectants on the growth of bacteria.

If the bacteria don't grow, it could be because they have been killed by the disinfectant. But the bacteria in your investigation may have died for some other reason. Another factor may be involved. To test whether any effects were down to the disinfectant, you need to set up the same practical, but this time using distilled water in place of the disinfectant. The distilled water is your control. If the bacteria are inhibited by the disinfectant, but grow normally in the dish containing distilled water, it's reasonable to assume that the disinfectant inhibited their growth.

> **Definition**
>
> An **experimental control** is used to find out whether the effect you obtain is from the treatment, or whether you get the same result in the absence of the treatment.

✹ Assessing and managing risk

Before you begin any practical work, you must assess and minimise the possible risks involved.

Before you carry out an investigation, you must identify the possible hazards. These can be grouped into biological hazards, chemical hazards and physical hazards.

> **Definition**
>
> A **hazard** is something that has the potential to cause harm. Even substances, organisms and equipment that we think of being harmless, used in the wrong way, may be hazardous.

Biological hazards include:

> microorganisms
> body fluids
> animals and plants.

Chemical hazards can be grouped into:

> irritant and harmful substances
> toxic
> oxidising agents
> corrosive
> harmful to the environment.

Physical hazards include:

> equipment
> objects
> radiation.

Scientists use an international series of symbols so that investigators can identify hazards.

Hazards pose risks to the person carrying out the investigation.

Many acids, for instance, while being corrosive in higher concentrations, are harmful or an irritant at low concentrations.

A risk posed by concentrated sulfuric acid, for example, will be lower if you're adding one drop of it to a reaction mixture to make an ester, than if you're mixing a large volume of it with water.

When you use hazardous materials, chemicals or equipment in the laboratory, you must use them in such a way as to keep the risks to an absolute minimum. For example, one way is to wear eye protection when using hydrochloric acid.

Hazard symbols are used on chemical bottles so that hazards can be identified

> **Definition**
>
> The **risk** is the likelihood of a hazard to cause harm in the circumstances it's being used in.

> **Assessment tip**
>
> Your method should show how you will manage risks and make your experiment safe.

✳ Risk assessment

Before you begin an investigation, you must carry out a risk assessment. Your risk assessment must include:

✔ all relevant hazards (use the correct terms to describe each hazard, and make sure you include them all, even if you think they will pose minimal risk)

✔ risks associated with these hazards

✔ ways in which the risks can be minimised

✔ results of research into emergency procedures that you may have to take if something goes wrong.

You should also consider what to do at the end of the practical. For example, used agar plates should be left for a technician to sterilise; solutions of heavy metals should be collected in a bottle and disposed of safely.

Assessment tip

Your method should show how you will manage the risks and make your experiment safe.

✳ Overall plan

You should write up your overall plan – including method, equipment, variables to test and control, and risk assessment – before beginning your experiment. Arrange your plan logically. Remember, another student should be able to use it to carry out the same experiment.

✳ Collecting primary evidence

✔ You should be sure to collect evidence that is appropriate for the topic.

✔ You should make sure that observations, if appropriate, are recorded in detail. For example, it's worth recording the appearance of your potato chips in your osmosis practical, in addition to the measurements you make.

✔ Measurements should be recorded in tables. Have one ready so that you can record your readings as you carry out the practical work.

✔ Think about the dependent variable and define this carefully in your column headings.

✔ You should make sure that the table headings describe properly the type of measurements you've made, for example 'time taken for magnesium ribbon to dissolve'.

✔ It's also essential that you include units – your results are meaningless without these.

✔ The units should appear in the column head, and not be repeated in each row of the table.

Definition

When you carry out an investigation, the data you collect are called **primary evidence.** The term 'data' is normally used to include your observations as well as any measurements you might make.

Repeatability and reproducibility of results

When making measurements, in most instances, it's essential that you carry out repeats.

These repeats are one way of checking your results.

Results will not be repeatable, of course, if you allow the conditions the investigation is carried out in to change.

You need to make sure that you carry out sufficient repeats, but not too many. In a titration, for example, if you obtain two values that are within $0.1\,cm^3$ of each other, carrying out any more will not improve the reliability of your results.

This is particularly important when scientists are carrying out scientific research and make new discoveries.

Collecting secondary evidence

As part of Controlled Assessment, you will be expected to collect **secondary evidence**. The secondary data you collect must be appropriate for the topic.

One of the simplest ways of doing this is to collect evidence from other groups in your class who have carried out an identical practical investigation.

You should also, if possible, search through the scientific literature – in textbooks, the internet, and databases – to find evidence from similar or identical practical investigations.

Ideally, you should use secondary evidence from a number of sources and record it appropriately.

You should review secondary data and evaluate it. Scientific studies are sometimes influenced by the **bias** of the experimenter.

✔ One kind of bias is having a strong opinion related to the investigation, and perhaps selecting only the results that fit with a hypothesis or prediction.

✔ Or the bias could be unintentional. In fields of science that are not yet fully understood, experimenters may try to fit their findings to current knowledge and thinking.

There have been other instances where the 'findings' of experimenters have been influenced by organisations that supplied the funding for the research.

You must fully reference any secondary data you have used, using one of the accepted referencing methods.

Referencing methods

The two main conventions for writing a reference are the:

✔ Harvard system
✔ Vancouver system.

In your text, the Harvard system refers to the authors of the reference, for example 'Smith and Jones (1978)'.

The Vancouver system refers to the number of the numbered reference in your text, for example '... the reason for this hypothesis is unknown.[5]'.

Assessment tip

One set of results from your investigation may not reflect what truly happens. Carrying out repeats enables you to identify any results that don't fit.

Definition

If, when you carry out the same experiment several times and get the same, or very similar, results, we say the results are **repeatable**.

Definition

Taking more than one set of results will improve the **reliability** of your data.

Definition

Secondary evidence is measurements/observations made by anyone other than you.

Assessment tip

Always comment on the quality of your secondary evidence – including bias.

Though the Harvard system is usually preferred by scientists, it is more straightforward for you to use the Vancouver system.

Harvard system

In your references list a book reference should be written:

> Author(s) (year of publication). *Title of Book*, publisher, publisher location.

The references are listed in alphabetical order according to the authors.

Vancouver system

In your references list a book reference should be written:

> 1 Author(s). *Title of Book*. Publisher, publisher location: year of publication.

The references are number in the order in which they are cited in the text.

✳ Processing evidence

Calculating the mean

Using your repeat measurements you can calculate the arithmetical mean (or just 'mean') of these data. We often refer to the mean as the 'average'.

Temperature, °C	Number of yeast cells, mm³			Mean number of yeast cells, mm³
	Test 1	Test 2	Test 3	
10	1000	1040	1200	1080
20	2400	2200	2300	2300
30	4600	5000	4800	4800
40	4800	5000	5200	5000
50	200	1200	700	700

You may also be required to use formulae when processing data. Sometimes, these will need rearranging to be able to make the calculation you need. Practise using and rearranging formulae as part of your preparation for assessment.

Significant figures

When calculating the mean, you should be aware of significant figures.

For example, for the set of data below:

18	13	17	15	14	16	15	14	13	18

The total for the data set is 153, and ten measurements have been made. The mean is 15, and not 15.3.

This is because each of the recorded values has two significant figures. The answer must therefore have two significant figures. An answer cannot have more significant figures than the number being multiplied or divided.

Assessment tip

Remember to process all your collected evidence – primary and secondary.

Definition

The **reproducibility** of data is the ability of the results of an investigation to be reproduced by someone else, who may be in a different lab, carrying out the same work.

Definition

The **mean** is calculated by adding together all the measurements, and dividing by the number of measurements.

Definition

Significant figures are the number of digits in a number based on the precision of your measurements.

Using your data

When calculating means (and displaying data), you should be careful to look out for any data that don't fit in with the general pattern.

It might be the consequence of an error made in measurement. But sometimes anomalies are genuine results. If you think an anomaly has been introduced by careless practical work, you should ignore it when calculating the mean. But you should examine possible reasons carefully before just leaving it out.

Presenting your evidence

Presenting your evidence – usually the means – makes it easy to pick out and show any patterns. It also helps you to pick out any anomalous results.

It is likely that you will have recorded your results in tables, and you could also use additional tables to summarise your results. The most usual way of displaying data is to use graphs. The table will help you decide which type to use.

Type of graph	When you would use the graph	Example
Bar charts or bar graph	Where one of the variables is discrete	'The diameters of the clear zones where the growth of bacteria was inhibited by different types of disinfectant'
Line graph	Where independent and dependent variables are both continuous	'The volume of carbon dioxide produced by a range of different concentrations of hydrochloric acid'
Scatter graph	To show an association between two (or more) variables	'The association between length and breadth of a number of privet leaves' In scatter graphs, the points are plotted, but not usually joined

If it's possible from the data, join the points of a line graph using a straight line, or in some instances, a curve. In this way graphs can also help us to process data.

Spread of data

Plotting a graph of just the means doesn't tell you anything about the spread of data that has been used to calculate the mean.

You can show the spread of the data on your graphs using error bars or range bars.

Range bars are very useful, but they don't show how the data are spread between the extreme values. It is important to have information about this range. It may affect the analysis you do of the data, and the conclusions you draw.

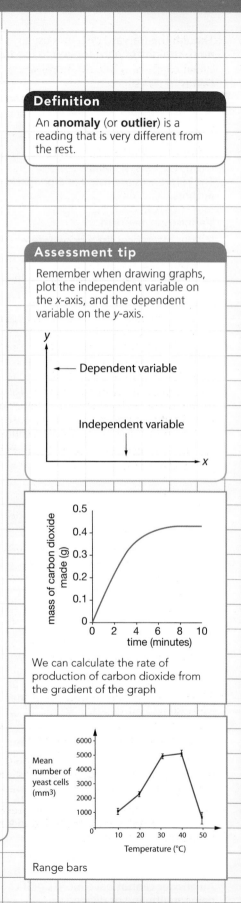

Definition

An **anomaly** (or **outlier**) is a reading that is very different from the rest.

Assessment tip

Remember when drawing graphs, plot the independent variable on the *x*-axis, and the dependent variable on the *y*-axis.

We can calculate the rate of production of carbon dioxide from the gradient of the graph

Range bars

✳ Differences in data sets and probability

When comparing two (or more) sets of data, we often compare the values of two sets of means.

Example 5

Investigation: Comparing the effectiveness of two disinfectants.

Two groups of students compared the effectiveness of two disinfectants, labelled A and B. Their results are shown in the table.

Disinfectant	Diameter of zone of inhibition (clear zone), mm										Mean dia., mm
	1	2	3	4	5	6	7	8	9	10	
A	15	13	17	15	14	16	15	14	13	18	15
B	25	23	24	23	26	27	25	24	23	22	24

When the means are compared it appears that disinfectant B is more effective in inhibiting the growth of bacteria. But can we be sure? The differences might have resulted from the treatment of the bacteria using the two disinfectants. But the differences could have occurred purely by chance.

Scientists use statistics to find the probability of any differences having occurred by chance. The lower this probability is, which is found out by statistical calculations, the more likely it is that it was (in this case) the disinfectant that caused the differences observed.

Statistical analysis can help to increase the confidence you have in your conclusions.

Assessment tip

You have learnt about probability in your Maths lessons.

Definition

If there is a relationship between dependent and independent variables that can be defined, we say there is a **correlation** between the variables.

✳ Drawing conclusions

Observing trends in data or graphs will help you to draw conclusions. You may obtain a linear relationship between two sets of variables, or the relationship might be more complex.

Example 6

The higher the concentration of acid, the shorter the time taken for the magnesium ribbon to dissolve.

When drawing conclusions, you should try to relate your findings – including mathematical relationships, primary evidence and secondary evidence – to the science involved. You should also relate your conclusion to your hypothesis.

In this example, your discussion should focus on the greater possibility/increased frequency of collisions between reacting particles as the concentration of the acid is increased.

But we sometimes see correlations between data in science which are coincidental, where the independent variable is not the cause of the trend in the data.

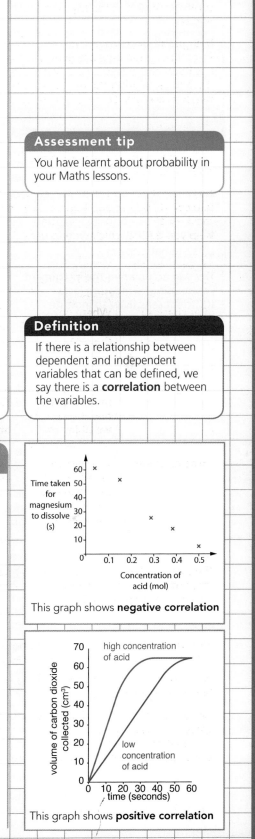

This graph shows **negative correlation**

This graph shows **positive correlation**

Example 7

Studies have shown that levels of vitamin D are very low in people with long-term inflammatory diseases. But there's no scientific evidence to suggest that these low levels are the cause of the diseases.

✳ Accounting for errors

Your conclusion will be based on your evidence, but must take into consideration any uncertainty in these introduced by any possible sources of error. You should discuss where these have come from in your evaluation.

The two types of errors are:

✔ random error
✔ systematic error.

This can occur when the instrument you're using to measure lacks sufficient sensitivity to indicate differences in readings. It can also occur when it's difficult to make a measurement. If two investigators measure the height of a plant, for example, they might choose different points on the compost, and the tip of the growing point to make their measurements.

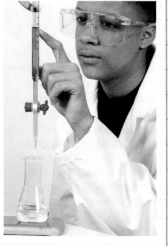

Your results may be either consistently too high or too low. One reason could be down to the way you are making a reading; for example, taking a burette reading at the wrong point on the meniscus. Another could be the result of an instrument being incorrectly calibrated, or not being calibrated.

The volume of liquid in a burette must be read to the bottom of the meniscus

✳ Accuracy and precision

When evaluating your investigation, you should mention accuracy and precision. But if you use these terms, it's important that you understand what they mean, and that you use them correctly.

Precise but not accurate

Precise and accurate

Neither precise nor accurate

The terms accuracy and precision can be illustrated using shots at a dartboard.

In science, the measurements you make as part of your investigation should be as precise as you can, or need to, make them. To achieve this, you should use:

✔ the most appropriate measuring instrument

✔ the measuring instrument with the most appropriate size of divisions.

The smaller the divisions you work with, the more precise your measurements. For example:

✔ in an investigation on how your heart rate is affected by exercise, you might decide to investigate this after a 100 m run. You might measure out the 100 m distance using a trundle wheel, which is sufficiently precise for your investigation

✔ in an investigation on how light intensity is affected by distance, you would make your measurements of distance using a metre rule with millimetre divisions; clearly a trundle wheel would be too imprecise

✔ in an investigation on plant growth, in which you measure the thickness of a plant stem, you would use a micrometer or Vernier callipers. In this instance, a metre rule would be too imprecise.

✸ Evaluating your method and conclusion

When evaluating your method, you should identify the strengths of your method and discuss how your investigation could be improved. This could be by improving; you should consider improving:

✔ the reliability of your data. For example, you could make more repeats, or more frequent readings, or 'fine-tune' the range you chose to investigate, or refine your technique in some other way

✔ the accuracy and precision of your data, by using more precise measuring equipment.

Taking this into account, you can evaluate your conclusion – how could you improve or extend your evidence to give further support to your conclusion? An important way to extend your evidence is by carrying out repeats.

✸ Does the evidence support your hypothesis?

You need to discuss, in detail, whether all, or which of your primary and the secondary evidence you have collected, support your original hypothesis. They may, or may not.

You should communicate your points clearly, using the appropriate scientific terms, and checking carefully your use of spelling, punctuation and grammar. You will be assessed on this written communication as well as your science.

Assessment tip

Your evaluation of method should be related to your hypothesis and reasons should be given for anomalies.

If your evidence does not completely match your hypothesis, it may be possible to modify the hypothesis or suggest an alternative one. You should suggest any further investigations that can be carried out to support your original hypothesis or the modified version.

It is important to remember, however, that if your investigation does support your hypothesis, it can improve the confidence you have in your conclusions and scientific explanations, but it can't prove your explanations are correct.

✳ Your controlled assessment

The assessment of your investigation will form part of what's called Controlled Assessment. Edexcel will provide the task for you to investigate.

You may be able to work in small groups to carry out the practical work, but you will have to work on your own to write up your investigation.

Controlled assessment is worth 25% of the marks for your GCSE. It's worth doing it well!

Your Science Controlled Assessment Task (CAT) will consist of three parts:

✔ Part A – Planning
✔ Part B – Observations
✔ Part C – Conclusions

To achieve a final grade in your Controlled Assessment Unit, you must complete all three parts of at least one CAT.

Part A – Planning

In Part A you must write a plan to test a specific hypothesis.

You will be briefed with an outline of a scientific concept and task.

In your **Science** CAT you will be given a hypothesis to test. In your **Additional** and **Separate Sciences** CATs you must write a hypothesis in line with the brief you have been given.

To produce a complete plan you must:

✔ Select and justify the equipment for your investigation
✔ Choose and explain the variables you will change, measure and control
✔ Identify risks and explain how you will manage them
✔ Write a plan that includes your method, equipment and variables, and reflects how risks will be managed.

Your plan must be clear and produce results that will test your hypothesis.

You will complete Part A under 'limited' controlled conditions. This means that you will be allowed to collaborate with other students and use research to complete the task.

Part B – Observations

In Part B you will carry out an experiment to test your hypothesis from Part A, using the plan you produced also in Part A.

You will use your plan to collect and record primary evidence.

You must also collect and record secondary evidence that is relevant to your hypothesis.

You may collect secondary evidence in class or at home from:

✔ the internet
✔ other students, or
✔ textbooks.

You will be expected to reference all secondary sources fully and comment on the quality of the source of evidence.

You will also complete Part B under 'limited' controlled conditions.

Part C – Conclusions

In Part C you will process and draw conclusions from the evidence you collected in Part B.

✔ Process all your evidence (primary and secondary) suitably using digital technology and maths as appropriate.
✔ Decide whether to include or exclude anomalies when processing evidence, explaining your reasons why.
✔ Produce a conclusion based on all processed evidence and appropriate scientific ideas. Does your evidence prove or disprove your hypothesis?
✔ Evaluate your method, describing strengths, weaknesses and improvements, and explaining reasons for anomalies.
✔ Suggest how you could improve or extend your evidence to support your conclusion further.
✔ Review your hypothesis in light of the evidence.

You will complete Part C under 'high' controlled conditions. This means that you must complete your write-up individually and completely under teacher supervision.

Quality of Written Communication

Be aware of the quality of your written communication in all parts of the CAT. You must ensure that the marker understands your ideas and evidence.

At all times you must communicate clearly using:

✔ an appropriate form and style
✔ clear and logical presentation, and
✔ scientific language where appropriate.

Assessment tip

If your plan from Part A was unusable – for example, because it was potentially dangerous – your teacher will give you a plan to work from for Part B. Remember, you will receive no marks for a Part A plan that is given to you.

Assessment tip

You will achieve top marks in Part B by:

> Collecting a suitable range of data.

> Carrying out repeat experiments as appropriate

> Recording all evidence – primary and secondary – appropriately.

Assessment tip

You will achieve top marks in Part C by:

> Presenting evidence so that you can draw conclusions from it

> Explaining your conclusions using maths, scientific ideas and data

> Relating your conclusion and evaluation back to your hypothesis.

Assessment tip

Your teacher will give you a copy of the Assessment Criteria so that you can see what you need to do to access all marks.

How to be successful in your GCSE science written assessment

Introduction

Edexcel uses assessments to test how good your understanding of scientific ideas is, how well you can apply your understanding to new situations, and how well you can analyse and interpret information you've been given. The assessments are opportunities to show how well you can do these.

To be successful in exams you need to:

✔ have a good knowledge and understanding of science
✔ be able to apply this knowledge and understanding to familiar and new situations, and
✔ be able to interpret and evaluate evidence that you've just been given.

You need to be able to do these things under exam conditions.

✺ The language of the external assessment

When working through an assessment paper, make sure that you:

✔ re-read a question enough times until you understand exactly what the examiner is looking for
✔ make sure that you highlight key words in a question
✔ look at how many marks are allocated for each part of a question. In general, you need to write at least as many separate points in your answer as there are marks.

✺ What verbs are used in the question?

A good technique is to see which verbs are used in the wording of the question and to use these to gauge the type of response you need to give. The table lists some of the common verbs found in questions, the types of responses expected and then gives an example.

Verb used in question	Response expected in answer	Example question
write down; state; give; identify	These are usually more straightforward types of question in which you're asked to give a definition, make a list of examples, or the best answer from a series of options	'Write down three types of microorganism that cause disease' 'State one difference and one similarity between radio waves and gamma rays'
calculate	Use maths to solve a numerical problem	'Calculate the cost of supplying the flu vaccine to the whole population of the UK'

estimate	Use maths to solve a numerical problem, but you do not have to work out the exact answer	'Estimate the number of bacteria in the culture after five hours'
describe	Use words (or diagrams) to show the characteristics, properties or features of, or build an image of, something	'Describe how antibiotic resistance can be reduced'
suggest	Come up with an idea to explain information you're given	'Suggest why eating fast foods, rather than wholegrain foods, could increase the risk of obesity'
demonstrate; show how	Use words to make something evident using reasoning	'Show how enzyme activity changes with temperature'
compare	Look for similarities and differences	'Compare the structure of arteries and veins'
explain	To offer a reason for, or make understandable, information you're given	'Explain why measles cannot be treated with antibiotics'
evaluate	To examine and make a judgement about an investigation or information you're given	'Evaluate the evidence for vaccines causing harm to human health'

✳ What is the style of the question?

Try to get used to answering questions that have been written in lots of different styles before you sit the exam. Work through past papers, or specimen papers, to get a feel for these. The types of questions in your assessment fit the three assessment objectives shown in the table.

Assessment objective	Your answer should show that you can...
AO1 Recall the science	Recall, select and communicate your knowledge and understanding of science
AO2 Apply your knowledge	Apply skills, knowledge and understanding of science in practical and other contexts
AO3 Evaluate and analyse the evidence	Analyse and evaluate evidence, make reasoned judgements and draw conclusions based on evidence

Assessment tip

Of course, you must revise the subject material adequately. But it's as important that you are familiar with the different question styles used in the exam paper, as well as the question content.

✹ How to answer questions on: AO1 Recall the science

These questions, or parts of questions, test your ability to recall your knowledge of a topic. There are several types of this style of question:

✔ Fill in the spaces (you may be given words to choose from)
✔ Multiple choice
✔ Use lines to link a term with its definition or correct statement
✔ Add labels to a diagram
✔ Complete a table
✔ Describe a process

Example 8

a What is meant by the term *metabolic rate*?

   A ☒ the amount of energy a person uses each hour

   B ☒ the amount of exercise a person does each day

   C ☒ the amount of food a person eats each day

AO1 questions on practical techniques

You may be asked to recall how to carry out certain practical techniques; either ones that you have carried out before, or techniques that scientists use.

To revise for these types of questions, make sure that you have learnt definitions and scientific terms. Produce a glossary of these, or key facts cards, to make them easier to remember. Make sure your key facts cards also cover important practical techniques, including equipment, where appropriate.

Example 9

1 Describe how to test the pH of a solution.

2 Describe how DNA fragments can be separated by electrophoresis.

Assessment tip

Don't forget that mind maps – either drawn by you or by using a computer program – are very helpful when revising key points.

✹ How to answer questions on: AO2 Apply skills, knowledge and understanding

Some questions require you to apply basic knowledge and understanding in your answers.

You may be presented with a topic that's familiar to you, but you should also expect questions in your science exam to be set in an unfamiliar context.

Questions may be presented as:

✔ short questions referring to an unfamiliar object, process or organism
✔ experimental investigations
✔ data or diagrams for you to interpret
✔ a short paragraph or article.

The information required for you to answer the question might be in the question itself, but, for later stages of the question, you may be asked to draw on your knowledge and understanding of the subject material in the question.

Practice will help you to become familiar with contexts that examiners use and question styles. But you will not be able to predict many of the contexts used. This is deliberate; being able to apply your knowledge and understanding to different and unfamiliar situations is a skill the examiner tests.

Practise doing questions where you are tested on being able to apply your scientific knowledge and your ability to understand new situations that may not be familiar. In this way, when this type of question comes up in your exam, you will be able to tackle it successfully.

> **Assessment tip**
>
> Work through the Preparing for Assessment: Applying your knowledge tasks in this book as practice.

Example 10

1 The diagram shows a pedigree chart.

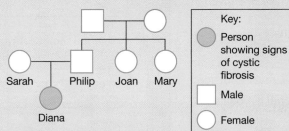

Key:

🔘 Person showing signs of cystic fibrosis

☐ Male

◯ Female

Sarah and Philip have been told that Diana, their baby daughter, has cystic fibrosis, which is an inherited disorder. As far as Sarah and Philip know, no one else in either of their families has the disorder. Mary, Philip's younger sister, is concerned that she might develop the disease.

Explain why this would not happen.

AO2 questions on practical investigations

Some opportunities to demonstrate your application of skills, knowledge and understanding will be based on practical investigations. You may have carried out some of these investigations, but others will be new to you, and based on data obtained by scientists. You will be expected to describe patterns in data from graphs you are given or that you will have to draw from given data.

Again, you will have to apply your scientific knowledge and understanding to answer the question.

Example 11

1 Look at the graph on the right showing the resistance of the bacterium, *Streptococcus pneumoniae,* to three different types of antibiotic.

   a Which antibiotic does there seem to be least resistance to, even when it has been used before?

   b Can you explain why this might be the case?

✹ How to answer questions on: AO3 Analysing and evaluating evidence

For these types of questions, you will analyse and evaluate scientific evidence or data given to you in the question. It's likely that you won't be familiar with the material.

Analysing data may involve drawing graphs and interpreting them, and carrying out calculations. Practise drawing and interpreting graphs from data.

When drawing a graph, make sure you:

✔ choose and label the axes fully and correctly

✔ include units, if this hasn't been done for you already

✔ plot points on the graph carefully – the examiner will check individual points to make sure that they are accurate

✔ join the points correctly; usually this will be by a line of best fit.

When reading values off a graph you have drawn or one given in the question, make sure you:

✔ do it carefully, reading the values as accurately as you can

✔ double-check the values.

When describing patterns and trends in the data, make sure you:

✔ write about a pattern or trend in as much detail as you can

✔ mention anomalies where appropriate

✔ recognise there may be one general trend in the graph, where the variables show positive or negative correlation

✔ recognise the data may show a more complex relationship. The graph may demonstrate different trends in several sections. You should describe what's happening in each

✔ describe fully what the data shows.

You must also be able to evaluate the information you're given. This is one of the hardest skills. Think about the validity of the scientific data: did the technique(s) used in any practical investigation allow the collection of accurate and precise data?

Your critical evaluation of scientific data in class, along with the practical work and Controlled Assessment work, will help you to develop the evaluation skills required for these types of questions.

Example 12

1 In the experiment shown, on the testing of the inhibition of bacterial growth by a new antibiotic, explain why further investigation is required to confirm the effectiveness of the antibiotic.

Your AO3 questions may also require you to demonstrate an understanding of how evidence is used and validated in the scientific community.

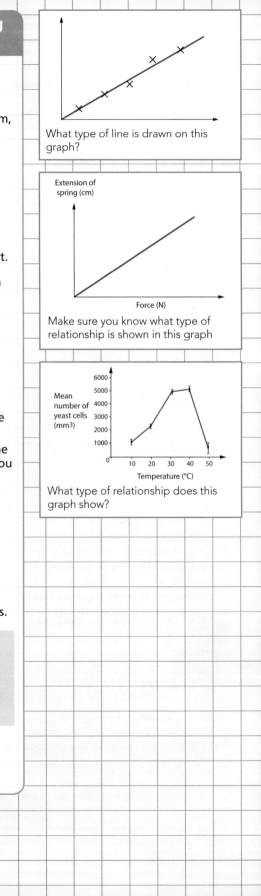

What type of line is drawn on this graph?

Make sure you know what type of relationship is shown in this graph

What type of relationship does this graph show?

✹ How to answer questions needing calculations

✔ The calculations you're asked to do may be straightforward; for example, the calculation of the mean from a set of practical data.

✔ Or they may be more complex; for example, calculating the yield of a chemical reaction.

✔ Other questions will require the use of formulae.

Remember, this is the same maths that you learnt in your Maths lessons.

> ### Example 13
>
> 1 Calculate the area on the agar plate, around the antibiotic disc, that is free from bacteria.
>
>   Use the formula:
>
>   area = πr^2
>
>   where π = 3.14

✹ The quality of your written communication

Scientists need good communication skills to present and discuss their findings. You will be expected to demonstrate these skills in the exam. Questions where quality of written communication is likely to be particularly important are marked with an *. However, this doesn't mean quality of written communication isn't important in other questions – it is!

✔ You must also try to make sure that your spelling, punctuation and grammar are accurate, so that it's clear what you mean in your answer. Examiners can't award marks for answers where the meaning isn't clear.

✔ Present your information in a form that suits the purpose. For example, think about the form, style of writing and level of complexity.

✔ Organise information clearly, coherently and logically.

✔ When describing and explaining science, use correct scientific vocabulary.

Practise answering some questions where quality of written communication is important. Look at how marks are awarded in mark schemes provided by Edexcel. You'll find these in the specimen question papers, and past papers.

You will also need to remember the writing and communication skills you've developed in English lessons. For example, make sure that you understand how to construct a good sentence using connectives.

Assessment tip

Remember, you calculate the mean by adding up all the numbers in the data set, and dividing by how many numbers there are.

Assessment tip

Formulae are often given to you on the question paper, but sometimes you will be expected to recall and use these. When completing your calculation, make sure you include the correct units.

Assessment tip

Check the specification, or check with your teacher, to make sure that you know the formulae that you have to learn and remember.

Assessment tip

Remember, when carrying out any calculations, you should include your working at each stage. You may get credit for getting the process correct, even if your final answer is wrong.

Assessment tip

Organising information clearly, coherently and logically is the most important skill in QWC.

Assessment tip

When answering questions, you must make sure that your writing is legible. An examiner can't award marks for answers that he or she can't read.

✺ Revising for your science exam

You should revise in the way that suits you best. But it's important that you plan your revision carefully, and it's best to start well before the date of the exams. Take the time to prepare a revision timetable and try to stick to it. Use this during the lead up to the exams and between each exam.

When revising:

✔ find a quiet and comfortable space in the house where you won't be disturbed. It's best if it's well ventilated and has plenty of light

✔ take regular breaks. Some evidence suggests that revision is most effective when you revise in 30 to 40 minute slots. If you get bogged down at any point, take a break and go back to it later when you're feeling fresh. Try not to revise when you are feeling tired. If you do feel tired, take a break

✔ use your school notes, textbook and, possibly, a revision guide. But also make sure that you spend some time using past papers to familiarise yourself with the exam format

✔ produce summaries of each topic or unit

✔ draw mind maps covering the key information on a topic or unit

✔ set up revision cards containing condensed versions of your notes

✔ ask yourself questions, and try to predict questions, as you're revising topics or units

✔ test yourself as you're going along. Try to draw key labelled diagrams, and try some questions under timed conditions

✔ prioritise your revision of topics. You might want to allocate more time to revising the topics you find most difficult.

Assessment tip

Try to make your revision timetable as specific as possible – don't just say 'science on Monday, and Thursday', but list the units that you'll cover on those days.

Assessment tip

Start your revision well before the date of the exams, produce a revision timetable, and use the revision strategies that suit your style of learning. Above all, revision should be an active process.

✺ How do I use my time effectively in the exam?

Timing is important when you sit an exam. Don't spend so long on some questions that you leave insufficient time to answer others. For example, in a 60-mark question paper, lasting one hour, you will have, on average, one minute per question.

If you're unsure about certain questions, complete the ones you're able to do first, then go back to the ones you're less sure of.

If you have time, go back and check your answers at the end of the exam.

✺ On exam day...

A little bit of nervousness before your exam can be a good thing, but try not to let it affect your performance in the exam. When you turn over the exam paper keep calm. Look at the paper and get it clear in your head exactly what is required from each question. Read each question carefully. Don't rush.

If you read a question and think that you have not covered the topic, keep calm – it could be that the information needed to answer the question is in the question itself or the examiner may be asking you to apply your knowledge to a new situation.

Finally, good luck!

Periodic table

Group

Group 1	Group 2												Group 3	Group 4	Group 5	Group 6	Group 7	Group 0
																		4 He 2 helium
7 Li 3 lithium	9 Be 4 beryllium						1 H 1 hydrogen						11 B 5 boron	12 C 6 carbon	14 N 7 nitrogen	16 O 8 oxygen	19 F 9 fluorine	20 Ne 10 neon
23 Na 11 sodium	24 Mg 12 magnesium												27 Al 13 aluminium	28 Si 14 silicon	31 P 15 phosphorus	32 S 16 sulfur	35 Cl 17 chlorine	40 Ar 18 argon
39 K 19 potassium	40 Ca 20 calcium	45 Sc 21 scandium	48 Ti 22 titanium	51 V 23 vanadium	52 Cr 24 chromium	55 Mn 25 manganese	56 Fe 26 iron	59 Co 27 cobalt	59 Ni 28 nickel	64 Cu 29 copper	65 Zn 30 zinc		70 Ga 31 gallium	73 Ge 32 germanium	75 As 33 arsenic	79 Se 34 selenium	80 Br 35 bromine	84 Kr 36 krypton
85 Rb 37 rubidium	88 Sr 38 strontium	89 Y 39 yttrium	91 Zr 40 zirconium	93 Nb 41 niobium	96 Mo 42 molybdenum	99 Tc 43 technetium	101 Ru 44 ruthenium	103 Rh 45 rhodium	106 Pd 46 palladium	108 Ag 47 silver	112 Cd 48 cadmium		115 In 49 indium	119 Sn 50 tin	122 Sb 51 antimony	128 Te 52 tellurium	127 I 53 iodine	131 Xe 54 xenon
133 Cs 55 caesium	137 Ba 56 barium	139 La 57 lanthanum	178 Hf 72 hafnium	181 Ta 73 tantalum	184 W 74 tungsten	186 Re 75 rhenium	190 Os 76 osmium	192 Ir 77 iridium	195 Pt 78 platinum	197 Au 79 gold	201 Hg 80 mercury		204 Tl 81 thallium	207 Pb 82 lead	209 Bi 83 bismuth	210 Po 84 polonium	210 At 85 astatine	222 Rn 86 radon
223 Fr 87 francium	226 Ra 88 radium	227 Ac 89 actinium																

You need to remember the symbols for the highlighted elements.

✸ Some useful formulae

The relationship between wave speed, frequency and wavelength:

wave speed   = frequency × wavelength
(metre/second, m/s)   (hertz, Hz)   (metre, m)

$v = f \times \lambda$

The relationship between wave speed, distance and time:

$$\text{wave speed (metre/second, m/s)} = \frac{\text{distance (metre, m)}}{\text{time (second, s)}}$$

$v = \dfrac{x}{t}$

The relationship between electric power, current and potential difference:

electrical power = current   × potential difference
   (watt, W)   (ampere, A)   (volt, V)

$P = I \times V$

Calculating the cost of electricity:

cost =   power   × time   × cost of 1 kilowatt-hour
     (kilowatts, kW) (hour, h)   (kW h)

The relationship between power, energy and time:

$$\text{power (watt, W)} = \frac{\text{energy used (joule, J)}}{\text{time taken (second, s)}}$$

$P = \dfrac{E}{t}$

The term efficiency calculated from:

$$\text{efficiency} = \frac{\text{(useful energy transferred by the device)}}{\text{(total energy supplied to the device)}} \times 100\%$$

Glossary

abuse non-medical use of drugs legally available only with a doctor's prescription

accommodation shape changes in the lens of the eye enabling a person to focus on near and far objects

acid rain rain with a pH of 2–5, usually caused by the emission of pollutants such as the oxides of sulfur and nitrogen

acquired characteristics non-hereditary or environmental changes in an organism

acquired immunodeficiency syndrome (AIDS) the collection of diseases associated with HIV infection

adaptation refers to characteristics that best suit the survival of an individual

adapted suited to surviving in a particular environment

addict a person who is dependent (hooked) on drugs or any other habit-forming substance

addition polymerisation the process of making polymers by adding monomers to the end of chains of monomers

algae aquatic organisms capable of photosynthesis

alkali a substance which makes a solution that turns red litmus paper blue

alkaloids compounds (e.g. nicotine, cocaine and morphine), often bitter tasting, derived from amino acids

alkanes a family of hydrocarbons found in crude oil containing only hydrogen and carbon, with single covalent bonds

alkenes a family of hydrocarbons found in crude oil with double carbon to carbon covalent bonds

alleles different versions of a gene which control a particular characteristic

alternating current (a.c.) a current that repeatedly changes direction

ammeter meter used in an electric circuit for measuring current

amperes (amps) units used to measure electrical current

amplitude maximum displacement of a wave measured from the mean position

animalia the animal kingdom

anode positively charged electrode

Anopheles the mosquito genus that transmits the malarial protozoan; *Anopheles gambiae* is the most common species in Africa

antacid a base or basic salt used to treat indigestion

antibacterials substances that prevent bacteria from multiplying but are toxic to ingest, e.g. antibacterial soap

antibiotic therapeutic drug acting to kill bacteria or prevent them from multiplying, which is taken into the body

antibodies proteins produced by a particular type of white blood cell (B-lymphocytes) that bind to substances on the surface of pathogens and destroy them

antifungals substances that kill fungi

antiseptics substances that prevent bacteria from multiplying on the body and other surfaces

atmosphere the layer of gases surrounding a planet

atom the basic 'building block' of an element which cannot be chemically broken down

atomic number the number of protons found in the nucleus of an atom

auto-immune disease disease caused by the body's immune system attacking its own tissues and organs, e.g. Type 1 diabetes

auxin a plant hormone involved in plant growth

axon a long projection from a nerve fibre that conducts impulses away from the body of a nerve cell

backbone a flexible rod running along the length of the body near to its upper surface; it supports the body

bacteria single-celled microorganisms which can either be free-living or parasites (they sometimes invade the body and cause disease); the cell does not contain a distinct nucleus

bactericides antibiotics that kill bacteria

bacteriostats antibiotics that prevent bacteria from multiplying

base any substance that neutralises an acid

base metal a common metal, not considered precious, e.g. lead, iron, copper

Big Bang an explosion some 14 billion years ago that created both space and time

Big Bang theory a theory that proposes the creation of the Universe from the Big Bang

binge drinking consumption of large amounts of alcohol in a short period of time

binomial system the method of giving an organism a two-part name consisting of genus and species

biodegradable a biodegradable material can be broken down by microorganisms

biodiversity range of different living organisms in a habitat, e.g. a woodland or pond

biofuels fuels made from plants and animal waste

biomass amount of organic material of an organism (usually measured as dry mass); waste wood and other natural materials which are burned in power stations

black dwarf the final stage of a white dwarf, when it has lost all its energy

black hole an extremely dense core of a supermassive star left behind after the supernova stage; light cannot escape its strong gravitational pull

body mass index (BMI) measure of someone's weight in relation to their height, used as a guide to thinness or fatness – values over 30 indicate obesity

calorimeter a device used to measure the heat of chemical reactions

carbohydrates organic molecules composed of carbon, hydrogen and oxygen with the generalised formula $C_nH_{2+n}O_n$

carbon monoxide a toxic gas formed during incomplete combustion

carbonate a compound containing carbonate ion, CO_3^{2-}

carrier someone who carries an abnormal gene but does not themselves have the disease

catalyst   substance added to a chemical reaction to alter the speed of the reaction

cathode   negatively charged electrode

cellulose   large polysaccharides made by plants for cell walls

chalk   porous, fine-grained rock composed mainly of calcareous shells of microorganisms

characteristics   the features of an organism, including its structure, the chemistry of its cells and the way its body works

charge   a physical property of particles which causes it to experience a force when near other electrically charged particles

chemical energy   energy available from atoms when electron bonds are broken

chemical property   property which cannot be observed just by looking at a substance – a chemical property depends on how that substance reacts chemically with other substances, e.g. flammability, reactions with acids and bases, and reactions started by light

chemosynthesis   the chemical reactions in different species of bacteria which utilise hydrogen from sources other than water to reduce carbon dioxide, forming sugars

chloroplasts   structures characteristic of plant cells and the cells of algae where photosynthesis takes place

chordata   a phylum of animals that possess a rod for supporting the body

chromosomes   thread-like structures in the cell nucleus that carry genetic information – each chromosome consists of DNA wound around a core of protein

classification   sorting living things that have characteristics in common into groups

climate change   usually used to refer to global warming

coefficients   numbers used in chemical equations to indicate the number of each reactant and product

combustion reaction   an oxidation reaction between a fuel and oxygen that releases energy

common ancestor   an individual from which organisms are directly descended

compaction   process of compressing sediments together and squeezing out water between the grains

competition   rivalry between competitors for supplies of limited resources

complete combustion   when fuels burn in an excess of oxygen to produce carbon dioxide and water only

compound   two or more elements which are chemically joined together, e.g. H_2O

compressions   regions where particles are pushed together and create a region of higher pressure in a sound wave

condensation   the process of vapour molecules forming a liquid

conservation of matter   the principle that states that atoms are neither created nor destroyed in a chemical reaction

consumers   organisms that feed on food already made

continuous variation   a characteristic that varies continuously shows a spread of values between extreme values of the characteristic in question, e.g. the height of people shows a range of values between short and tall

control experiment   an experiment in which all of the conditions (variables) of an experiment are unaltered, which allows comparison with the results of an experiment where one condition (variable) is altered

conventional current   the flow of positive charges

converging lens   a lens that focuses parallel rays of light to a point

cosmic microwave background (CMB) radiation   the 'left-over' radiation from the Big Bang – radiation coming very faintly from all directions in space

coulomb   the unit for charge

covalent bonds   bonds between atoms where electrons are shared

cracking   the thermal decomposition of long-chain hydrocarbons into smaller and more useful hydrocarbons

cross-breeding   mating (or plant equivalent) between two individuals resulting in offspring

cross-linking   chemical bonds between individual polymer strands

crude oil   a complex mixture of hydrocarbons mined from the Earth from which petrol and many other products are made

cryogenics   the study of substances at low temperatures

current   the rate of flow of charge

cystic fibrosis   a recessive genetic disorder in which thick, sticky mucus is produced, affecting the lungs and digestive tract in particular

data   information about what is happening or has happened – experimental data is the results of an experiment

decompose   separation of a chemical compound into simpler compounds

decomposers   fungi and bacteria whose feeding activities cause decomposition

decomposition   process resulting from the feeding activities of fungi and bacteria that release nutrients from dead organic matter into the environment

deforestation   clear cutting of large tracts of land

dendrite   the fine branches at the end of axons and dendrons

dendron   a long projection of a nerve fibre that conducts impulses to the nerve cell

denitrifying bacteria   bacteria that convert nitrates into nitrogen gas

density   the density of a substance is found by dividing its mass by its volume

depressant   a substance that slows down responses

diabetes   disease where the body cannot control its blood sugar levels

diffraction   the spreading of a wave at an opening

diminished   an image that is smaller than the object

direct current   an electric current that flows in one direction only

discontinuous variation   a characteristic that only has a limited number of values, e.g. blood group, shoe size

disinfectant   substance applied to an object to kill microorganisms

displacement   distance moved in a specific direction

diverging lens a lens that makes parallel rays of light spread out rather than focus to a point

DNA molecule found in all body cells in the nucleus – its sequence determines how our bodies are made (e.g. do we have straight or curly hair), and gives each one of us a unique genetic code

dominant characteristic any characteristic that appears in the heterozygote

dominant refers to an allele which controls the development of a characteristic even if it is present on only one of the chromosomes of a pair of chromosomes

donor a person who gives (donates) an organ

Doppler effect the change in the wavelength or frequency of a wave as a result of relative motion between the source and observer

drug a substance from outside the body that affects chemical reactions inside the body

dry mass the mass of organic material minus the percentage mass of water

ductile capable of being drawn into a wire

echolocation a technique similar to sonar used by some animals to navigate and find their prey

ecosystem a habitat and all the living things in it

ectoparasites parasites that live on the external surfaces of the host

efficiency the proportion of the input energy that is transferred to useful form, calculated using the equation: efficiency = (useful energy transferred by the device/ total energy supplied to the device) × 100%

elastic potential energy energy gained and stored when an elastic object is stretched

electrical energy energy from the flow of electrons through a circuit (e.g. devices with plugs or batteries use electrical energy)

electrical power the rate of energy transfer

electrochemical cell a device for converting chemical energy into electrical energy, consisting of a container, electrodes and an electrolyte

electrode bars of metal or carbon that carry electric current into a liquid

electrolysis process in which compounds are decomposed by passing a d.c. electric current through a solution which conducts electricity

electromagnetic spectrum electromagnetic waves ordered according to wavelength and frequency, ranging from low-frequency radio waves to high-frequency gamma rays

electromagnetic waves a group of transverse waves that carry different amounts of energy, ranging from radio waves to gamma rays – they can travel through a vacuum at 300 million m/s

electrons tiny negatively charged particles within an atom that orbit the nucleus – responsible for current in electrical circuits

elements substances made out of only one type of atom

endocrine glands glands that release the substances produced (hormones) directly into the blood

endoparasites parasites that live inside the host's body

endotoxin a poison produced by a pathogen within the body

enzymes biological catalysts (usually proteins) produced by cells which control the rate of chemical reactions in cells

erosion where rock is worn away by wind or rain

ethene a gas that is an alkene (C_2H_4), which is used to make polymers and is also a plant hormone

ethics the actions taken as the result of moral judgements

eutrophication the processes that occur when water is enriched with nutrients (from fertilisers) which allow algae to grow and use up all the oxygen

evolution the process whereby organisms change through time – present-day living things are descended from organisms that were different from them

exocrine glands glands that release the substances produced (e.g. digestive enzymes) into a duct (tube)

exoskeleton surrounds the body of insects (and spiders, centipedes, millipedes and Crustacea) – the prefix exo- means 'outside'

expressed refers to the activity of genes which results in the production of protein (characteristics)

extinction when species die out (cease to exist)

extraterrestrial a term used to describe things 'beyond Earth'

extrusive rock igneous rock formed by rapid cooling of lava when exposed to the air or seawater

eyepiece the lens at the end of a telescope which you look through

family a group consisting of several genera (used in classification of living things)

feedback regulation of a process by the results (outcomes) of the process

fermentation the conversion of carbohydrates to alcohol and carbon dioxide by yeast or bacteria

fertile able to reproduce sexually

fertilisation the moment when the nucleus of a sperm fuses with the nucleus of an egg

fineness system a system for denoting the purity of gold, platinum and silver, indicating parts per thousand

fluoresce when materials emit intense visible light upon exposure to ultraviolet

focal length the distance between the centre of the lens and the focal point

food web flow chart to show how a number of living things get their food (more complicated than a food chain)

force of gravity an attractive force between all particles that have mass

fossil fuels fuel (coal, natural gas, oil) formed from the compressed remains of plants and other organisms that died millions of years ago

fossilisation the process of forming a fossil

fossils the preserved remains of organisms that lived long ago

frequency the number of vibrations per second or number of complete waves passing a set point per second

fuel cell a cell that produces energy by combining a fuel and an oxidant

fungi organisms which can break down complex organic substances (some are pathogens and harm the body)

fuse a thin wire used in an electrical circuit as a safety device

galaxy a collection of billions of stars held together by the force of gravity

galvanising method of corrosion protection that uses a layer of zinc to protect the underlying metal

gametes the male and female sex cells (sperm and eggs)

gene section of DNA that codes for a particular characteristic, by controlling the production of a particular protein or part of a protein by cells

generator a device used for producing electrical energy by moving wires through a magnetic field

genetic code the information contained in a gene which determines the type of protein produced by cells

genetic disorder an inherited disease that arises as the result of a mutated gene, passed on from parents to children

genetic engineering techniques that make it possible to manipulate genes in the cells of organisms

genetic material DNA that is inherited by offspring from parents

genetically modified (GM) a GM organism has had its DNA has modified by the insertion of DNA from another species

genetics the study of the pattern of inheritance of characteristics by offspring from their parents

genotype all of the genes of an organism

genus a group consisting of more than one species (used in classification of living things)

geocentric model Earth-centred model of the Solar System

geotropism (or gravitropism) growth movement in response to the stimulus of gravity

gibberellin plant hormone that regulates growth and influences developmental processes

glucagon hormone produced by the pancreas that promotes the conversion of glycogen to glucose

glycogen a type of carbohydrate whose molecule consists of many glucose units joined together

gravitational potential energy energy due to the position of an object in the Earth's gravitational field

greenhouse effect a process in which the atmosphere is warmed up by infrared radiation; it then re-radiates some of the infrared radiation back towards the Earth's surface, which warms the surface

greenhouse gases gases in the atmosphere whose absorption of infrared solar radiation is responsible for the greenhouse effect, e.g. carbon dioxide, methane and water vapour

haemoglobin chemical found in red blood cells which carries oxygen

hallucinogens substances that give a false sense of reality

hazard labels a standardised system of labels to indicate the hazards associated with chemicals

heliocentric model Sun-centred model of the Solar System

herbicide the technical name for weedkiller

heterozygous refers to the pair of alleles of a gene where the alleles are different

homeostasis self-adjusting mechanisms that allow the body to keep a constant internal environment

homeotherms animals that regulate their body temperature

homologous series a group of compounds that change in some incremental way

homozygous refers to the pair of alleles of a gene where the alleles are the same

hormones substances produced by animals and plants that regulate activities; in animals, hormones are produced by and released from endocrine tissue into the blood to act on target organs, and help to coordinate the body's response to stimuli

host the individual infected with a pathogen transmitted by a vector; the organism on which a parasite lives (the parasite takes food from the host)

huddling grouping together

human immunodeficiency virus (HIV) the virus that causes AIDS

hybrid the offspring of parents which are not the same species

hydrocarbon molecules containing only carbon and hydrogen – many fuels are hydrocarbons, e.g. natural gas (methane) and petrol (a complex mixture)

hydrothermal vent cracks in the seabed where water is heated as a result of volcanic activity

hypothalamus part of the brain that has several functions, the most important being to link the nervous system to the endocrine system

igneous rock rock formed from magma or lava

incomplete combustion when fuel burns in a small amount of oxygen so that carbon monoxide, particles and water are produced

indicator species the presence or absence of these species indicates how polluted (or not) a particular environment is

induced a term used to mean 'created'

infectious a disease that passes (is transmitted) from person to person

inflammatory response the symptoms which result from white blood cells called phagocytes migrating from the blood to the site of infection and destroying the pathogens that caused the infection

infrared radiation part of the electromagnetic spectrum, thermal energy

infrared waves non-ionising waves with a wavelength longer than red light that are radiant heat

infrasound sound with a frequency less than 20 Hz

insoluble a substance that will not dissolve (something that will not dissolve in water may dissolve in other liquids)

insulin hormone produced by the pancreas that promotes the conversion of glucose to glycogen

insulin insensitivity a condition in which target tissues (e.g. liver, muscles) do not respond to insulin

intrusive rock igneous rock formed by slow cooling when magma oozes into cracks and voids in the Earth's crust

invertebrates animals that do not have a backbone

involuntary response an automatic response to a stimulus that you do not think about

ion an atom with an electrical charge (can be positive or negative)

ionisation a process in which radiation transfers some or all of its energy to liberate an electron from an atom

ionosphere   a region of charged particles around the Earth that reflects radio waves

key   a chart of alternative statements that identifies organisms

kilowatt-hour   a kilowatt-hour is the energy used by an appliance of power 1 kW used for 1 hour – it is a unit of energy used by electrical suppliers

kinetic energy   the energy that moving objects have

kingdom   used in classification and refers to the largest grouping (except for domain) of organisms which have characteristics in common

lander   a robotic space probe sent to planets and moons to carry out soil analysis

landfill   the operation that dumps non-toxic industrial waste and domestic waste into large pits in the ground

leguminous   plants whose roots carry nodules that contain nitrogen-fixing bacteria

lichens   a combination of fungi and algae – the relationship between the organisms is an example of mutualism

life cycle   a term used to describe the journey of a star in time

light energy   energy due to light (electromagnetic) waves – anything that glows (such as a light bulb) gives out light energy

light-year   the distance travelled by light in a vacuum in 1 year

limestone   sedimentary rock composed mainly of calcite or dolomite

limewater   an aqueous solution of calcium hydroxide

limewater test   limewater is a clear liquid that turns milky in the presence of carbon dioxide

lineage   known ancestry

locus   the position of an allele on its chromosome

longitudinal waves   waves with vibrations parallel to the direction in which they travel

magma   hot molten rock found in the mantle, below the Earth's surface

magnified   an image that is larger than the object

main sequence star   an average star, just like our Sun

malleable   capable of being shaped by hammering

mantle   semi-liquid layer of the Earth beneath the crust

marble   metamorphosed limestone produced by recrystallisation

mean   the midpoint in an arithmetic progression

melting point   the temperature at which a solid becomes a liquid

metabolism   all of the chemical reactions taking place in a cell

metamorphic rock   sedimentary rock that is transformed by heat and pressure

Milky Way   the name of our galaxy

minerals   solid metallic or non-metallic substances found naturally in the Earth's crust

monohybrid   refers to the inheritance of a single characteristic

monomer   small molecule that may become chemically bonded to other monomers to form a polymer

morals   deciding what is right or wrong

MRSA   methicillin-resistant *Staphylococcus aureus*

mucus   sticky material consisting of a mixture of substances produced by goblet cells

multicellular   consisting of many cells

mutation   permanent change in the structure of a gene – the DNA within cells is altered (this happens in cancer)

mutualism   relationship between individuals of different species where both benefit

nanotechnology   engineering systems constructed at the molecular level

narcotic   a substance that induces sleep, drowsiness or insensibility

National Grid   network of pylons, high-voltage cables and transformers that carries electricity from power stations across the country

natural selection   process that results in the individuals of a population with characteristics suited to a particular environment surviving, reproducing and therefore passing on the genes controlling the characteristics to their offspring – natural selection is the mechanism of evolution

nebula   a cloud of dust and gas from which stars form

negative tropism   growth movement away from a particular stimulus

nerve impulses   electrical impulses that pass along a neurone

neurone   a nerve cell that carries nerve impulses

neurotransmitter   a chemical released from the end of a neurone into a synapse and which stimulates the next neurone to trigger new nerve impulses

neutralisation reaction   a reaction between an acid and an alkali that produces a neutral solution

neutron star   a very dense core of a massive star left behind after the supernova stage

nitrifying bacteria   bacteria that convert ammonium compounds into nitrates

nitrogen-fixing bacteria   bacteria that convert gaseous nitrogen into nitrogen-containing compounds

non-renewable resources   resources which are being used up more quickly than they can be replaced, e.g. fossil fuels; they will eventually run out

normal distribution curve   a graph that shows variables in a bell-shaped curve

nuclear energy   energy that is stored inside the nuclei of atoms

nuclear fusion   the fusing together of hydrogen nuclei to produce helium nuclei

nucleus   (1) the central core of an atom, which contains protons and neutrons and has a positive charge (2) a distinct structure in the cytoplasm of cells that contains the genetic material

nutrients   substances essential to maintaining living processes

objective lens   lens at the front of a telescope

oral rehydration therapy (ORT)   a mixture of salts and sugar dissolved in water and given to people suffering life-threatening diarrhoea; promotes reabsorption of water from the intestines and replaces salts lost from the body

order   a group consisting of several families (used in classification of living things)

ores   rocks that contain minerals, including metals, e.g. iron ore

organic compounds   chemicals containing carbon

osmoregulation   the control of an organism's fluid balance

oviparous   animals that lay eggs, the embryo does not develop within the mother's body

oxidation reaction   a reaction in which molecules gain oxygen

oxidation–reduction reaction   the combined reactions of adding oxygen to one substance and removing it from another

P wave   primary (longitudinal) seismic wave

painkiller   a drug that affects the nervous system, deadening pain

pancreas   organ that produces the hormones insulin and glucagon (from endocrine tissue) and digestive enzymes (from exocrine tissue)

paraffin   a fraction of crude oil

parallel   when components are connected across each other in a circuit

parasitism   relationship between individuals of different species where one benefits (parasite) and the other is harmed (host)

pathogen   a harmful organism which invades the body and causes disease

payback time   the number of years it takes to get back the cost of an energy-saving method

peak   uppermost point of a wave

pedigree   known genetic line of descent from generation to generation

peer review   the process of evaluating the quality of research using anonymous review by experts in a particular field

pentadactyl limb   the basic arrangement of five digits for most vertebrates

pH   scale running from 0 to 14 which shows how acidic or alkaline a substance is

phase   non-circular shape that includes a crescent

phenotype   all of the characteristics of an organism

photography   the process of producing permanent images

photosynthesis   process carried out by green plants where sunlight, carbon dioxide and water are used to produce glucose and oxygen

phototropism   growth movement in response to the stimulus of light

physical properties   properties that can be observed without changing the chemical composition of a substance, e.g. colour, density, melting point and boiling point

plantae   the plant kingdom

plasma membrane   the membrane that surrounds a cell

Plasmodium   the protozoan genus that causes malaria – *Plasmodium fulciparum* is the most dangerous species, *P. vivax* the least

plasticity   a physical property of materials that means they can be formed or shaped

poikilotherms   animals that cannot regulate their body temperature

pollutants   substances released into the environment that are harmful to health and wildlife

pollution   the effects of pollutants which contaminate or destroy the environment

polymer   large molecule made up of chains of monomers

polymerisation reaction   chemical process that combines monomers to form a polymer – this is how polythene is formed

population   organisms of the same species that live in the same geographical area

positive tropism   growth movement towards a particular stimulus

potential difference   another term for voltage (a measure of the energy carried by the electric charge)

precipitate   insoluble solid formed in a solution during a chemical reaction

predator   an animal that feeds on other animals

prescription   a doctor's written orders for the preparation and administration of a drug

prey   an animal that is eaten on by a predator

primary coil   the input coil of a transformer

principal focus   rays parallel to the principal axis of the lens meet at this point after being refracted twice by the lens (also known as the focus or focal point)

principle of conservation of energy   energy cannot be created or destroyed, it can simply be transferred from one form to another

prioritise   to rank in order

prism   a block of glass used to split white light into a visible spectrum

producers   organisms that synthesise sugars (food) by photosynthesis or chemosynthesis

products   chemicals produced by a chemical reaction

prokaryotes   single-celled organisms that lack a distinct nucleus

protists   single-celled organisms that contain a distinct nucleus

Protoctista   single-celled organisms that have a distinct nucleus; also some simple multicellular (many-celled) organisms such as seaweed

protons   small positively charged particles found in the nucleus of an atom

psychological behaviour   the mental processes used when assessing a situation

Punnett square   a type of genetic diagram that sets out the results of genetic crosses in the form of a table

pure-bred   a characteristic of an organism passes unchanged from generation to generation – the organism is homozygous for the characteristic in question

pyramid of biomass   diagram representing the biomass of the trophic levels of a community

radiotherapy   a technique that uses gamma rays to kill cancer cells in the body

rarefactions   regions where particles are pulled apart and create regions of low pressure in sound waves

rate of reaction   the speed with which a chemical reaction takes place

reactants   the chemicals that react in a chemical reaction

reaction time   the time taken to respond to a stimulus

reactivity series   a list of elements in order of decreasing reactivity used in metal extraction

real image   image formed on the other side of the lens to the object – a real image can be formed on a screen

receptor   part of a neurone that detects stimuli and converts them into nerve impulses

recessive   refers to an allele which controls the development of a characteristic only if its dominant partner allele is not present

recessive characteristic   an allele that does not develop a particular characteristic when present with a dominant allele

recipient   a person who receives a donated organ

recycling   reprocessing of materials to make new products

red blood cells   blood cells which are adapted to carry oxygen

red giant   a huge expanded star with a cooler surface

red-shift   the increase in the wavelength of light from distant galaxies – if an object has a red-shift it is moving away from us

reduction reaction   the removal of oxygen from a compound

reflecting telescope   telescope with a concave mirror, a flat mirror and an eyepiece

reflection   when a wave is bounced off a surface

reflex arc   pathway taken by nerve impulse from a receptor, through the nervous system, to an effector (does not go through brain) , bringing about a reflex response

reflex response   an automatic action not controlled by the brain, made in response to a stimulus

refracting telescope   telescope that uses two convex lenses to collect and focus light

refraction   the bending of a wave caused by the change in its speed – when a light ray travelling through air enters a glass block it changes direction

rejection   destruction of the donor organ because of the activity of the recipient's immune system

renewable energy resources   energy resources that can be replenished at the same rate that they are used up, e.g. biofuels – they will not run out

resistance   refers to pathogens, e.g. bacteria, that are not affected by drugs that previously were effective treatments

resource   what an individual's environment provides, enabling that individual to survive, e.g. food, water, light and living space

resources   the raw materials taken from the environment and used to run industry, homes and transport, and to manufacture goods

respiration   the series of chemical reactions that oxidise (break down) glucose, releasing energy: in the presence of oxygen, glucose is oxidised to carbon dioxide and water

response   the action taken as the result of a stimulus

retina   covering of light-sensitive cells at the back of the eyeball

retrograde motion   the backward motion of a planet against the background of stars

ring species   a connected geographical sequence of neighbouring species that can interbreed with one another; however, the two 'end' species of the sequence cannot interbreed

rods and cones   different types of photoreceptor

S wave   secondary (transverse) seismic wave

sacrificial protection   method of corrosion protection using blocks of reactive metals to corrode instead of the object being protected

Sankey diagram   a diagram showing the transfer of energy to different forms

saprophytic   feeding from dead organic matter

saturated hydrocarbons   hydrocarbons that contain no carbon–carbon double bonds

scavenger   an animal that feeds on dead animals

scientific conferences   meetings where participants exchange and present new ideas for research

scientific journals   periodic publications with articles contributed by scientists reporting on their new research

secondary coil   the output coil of a transformer

sedimentary rock   rock formed by the sedimentation of material on riverbeds and ocean floors

sedimentation   the gradual settling of grains of rock

seedling   a germinating seed which is at a stage where shoots and roots are visibly developing

seismic waves   shock waves from earthquakes

seismometer   an earthquake-detecting instrument

selective weedkiller   a substance that at a particular concentration kills weeds but not crop plants

series   when components are connected end-to-end in a circuit

shells   electrons are arranged in shells (or orbits) around the nucleus of an atom

sickle cell crisis   the periods of pain experienced when sickled red blood cells clump together, restricting blood flow to the organs of the body; each crisis may last for days, weeks or months

sickle cell disease   recessive genetic disorder in which the shape of haemoglobin molecules is altered, so they absorb less oxygen

slag   calcium silicate impurities that float on the surface of the molten iron during smelting

smelting   method of extracting metals from their ore using carbon and high temperatures

Solar System   the Sun and all the objects orbiting it (planets, asteroids, comets, etc.)

soluble   able to dissolve in a solvent to form a solution

sonar   a technique used by ships to determine the depth of water: it stands for Sound Navigation And Ranging

sound energy   energy due to vibrations of air particles – anything making a noise gives out sound energy

speciation   an evolutionary process that results in new species

species   a group of individuals able to mate and reproduce offspring, which themselves are able to mate and reproduce

specific heat capacity   the heat which a unit mass of a substance requires to raise its temperature by one degree

specific   relating to a particular thing or event, e.g. a particular hormone affects only a particular target tissue

spectrometer   a device used to analyse light from various sources

speed   how fast an object travels, calculated using the equation: speed (metres per second) = distance/time

starch   large polysaccharides made by plants as a form of food storage

Steady State theory   a theory that proposes a Universe in which matter is created from empty space to keep its density the same

stem cutting   a piece of stem cut from a parent plant, which has the potential to develop roots and grow into a new plant

step-down transformer   device used to change the voltage of an a.c. supply to a lower voltage

step-up transformer   device used to change the voltage of an a.c. supply to a higher voltage

sterilisation   technique used to kill bacteria by exposure to radiation

stimulant   a substance that speeds up responses

stimulus   a change in the environment that causes a response by stimulating receptor nerve cells, e.g. a hot surface

subcutaneous fat   literally means 'fat under the skin'

subspecies   a subdivision of a species; it is possible that characteristics can become so different from the original species that they form a new species

super red giant   a huge expanded star larger than a red giant

supernova   an exploding star

symptoms   indicators of a disease

synapse   the gap between two adjacent neurones

target tissues   tissues that respond to hormones

tectonic plates   the several solid parts of the Earth's crust

telescope   a device using lenses (or mirrors) to magnify distant objects

thermal decomposition   the breaking down of a compound due to the action of heat

thermal (heat) energy   energy emitted by an object that is hotter than its surroundings

thermograph   an image produced using infrared waves

thermoregulation   the processes that enable an animal to keep its body temperature constant

thermosetting   the property of polymers that causes cross-links to form when heated, making them rigid

thermosoftening   the property of polymers that allows them to be heated and shaped

titration   common laboratory method used to determine the unknown concentration of a known reactant

total internal reflection   a phenomenon where 100% of the light is reflected back into a material, when the ray hits the glass/air boundary at an angle that is greater than the critical angle

tracer   a radioactive material injected into a patient for locating cancer or diagnosing a function of the body

transformer   device which converts the voltage of an a.c. supply to another voltage

transplantation tourism   travelling to another country to buy organs

transverse waves   waves with vibrations at right angles to the direction in which the wave is travelling

trophic   literally means relating to feeding

tropism   growth movement by plants in response to stimuli coming mainly from one direction

trough   lowest point of a wave

ultrasound   sound with frequencies greater than 20 kHz – too high for detection by human ears

ultraviolet waves   electromagnetic waves with a wavelength shorter than violet (blue) light

unicellular   consisting of a single cell

Universe   the whole of space containing all the galaxies

unsaturated hydrocarbons   hydrocarbons that contain carbon–carbon double bonds

vacuum   empty space that has no particles

validated   to establish the soundness of, or to corroborate, evidence

variation   the difference in characteristics between species and the range of a characteristic in individuals of the same species

vasoconstriction   narrowing of the lumen (internal space) of blood vessels in cold conditions – this reduces the flow of blood

vasodilation   widening of the lumen (internal space) of blood vessels in hot conditions – this increases the flow of blood

vector   an organism that transmits pathogens from host to host – insects are common disease vectors

vertebrates   animals that have the characteristic of a backbone in common

virtual image   image formed on the same side of the lens as the object – a virtual image can be seen by looking through the lens, it cannot be projected onto a screen

viruses   very small infectious organisms that reproduce within the cells of living organisms and often cause disease; consist of a protein layer surrounding a strand of nucleic acid

viviparous   animals that do not lay eggs, the embryo develops within the mother's body

volt   the unit of voltage

voltage   the energy transferred per unit charge – a measure of the energy carried by electric charge (also called the potential difference)

voltmeter   a device used to measure the voltage across a component

voluntary response   a response to a stimulus that you think about and can control

watt   the unit for power

wave equation   the equation: speed = frequency × wavelength

wavelength   distance between neighbouring wave peaks (or troughs)

weedkiller   a substance that kills weeds (unwanted plants)

white dwarf   a hot and dense core of a star (such as our Sun) left behind after the red giant stage

xenotransplantation   transplantation of organs from another species X-rays   electromagnetic waves with very short wavelength of the order of 0.000 000 001 m

X-rays   electromagnetic waves with very short wavelength of the order of 0.000 000 001 m

Index

William Collins' dream of knowledge for all began with the publication of his first book in 1819. A self-educated mill worker, he not only enriched millions of lives, but also founded a flourishing publishing house. Today, staying true to this spirit, Collins books are packed with inspiration, innovation and practical expertise. They place you at the centre of a world of possibility and give you exactly what you need to explore it.

Collins. Freedom to teach

Published by Collins
An imprint of HarperCollinsPublishers
77–85 Fulham Palace Road
Hammersmith
London
W6 8JB

Browse the complete Collins catalogue at
www.collinseducation.com

© HarperCollinsPublishers Limited 2011

10 9 8 7 6 5 4 3 2 1

ISBN-13 978 0 00 741514 4

John Adkins, David Applin and Gurinder Chadha assert their moral rights to be identified as the authors of this work

British Library Cataloguing in Publication Data
A Catalogue record for this publication is available from the British Library

Commissioned by Letitia Luff
Project managed by Alexandra Riley and Gray Publishing
Production by Kerry Howie

Designed, edited, proofread and indexed by Gray Publishing
New illustrations by Gray Publishing
Picture research by Caroline Green and Thelma Gilbert
Concept design by Anna Plucinska
Cover design by Julie Martin
Development editor Lesley Gray
Technical review by Dr Christopher R.J. Woolston
Contributing authors John Beeby, Ed Walsh, Pam Large and Lyn Nicholls
'Bad Science' pages based on the work of Ben Goldacre

Printed and bound by L.E.G.O. S.p.A. Italy.

Edexcel disclaimer
This material has been endorsed by Edexcel and offers high quality support for the delivery of Edexcel qualifications.

Edexcel endorsement does not mean that this material is essential to achieve any Edexcel qualification, nor does it mean that this is the only suitable material available to support any Edexcel qualification. No endorsed material will be used verbatim in setting any Edexcel examination and any resource lists produced by Edexcel shall include this and other appropriate texts. While this material has been through an Edexcel quality assurance process, all responsibility for the content remains with the publisher.

Copies of official specifications for all Edexcel qualifications may be found on the Edexcel website – www.edexcel.com

Acknowledgements
The publishers wish to thank the following for permission to reproduce photographs. Every effort has been made to trace copyright holders and to obtain their permission for the use of copyright materials. The publishers will gladly receive any information enabling them to rectify any error or omission at the first opportunity.

Alamy: p.18t Lebrecht Music and Arts Photo Library, 59r Dominic Harrison, 62tr Peter Scholey, 68t Mary Evans Picture Library, 79 Mary Evans Picture Library, 116t imagebroker, 135b Mar Photographics, 152t Photofusion Picture Library, 162 Ted Foxx, 164t Moviestore collection Ltd, 200cr picturebox-uk.com, 244t Paul Glendell. Corbis: p.12t D. Bayes/Lebrecht Music & Arts, 66 CDC/Phil, 109T Roger Wood. Cynthia Goldsmith/courtesy of Dr. F. A. Murphy: p.56t. David Applin: p.34b. Fortean Picture Library: p.236t. Getty Images: p.17tr Wolfgang Kaehler, 44tr Time & Life Pictures, 63 AFP. Gurinder Chadha: p.208l, 2018r. iStockphoto: p.8t, 8u, 8l, 8b, 9u, 9l, 9b, 11, 12bl, 14bl, 14bl, 14bl, 14bl, 14bl, 14bl, 16, 18b, 20br, 21br, 22, 24, 26t, 32tr, 32bl, 32br, 34t, 36, 38, 40t, 45tl, 46tr, 46l, 53, 56u, 56l, 56b, 57t, 57u, 57l, 57b, 58tr, 59l, 64tr, 65tr, 67r, 68l, 69tr, 69bl, 70t, 71l, 71r, 72tr, 73cl, 73cr, 74tr, 76, 78c, 82, 84, 85t, 85l, 86tl, 86br, 94t, 94c, 94b, 97c, 100br, 104t, 106bl, 107tr, 109cr, 111l, 114tr, 115, 127, 130u, 130l, 130b, 131t, 131u, 131l, 131b, 132t, 135t, 136l, 136r, 138tr, 138cl, 142, 144t, 144cr, 145r, 149tr, 152l, 152r, 154bl, 167, 174t, 174c, 175c, 180t, 182, 186t, 186r, 190, 194cr, 196cr, 196br, 205b, 205c, 205f, 220, 224t, 224c, 224b, 225t, 225c, 225b, 229r, 232, 234t, 236l, 246, 249, 250, 251br, 254bl, 254r, 256. Lowell Observatory Archives: p.178l. NASA: p.30, 150, 174b, 204t, 205br, 206b, 207tr, 212, 214t, 217b. Rex Features: p.112t Chad Ehlers/Stock Connection, 121 CSU Archv/Everett, 200tr Shout. Robert Gray: p.10, 14cl, 198b. Science Museum/Science & Society Picture Library: p.189t. Science Photo Library: p.12c Bob Gibbons, 12br Tony Camacho, 17bl Dr Ken Macdonald, 20tr Eye of Science, 26b Simon Fraser/RVI/Newcastle-Upon-Tyne, 27 Eye of Science, 40r Cordelia Molloy, 42t John Kaprielian, 44cr Rosenfeld Images Ltd, 44bl Helmut Partsch, 45r Nigel Cattlin, 54 Eye of Science, 58c Patrick Landmann, 62l CIOT, 62br Life in View, 64br CNRI, 65tl Matt Meadows/Peter Arnold Inc., 67l Dr Gopal Murti, 70l SCIMAT, 70tr Juergen Berger, 70br Claude Huridsany & Marie Perennou, 73tr Eye of Science, 73bl Dr Jeremy Burgess, 73br Dr Ken Macdonald, 78tr Graeme Ewens, 80 Martin Bond, 81 Geoff Kidd, 92 Dr Jeremy Burgess, 95t NASA Goddard Space Flight Center (NASA-GSFC), 95c Martin Bond, 98c NASA Goddard Space Flight Center (NASA-GSFC), 98cr Steve Gschmeissner, 99tr Martin Dohrn, 101br Charles D. Winters, 103 NASA Goddard Space Flight Center (NASA-GSFC), 104bl Michael Marten, 104bc Michael Marten, 104br Dr Keith Wheeler, 105l Andrew Lambert Photography, 105r Joyce Photographics, 106br Dirk Wiersma, 107cr Pascal Goetgheluck, 107br M.I. Walker, 108t Carlos Dominguez, 108b Mark Thomas, 109br Martin Bond, 110r Andrew Lambert Photography, 111r Jerry Mason, 113 Andrew Lambert Photography, 117t Andrew Lambert Photography, 117c Martyn F. Chillmaid, 118tr James Holmes, Hays Chemicals, 118c Charles D. Winters, 119l Andrew Lambert Photography, 119r Trevor Clifford Photography, 120b Andrew Lambert Photography, 129 Martin Bond, 133l Joel Arem, 133r Ben Johnson, 139 Alex Bartel, 143tr Paul Rapson, 146 Martyn F. Chillmaid, 147tr Martyn F. Chillmaid, 147bl REVY/ISM, 148 Adam Hart-Davis, 149cr Sheila Terry, 151bl NASA/GSFC, 151r Pasieka, 153 David Nunuk, 154tr NASA, 155 Martin Bond, 158 Science Photo Library, 159l Andrew Lambert Photography, p159c Andrew Lambert Photography, 159r Andrew Lambert Photography, 160 Paul Rapson, 164c James King-Holmes, 165l Paul Rapson, 165r Sheila Terry, 176t Dr Jeremy Burgess, 177t David A Hardy, 178t Gianni Tortoli, 178r Eckhard Slawik, 178fr NASA/JPL/University of Arizona, 179t Jacopin, 179r NASA/CXC/UMass Amherst/Q.D.Wang et al., 180cl GIPhotostock, 181l GIPhotostock, 181r Southern Illinois University, 184t Emlio Serge Visual Archives, 184r Royal Greenwich Observatory, 185 NASA, 189l Gary Hincks, 189bl Gary Hincks, 189br James King-Holmes, 195r NASA, 196tr Cordelia Molloy, 198tr Edward Kinsman, 201cl CNRI, 202tr Science Photo Library, 202cr Science Source, 203br Hank Morgan, 204r Allan Morton/Dennis Milon, 205d Science Photo Library, 205e Adam Block, 206t Mark Garlick, 207b NASA, p.209l GIPhotostock, 209cl Physics Dept/Imperial College, 209cr GIPhotostock, 209r Dept of Physics/Imperial College, 210t European Southern Observatory, 210b European Southern Observatory, 211 John Sanford, 214b Mark Garlick, 215br Physics Today Collection/American Institute of Physics, 216 Tony Hallas, 217t Julian Baum, 221 Tony Hallas, 226t Zephyr, 227l D.Ouelette, Publiphoto Diffusion, 228t Christian Darkin, 229l Gary Hincks, 229br Sinclair Stammers, 230 Gary Hincks, 234c Trevor Clifford Photography, 238 Sheila Terry, 239 Adrienne Hart-Davis, 240 Cordelia Molloy, 241 US Department of Energy, 242 W.T. Sullivan III & Hansen Planetarium, 244cl Martin Bond, 245 Martin Bond, 254t Cordelia Molloy, 255tr Daniel Sambraus, 260r Christian Darkin. Shutterstock: p.9t, 13tr, 13br, 20bl, 21l, 28, 42bl, 52tl, 60tr, 72br, 86tr, 95b, 96, 97tl, 97r, 98br, 99br, 100l, 100tr, 101tr, 106tr, 110t, 114br, 116c, 120t, 122, 132r, 134, 136t, 140-141, 161, 175t, 180bl, 188, 194tr, 195l, 199tr, 205a, 207cr, 208t, 226c, 227r, 251cl, 252tr, 252cr 9t, 13tr, 13br, 20bl, 21l, 28, 42bl, 52tl, 60tr, 72br, 86tr, 95b, 96, 97tl, 97r, 98br, 99br, 100l, 100tr, 101tr, 106tr, 110t, 114br, 116c, 120t, 122, 132r, 134, 136t, 140-141, 161, 175t, 180bl, 188, 194tr, 195l, 199tr, 205a, 207cr, 208t, 226c, 227r, 251cl, 252tr, 252cr. Wikimedia Commons: p.13l.